contents

5. WATER

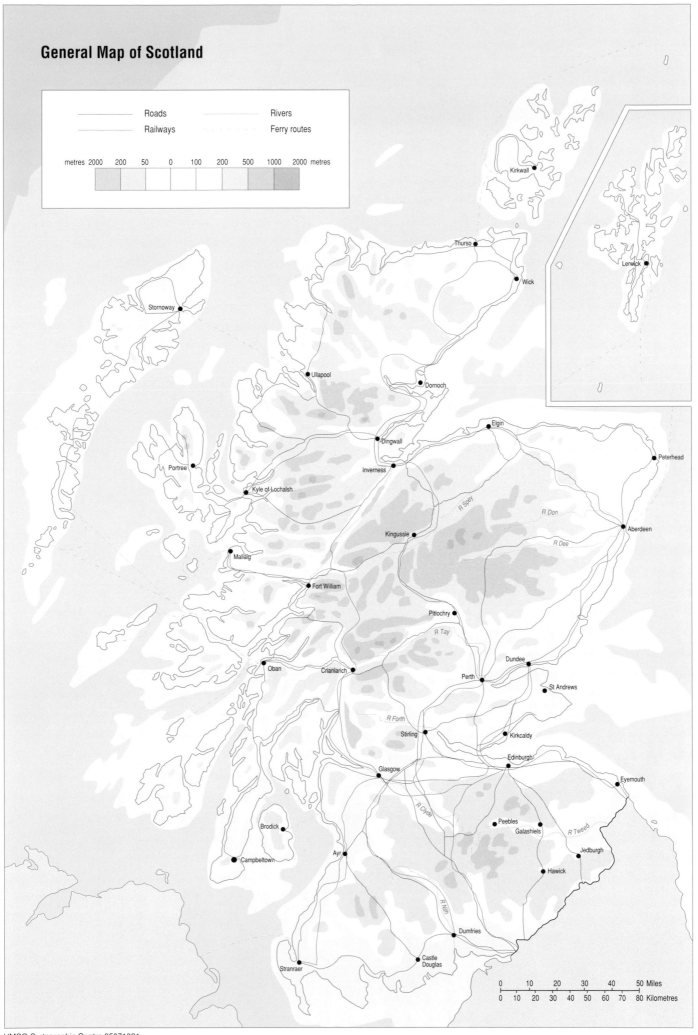

General Map of Scotland

Roads
Railways
Rivers
Ferry routes

metres 2000 200 50 0 100 200 500 1000 2000 metres

Kirkwall

Lerwick

Thurso
Wick

Stornoway

Ullapool
Dornoch

Elgin
Dingwall
Peterhead
Inverness

Portree

Kyle of Lochalsh

Kingussie
Aberdeen
R Spey
R Don
R Dee

Mallaig

Fort William

Pitlochry
R Tay

Dundee
Oban
Crianlarich
Perth
St Andrews

R Forth
Stirling
Kirkcaldy

Edinburgh

Glasgow
Eyemouth

R Clyde
Peebles
Brodick
Galashiels
R Tweed
Jedburgh
Ayr
Campbeltown
Hawick

R Nith

Dumfries

Stranraer
Castle
Douglas

0 10 20 30 40 50 Miles
0 10 20 30 40 50 60 70 80 Kilometres

population

1 population

1.1　　The Registrar General for Scotland is responsible for collecting statistics of population and vital events. The main source for the former is the decennial census. For the latter, information is obtained from registration of births and deaths.

POPULATION ESTIMATES

1.2　　The population estimates for 1991 presented in this section are based on the 1991 Census counts of residents. However, they incorporate adjustments to allow for differences in timing and in definition of residence (i.e. for students), and for estimated under counting of residents in the census. The estimates for 1992 onwards take account of subsequent births, deaths, and migration. Estimates for 1982 to 1990 have been revised to take account of the final census based estimates for 1991. The population is defined as including all persons usually resident in Scotland regardless of their nationality. Members of HM and non-UK armed forces stationed in Scotland are included; HM Forces stationed outside Scotland are excluded. Students are treated as being resident at their term time address.

HOUSEHOLD ESTIMATES

1.3　　Table 1.2 was supplied by the Housing Statistics Unit of the Scottish Office. Further details are available in the series of statistical bulletins "Annual Estimates of Households in Scotland".

POPULATION PROJECTIONS

1.4　　Population projections for Scotland are prepared at regular intervals by the Government Actuary's Department in association with the Registrar General. The latest projection was based on the Registrar General's population estimates for mid 1994. The assumptions on fertility, mortality, and migration used in this projection are described below:

Fertility:　The fertility rates used were based on assumptions about the average completed family size of successive cohorts of women. It has been assumed that the average completed family size will continue to decline from the current figure of over 2 children per woman for those now in their forties, to 1.81 for those born in 1965, before rising to 1.90 for those born in 1975 and later. The annual number of births is projected to rise slightly initially, but to fall below 60,000 in 2004-2005 and remain so for the rest of the projection period.

Mortality: The mortality rates for the first year of the projection, 1992-93, were based on estimates of the numbers of deaths in that period that were available in the Autumn of 1992. The mortality rates for later years are based on trends in the years up to 1992-93 in England and Wales. However, it has been assumed that the mortality differentials between Scotland and England and Wales, as shown by their experience in 1989-1991, will continue unchanged. For males aged between 23 and 42, it is assumed that mortality rates will increase for about 15 years. There is also initially very little reduction for women in their 20s.

EXPECTATION OF LIFE

1.5   The latest figures in table 1.8 are calculated on the mortality rates experienced during 1994 and the estimated population at 30 June 1994. At each age shown, the expectation of life is the average number of years of life left to persons aged X who are subject to the 1994 mortality rates from age X onwards.

LOCALITIES

1.6   The number and population of rural areas and localities are shown in tables 1.9 and 1.10. A locality is defined as a group of adjacent urban post-codes which had a resident population of 500 or more at the time of the 1991 census.

SOURCES

1.7   The source of data in this section, except for table 1.2, is the General Register Office for Scotland and the data is reproduced by permission of the Registrar General for Scotland. Further information may be found in the Registrar General's Annual Report and in census reports such as "Key Statistics for Urban and Rural Areas, Scotland" (HMSO).

Table 1.1   **Population, by district, 1981, 1991 and 1994**

Area	Estimated Population		Estimated Population 30 June 1994			Density[1]
	1981	1991	Persons	Males	Females	
Scotland	**5,180,200**	**5,107,000**	**5,132,400**	**2,486,237**	**2,646,163**	**67**
Borders	**101,256**	**104,100**	**105,700**	**50,807**	**54,893**	**23**
Berwickshire	18,342	19,120	19,420	9,355	10,065	22
Ettrick & Lauderdale	33,312	34,390	35,490	17,123	18,367	26
Roxburgh	35,330	35,320	35,230	16,940	18,290	23
Tweeddale	14,272	15,270	15,560	7,389	8,171	17
Central	**273,515**	**272,900**	**273,400**	**132,511**	**140,889**	**104**
Clackmannan	48,218	48,400	48,850	23,861	24,989	305
Falkirk	145,036	143,020	142,530	69,134	73,396	489
Stirling	80,261	81,480	82,020	39,516	42,504	38
Dumfries and Galloway	**145,502**	**147,700**	**147,800**	**71,779**	**76,021**	**23**
Annandale & Eskdale	35,633	37,110	37,070	18,102	18,968	24
Nithsdale	56,723	57,090	57,310	27,767	29,543	40
Stewartry	22,885	23,540	23,710	11,476	12,234	14
Wigtown	30,261	29,960	29,710	14,434	15,276	17
Fife	**341,589**	**349,400**	**352,100**	**171,461**	**180,639**	**269**
Dunfermline	126,508	130,120	130,060	64,275	65,785	431
Kirkcaldy	149,527	148,820	148,490	71,777	76,713	598
North East Fife	65,554	70,460	73,550	35,409	38,141	97
Grampian	**484,899**	**515,600**	**532,500**	**262,987**	**269,513**	**61**
Aberdeen City	212,494	214,950	219,090	106,965	112,125	1,188
Banff & Buchan	82,784	85,600	88,460	43,821	44,639	58
Gordon	63,746	77,080	80,400	40,127	40,273	36
Kincardine & Deeside	42,393	53,780	57,200	28,476	28,724	22
Moray	83,482	84,190	87,350	43,598	43,752	39
Highland	**194,903**	**204,100**	**207,500**	**101,836**	**105,664**	**8**
Badenoch & Strathspey	9,860	10,980	11,180	5,479	5,701	5
Caithness	27,636	26,710	26,080	12,956	13,124	15
Inverness	57,105	62,480	64,290	31,158	33,132	23
Lochaber	19,491	19,310	19,400	9,500	9,900	4
Nairn	9,953	10,610	10,940	5,342	5,598	26
Ross & Cromarty	46,924	49,100	50,460	25,085	25,375	10
Skye & Lochalsh	10,621	11,740	11,970	5,895	6,075	4
Sutherland	13,313	13,170	13,180	6,421	6,759	2
Lothian	**749,591**	**751,000**	**758,600**	**367,515**	**391,085**	**432**
East Lothian	80,715	84,920	86,800	42,082	44,718	122
Edinburgh City	446,165	439,660	443,600	213,373	230,227	1,699
Midlothian	83,397	80,050	80,010	39,212	40,798	223
West Lothian	139,314	146,370	148,190	72,848	75,342	350
Strathclyde	**2,414,813**	**2,298,200**	**2,287,800**	**1,100,863**	**1,186,937**	**169**
Argyll & Bute	65,018	65,520	63,620	30,519	33,101	10
Bearsden & Milngavie	39,217	40,900	41,400	20,001	21,399	1,137
Clydebank	52,809	46,390	46,730	21,960	24,770	1,319
Clydesdale	57,276	58,110	58,660	28,650	30,010	44
Cumbernauld & Kilsyth	62,245	63,470	63,980	31,420	32,560	621
Cumnock & Doon Valley	44,921	42,950	42,630	20,648	21,982	53
Cunninghame	137,304	139,060	139,090	66,852	72,238	158
Dumbarton	78,922	79,400	78,310	38,576	39,734	166
East Kilbride	83,204	84,200	85,180	41,588	43,592	299
Eastwood	53,824	60,340	62,670	30,189	32,481	544
Glasgow City	774,068	688,600	680,000	323,952	356,048	3,438
Hamilton	109,358	106,770	107,150	51,823	55,327	818
Inverclyde	101,182	91,580	89,380	42,793	46,587	567
Kilmarnock & Loudoun	82,442	81,340	80,920	38,965	41,955	217
Kyle & Carrick	113,187	113,550	114,360	54,567	59,793	87
Monklands	111,271	104,010	102,520	49,519	53,001	626
Motherwell	151,235	144,740	143,710	69,776	73,934	835
Renfrew	209,923	200,900	201,690	97,207	104,483	656
Strathkelvin	87,407	86,370	85,800	41,858	43,942	523
Tayside	**397,055**	**392,500**	**395,000**	**190,459**	**204,541**	**53**
Angus	93,035	95,240	98,000	47,872	50,128	48
Dundee City	184,741	172,420	167,820	80,268	87,552	714
Perth & Kinross	119,279	124,840	129,180	62,319	66,861	25
Orkney Islands	**19,182**	**19,560**	**19,810**	**9,786**	**10,024**	**20**
Shetland Islands	**26,347**	**22,540**	**22,880**	**11,617**	**11,263**	**16**
Western Isles	**31,548**	**29,400**	**29,310**	**14,616**	**14,694**	**10**

Source: General Register Office (Scotland)

(1)   Persons per sq km

Map 1.1 Population density per square kilometre by district, 1994 (see table 1.1)

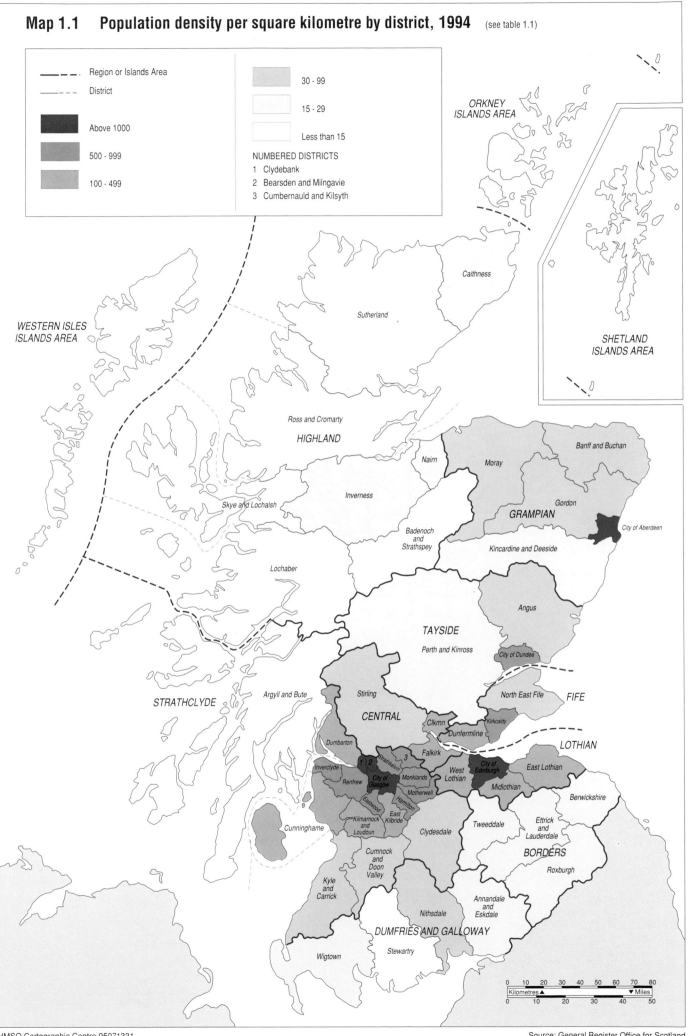

Region or Islands Area

District

Above 1000

500 - 999

100 - 499

30 - 99

15 - 29

Less than 15

NUMBERED DISTRICTS
1 Clydebank
2 Bearsden and Milngavie
3 Cumbernauld and Kilsyth

ORKNEY ISLANDS AREA

WESTERN ISLES ISLANDS AREA

SHETLAND ISLANDS AREA

Caithness

Sutherland

Ross and Cromarty

HIGHLAND

Nairn

Moray

Banff and Buchan

Gordon

GRAMPIAN

City of Aberdeen

Inverness

Skye and Lochalsh

Badenoch and Strathspey

Kincardine and Deeside

Lochaber

Angus

TAYSIDE

Perth and Kinross

City of Dundee

Argyll and Bute

STRATHCLYDE

Stirling

North East Fife

FIFE

CENTRAL

Clkmn

Kirkcaldy

Dunfermline

LOTHIAN

Dumbarton

2

Strathkelvin

3

Falkirk

West Lothian

City of Edinburgh

East Lothian

Inverclyde

Renfrew

City of Glasgow

Monklands

Midlothian

Berwickshire

Eastwood

Motherwell

Hamilton

Kilmarnock and Loudoun

East Kilbride

Cunninghame

Clydesdale

Tweeddale

Ettrick and Lauderdale

BORDERS

Roxburgh

Cumnock and Doon Valley

Kyle and Carrick

Nithsdale

Annandale and Eskdale

DUMFRIES AND GALLOWAY

Wigtown

Stewartry

Kilometres ▲

▼ Miles

0 10 20 30 40 50 60 70 80

0 10 20 30 40 50

Source: General Register Office for Scotland

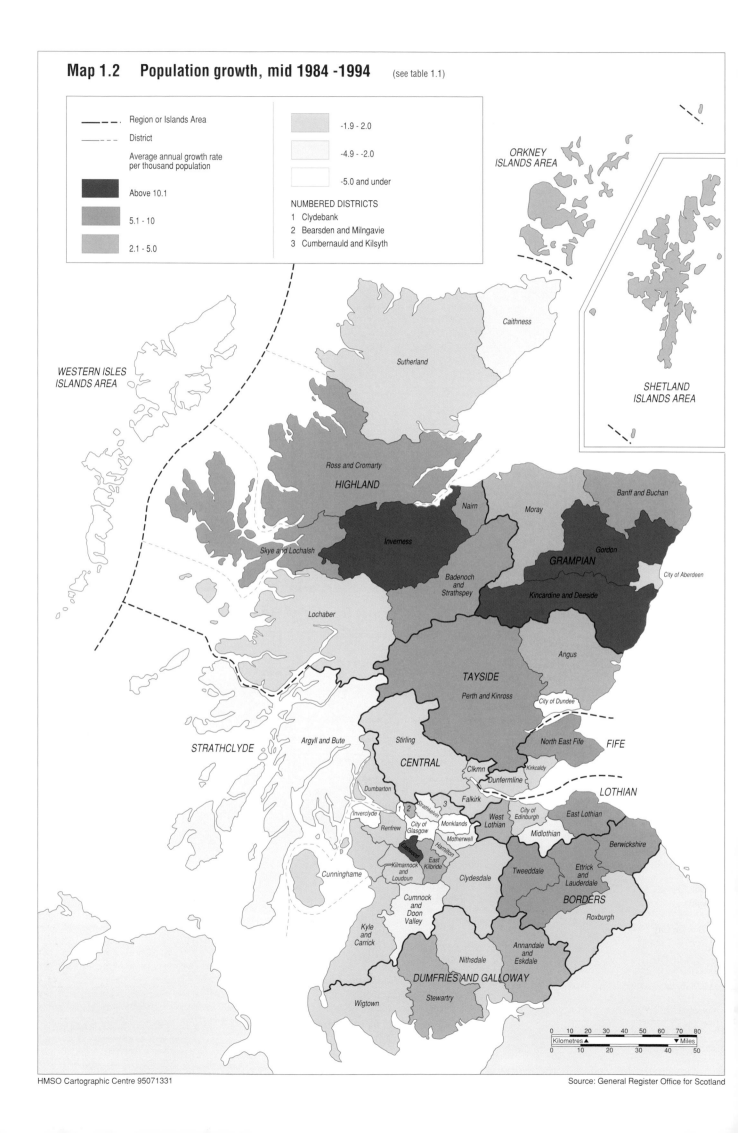

Map 1.2   Population growth, mid 1984 -1994   (see table 1.1)

Region or Islands Area

District

Average annual growth rate
per thousand population

Above 10.1

5.1 - 10

2.1 - 5.0

-1.9 - 2.0

-4.9 - -2.0

-5.0 and under

NUMBERED DISTRICTS
1 Clydebank
2 Bearsden and Milngavie
3 Cumbernauld and Kilsyth

ORKNEY
ISLANDS AREA

WESTERN ISLES
ISLANDS AREA

SHETLAND
ISLANDS AREA

Caithness

Sutherland

Ross and Cromarty

HIGHLAND

Nairn

Moray

Banff and Buchan

Skye and Lochalsh

Inverness

Gordon

GRAMPIAN

City of Aberdeen

Badenoch
and
Strathspey

Kincardine and Deeside

Lochaber

Angus

TAYSIDE

Perth and Kinross

City of Dundee

Argyll and Bute

Stirling

North East Fife

FIFE

STRATHCLYDE

CENTRAL

Clkmn

Kirkcaldy

Dunfermline

Dumbarton

Falkirk

LOTHIAN

Inverclyde

1 2

Strathkelvin

3

West
Lothian

City of
Edinburgh

East Lothian

Renfrew

City of
Glasgow

Monklands

Midlothian

Berwickshire

Motherwell

Eastwood

Hamilton

East
Kilbride

Tweeddale

Ettrick
and
Lauderdale

Kilmarnock
and
Loudoun

Cunninghame

Clydesdale

BORDERS

Cumnock
and
Doon
Valley

Roxburgh

Kyle
and
Carrick

Nithsdale

Annandale
and
Eskdale

DUMFRIES AND GALLOWAY

Wigtown

Stewartry

0 10 20 30 40 50 60 70 80
Kilometres ▲
0   10   20   30   40   50
▼ Miles

Source: General Register Office for Scotland

Table 1.2 Estimated number of households, 1981, 1986-1992[(1)(2)]

	1981	1986	1987	1988	1989	1990	1991	1992
Scotland	1,853,630	1,933,610	1,949,850	1,967,070	1,983,660	2,002,860	2,052,010	2,066,810
Borders	**39,190**	**40,410**	**40,690**	**41,000**	**41,270**	**41,770**	**43,610**	**43,960**
Berwickshire	7,040	7,310	7,360	7,400	7,450	7,510	7,960	8,050
Ettrick & Lauderdale	12,830	13,160	13,260	13,390	13,490	13,740	14,340	14,420
Roxburgh	13,740	14,140	14,170	14,240	14,300	14,420	14,890	15,030
Tweeddale	5,580	5,820	5,890	5,960	6,020	6,100	6,420	6,460
Central	**96,720**	**101,200**	**101,910**	**102,910**	**104,350**	**105,140**	**106,900**	**107,950**
Clackmannan	17,040	17,550	17,650	17,830	18,290	18,450	18,880	19,080
Falkirk	51,720	54,440	54,790	55,240	55,770	56,250	56,850	57,400
Stirling	27,950	29,210	29,460	29,850	30,290	30,440	31,170	31,470
Dumfries and Galloway	**52,460**	**54,900**	**55,450**	**55,790**	**55,450**	**55,980**	**59,660**	**60,020**
Annandale & Eskdale	12,950	13,610	13,690	13,850	13,820	13,980	14,860	15,000
Nithsdale	20,220	21,130	21,420	21,610	21,650	21,820	23,000	23,130
Stewartry	8,460	8,840	8,910	8,910	8,760	8,870	9,720	9,760
Wigtown	10,820	11,310	11,440	11,420	11,230	11,310	12,080	12,140
Fife	**123,670**	**130,080**	**131,110**	**131,460**	**130,580**	**131,750**	**138,970**	**139,980**
Dunfermline	44,730	46,890	47,380	47,510	46,960	47,440	50,410	50,810
Kirkcaldy	54,620	57,300	57,670	57,780	57,840	58,290	61,070	61,480
North East Fife	24,330	25,890	26,060	26,170	25,770	26,020	27,490	27,690
Grampian	**174,520**	**187,920**	**190,110**	**191,070**	**193,320**	**196,100**	**204,400**	**207,470**
Aberdeen City	79,600	85,070	85,950	86,020	87,180	88,380	90,600	92,280
Banff & Buchan	28,610	30,120	30,370	30,600	30,760	31,080	32,780	33,070
Gordon	22,260	25,300	25,610	25,800	26,150	26,700	28,340	28,910
Kincardine & Deeside	15,030	17,080	17,460	17,670	18,070	18,520	19,840	20,150
Moray	29,030	30,340	30,720	30,990	21,170	31,430	32,840	33,060
Highland	**67,560**	**71,760**	**72,720**	**73,600**	**74,540**	**75,720**	**80,170**	**81,190**
Badenoch & Strathspey	3,450	3,760	3,810	3,880	4,020	4,120	4,410	4,510
Caithness	9,680	9,770	9,880	10,000	9,890	9,970	10,610	10,660
Inverness	19,610	21,530	21,950	22,300	22,730	23,170	24,600	25,060
Lochaber	6,800	7,020	7,100	7,160	7,190	7,240	7,410	7,430
Nairn	3,550	3,690	3,730	3,770	3,800	3,890	4,160	4,220
Ross & Cromarty	15,730	16,750	16,880	17,060	17,220	17,440	18,690	18,870
Skye & Lochalsh	3,770	4,080	4,180	4,220	4,310	4,410	4,630	4,710
Sutherland	4,970	5,160	5,200	5,280	5,380	5,490	5,670	5,720
Lothian	**276,650**	**289,310**	**291,960**	**297,500**	**301,140**	**303,890**	**310,700**	**312,710**
East Lothian	29,200	31,030	31,520	32,080	32,750	32,960	34,530	34,840
Edinburgh City	172,260	179,280	180,730	185,060	186,920	188,010	190,770	191,460
Midlothian	28,170	28,690	28,810	28,920	29,150	29,350	29,780	29,950
West Lothian	47,030	50,320	50,890	51,440	52,320	53,570	55,620	56,460
Strathclyde	**848,240**	**876,550**	**882,900**	**889,580**	**897,780**	**905,620**	**917,250**	**922,130**
Argyll & Bute	24,280	24,470	24,510	24,680	24,930	25,090	27,020	26,380
Bearsden & Milngavie	13,600	14,120	14,190	14,300	14,340	14,510	14,850	14,950
Clydebank	18,120	18,300	18,520	18,690	18,880	18,880	18,900	18,980
Clydesdale	19,890	20,990	21,160	21,300	21,470	21,620	22,050	22,240
Cumbernauld & Kilsyth	19,980	21,190	21,190	21,480	41,940	22,370	23,220	23,500
Cumnock & Doon Valley	15,600	15,850	15,950	16,040	16,150	16,240	16,630	16,600
Cunninghame	48,750	50,850	51,250	51,560	51,990	52,510	55,060	55,510
Dumbarton	27,490	28,630	28,900	29,130	29,360	29,710	30,150	30,360
East Kilbride	27,710	29,510	29,890	30,340	30,920	31,670	32,200	32,710
Eastwood	19,030	20,230	20,630	21,170	21,650	21,900	22,680	22,850
Glasgow City	281,900	289,350	291,210	292,880	294,310	296,190	294,420	295,690
Hamilton	36,790	37,990	38,230	38,640	39,190	39,560	40,610	40,950
Inverclyde	35,110	35,770	36,000	36,140	36,470	36,630	36,640	36,700
Kilmarnock & Loudoun	29,970	30,140	30,740	31,060	31,330	31,580	32,490	32,610
Kyle & Carrick	41,610	43,180	43,400	43,670	44,120	44,510	45,540	45,840
Monklands	35,800	37,020	37,200	37,440	37,850	38,090	38,420	38,620
Motherwell	51,030	53,220	53,520	53,730	54,220	54,760	55,210	55,640
Renfrew	73,580	76,170	76,670	77,420	78,640	79,520	80,560	81,210
Strathkelvin	28,010	29,570	29,740	29,930	30,100	30,270	30,600	30,790
Tayside	**149,680**	**155,110**	**154,480**	**157,510**	**158,610**	**160,010**	**163,160**	**163,810**
Angus	34,970	36,200	36,620	36,850	36,990	37,300	38,670	39,000
Dundee City	70,430	72,070	72,610	72,900	73,180	73,420	73,830	73,650
Perth & Kinross	44,290	46,840	47,250	47,760	48,440	49,300	50,660	51,160
Orkney Islands	**6,820**	**7,100**	**7,080**	**7,090**	**7,160**	**7,270**	**7,770**	**7,900**
Shetland Islands	**7,790**	**8,230**	**8,300**	**8,350**	**8,470**	**8,560**	**8,400**	**8,540**
Western Isles	**10,330**	**11,060**	**11,150**	**11,160**	**10,990**	**11,060**	**11,020**	**11,150**

Source: Housing Statistics Unit SODD

1) All numbers individually rounded to nearest 10.

2) Figures for 1981 and 1986-1990 have not been revised following the 1991 Census of Population and are therefore not strictly comparable with the estimates for 1991 and 1992.

7

Table 1.3 Intercensal and annual changes in births, deaths and migration and their effect on the population of Scotland, 1861 to 1994

('000s)

Year	Population	Population change	Births	Deaths[1]	Natural Change	Estimated net civilian migration			Other changes[2]
						Total	Rest of UK	Overseas	
	Census population present								
1861	3,062.3						-	-	-
		297.7	1,124.3	708.0	416.3	-118.6	-	-	-
1871	3,360.0						-	-	-
		375.6	1,234.3	765.5	468.8	-93.2	-	-	-
1881	3,735.6						-	-	-
		290.1	1,252.6	744.8	507.9	-217.9	-	--	-
1891	4,025.6						-	-	-
		446.5	1,280.5	780.7	499.8	-53.4	-	-	-
1901	4,472.1						-	-	-
		288.8	1,305.6	762.7	542.9	-254.1	-	-	-
1911	4,760.9						-	-	-
		121.6	1,184.6	824.4	360.2	-238.6	-	-	-
1921	4,882.5						-	-	-
		-39.5	1,004.9	652.5	352.4	-390.0	-330.0	-60.0	-1.9
1931	4,843.0								
		253.4	1,849.3	1,347.0	502.3	-220.0	-210.0	-10.0	-28.9
1951	5,096.4								
		82.9	958.6	619.3	339.3	-282.0	-140.0	-142.0	25.6
1961	5,179.3								
		49.6	975.0	628.7	346.3	-326.5	-169.0	-157.5	29.9
1971	5,229.0								
		-98.3	696.7	638.1	58.6	-151.2	-52.1	-99.1	-5.7
1981	5,130.7								
		-168.6	663.7	635.7	28.0	-102.6	-45.9	-56.7	-94.0
1991	4,962.2[3]								
	Mid-year population estimate[4]								
1981	5,180.2								
		-13.4	67.2	65.8	1.5	-14.6	-0.9	-13.7	-0.3
1982	5,166.8								
		-14.2	65.8	63.9	1.8	-17.5	-5.0	-12.5	-1.5
1983	5,152.6								
		-7.0	64.3	62.9	1.4	-9.8	-9.0	-0.8	1.4
1984`	5,145.6								
		-8.7	66.1	62.4	3.7	-12.7	-9.7	-3.0	-0.3
1985	5,136.9								
		-13.9	66.8	65.2	1.6	-15.4	-11.5	-3.9	-0.1
1986	5,123.0								
		-10.4	66.0	61.2	4.7	-15.7	-11.4	-4.3	0.6
1987	5,112.6								
		-19.2	66.9	62.0	4.9	-24.9	-16.6	-8.3	0.8
1988	5,093.4								
		3.2	64.6	61.5	3.1	-0.5	0.1	-0.6	0.5
1989	5,096.6								
		5.6	64.1	65.5	-1.4	7.5	5.5	2.0	-0.5
1990	5,102.2								
		4.8	66.5	60.7	5.8	0.8	12.4	-11.6	-1.9
1991	5,107.0[3]								
		4.2	67.0	61.1	5.9	0.3	9.5	-9.2	-2.0
1992	5,111.2								
		9.0	64.3	61.9	2.4	4.9	7.4	-2.5	1.7
1993	5,120.2								
		12.2	63.1	62.6	0.5	9.8	7.2	2.6	1.9
1994	5,132.4								

Source: General Register Office for Scotland

(1) Includes estimated war deaths of non-civilians and merchant seamen abroad (74,000 in 1914-18 and 34,000 in 1939-45).

(2) The 'Other changes' component is a residual requirement to balance the detailed components with the overall population change. For the intercensal periods it includes any accumulated errors in the estimates of migration, any difference in the numbers of people away from home at the time of the census and any differences in the level of enumeration achieved by successive censuses. For the single years 1981 onwards, it includes movements to/from the armed forces and changes in the number of armed forces stationed in Scotland.

(3) The mid-year estimate for 1991 is significantly more than the population present at the 1991 Census mainly because of allowances made for underenumeration in the Census.

(4) Data for 1982 to 1990 were revised in 1993 to take account of final census-based population estimates for 1991.

Table 1.4(a)   **Proportional Distribution of area and population in Scotland by Region, 1891-1994**

	Area	Population								
		1891	1911	1931	1951	1961	1971	1981	1991	1994
Borders	6	3	2	2	2	2	2	2	2	2
Central	3	4	4	4	5	5	5	5	5	5
Dumfries and Galloway	8	4	3	3	3	3	3	3	3	3
Fife	2	5	6	6	6	6	6	6	7	7
Grampian	11	10	10	9	9	9	8	9	10	10
Highland	33	5	4	3	3	3	3	4	4	4
Lothian	2	13	13	13	14	14	14	14	15	15
Strathclyde	17	44	48	50	50	50	49	47	45	45
Tayside	10	10	8	8	8	8	8	8	8	8
Islands	7	3	2	2	1	1	1	2	1	1
Scotland	**100**	**100**	**100**	**100**	**100**	**100**	**100**	**100**	**100**	**100**

Source: General Register Office (Scotland)

Table 1.4(b)   **Proportional Distribution of area and population in Great Britain, 1891-1994**

	Area	Population								
		1891	1911	1931	1951	1961	1971	1981	1991	1994
England	57	82	82	83	84	85	85	85	86	86
Wales	9	5	6	6	5	5	5	5	5	5
Scotland	34	12	12	11	10	10	10	9	9	9
Great Britain	**100**	**100**	**100**	**100**	**100**	**100**	**100**	**100**	**100**	**100**

Source: General Register Office (Scotland)

Table 1.5   **Distribution of actual and projected population, by age and sex, 1911-2021[1]**

	Estimated population								Projected population[2]		
	1911	1921	1931	1951	1961	1971	1981	1991	2001	2011	2021
Persons *(thousands)*	4,751	4,882	4,843	5,102	5,184	5,236	5,180	5,107	5,134	5,082	5,040
Males *(thousands)*	2,304	2,348	2,326	2,439	2,485	2,516	2,495	2,470	2,502	2,493	2,478
Females *(thousands)*	2,447	2,535	2,517	2,664	2,699	2,720	2,685	2,637	2,632	2,590	2,562
Distribution											
Total	**1,000**	**1,000**	**1,000**	**1,000**	**1,000**	**1,000**	**1,000**	**1,000**	**1,000**	**1,000**	**1,000**
0-4	112	97	87	93	91	85	61	64	56	54	54
5-14	211	198	182	154	168	174	151	124	125	112	109
15-29	266	263	258	217	200	210	237	230	190	188	175
30-44	201	199	198	213	193	174	188	213	235	198	181
45-59	129	150	162	180	192	177	170	167	190	219	217
60-64	28	33	40	44	50	56	50	52	50	64	70
65-74	38	42	53	67	69	82	89	86	86	91	111
75+	16	17	20	32	37	42	54	64	68	74	84
Males											
Total	**1,000**	**1,000**	**1,000**	**1,000**	**1,000**	**1,000**	**1,000**	**1,000**	**1,000**	**1,000**	**1,000**
0-4	116	102	92	99	97	91	65	68	59	57	56
5-14	219	207	191	164	179	186	160	132	132	117	113
15-29	267	261	263	218	205	220	250	242	199	197	183
30-44	200	192	189	215	196	177	194	220	241	203	187
45-59	126	152	160	175	191	175	170	168	192	221	219
60-64	26	32	39	40	46	53	47	50	49	63	69
65-74	34	39	49	61	58	70	78	78	79	86	105
75+	12	13	16	27	29	28	35	43	49	56	66
Females											
Total	**1,000**	**1,000**	**1,000**	**1,000**	**1,000**	**1,000**	**1,000**	**1,000**	**1,000**	**1,000**	**1,000**
0-4	107	93	83	87	85	79	58	60	53	52	52
5-14	204	189	174	145	157	163	142	117	119	106	104
15-29	265	264	254	215	195	201	226	219	181	179	167
30-44	202	205	205	210	190	171	182	207	229	193	175
45-59	131	149	164	185	193	178	170	166	188	217	215
60-64	29	34	40	48	54	59	53	53	52	65	71
65-74	43	45	56	73	80	93	99	94	92	96	116
75+	19	21	24	37	45	55	72	84	87	91	100

Source: General Register Office (Scotland)

(1)   See introductory notes, paragraph 1.4 for details of assumptions made in this table.
(2)   Based on mid-1992 estimate of resident population.

Chart 1.1a Population Densities by Local Authority area in Scotland, 1994

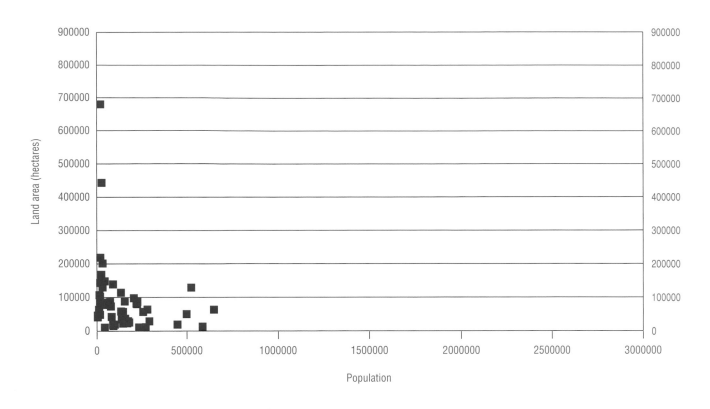

Chart 1.1b Population Densities of Counties in England, 1994

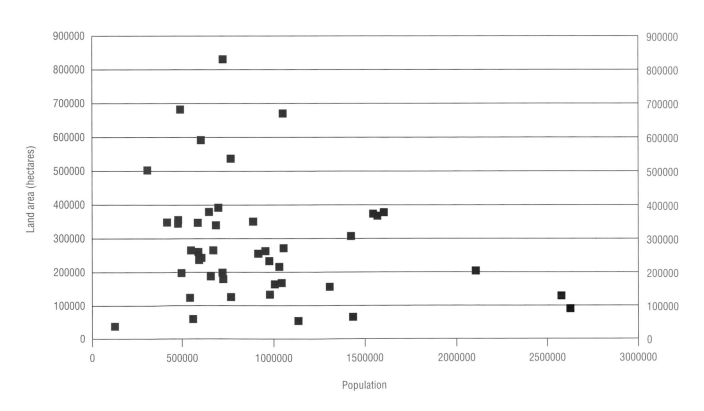

Source: General Register Office (Scotland)

Table 1.6   **Projected[1] number of dependants per 100 population of working age; Scotland: 1994-2032**

Age group	1994[2]	2001	2006	2011	2016	2021	2026	2031	2034
All dependants	**61**	**60**	**59**	**60**	**63**	**68**	**74**	**80**	**82**
Children under 16	**33**	**31**	**30**	**28**	**29**	**29**	**30**	**31**	**31**
Persionable ages 65/60[3] & over	**29**	**29**	**30**	**32**	**35**	**39**	**44**	**49**	**51**
65/60[3] - 74	19	18	18	20	22	25	27	30	31
75 & over	10	11	11	12	13	14	17	19	20

Source: General Register Office for Scotland

1) 1994-based projection.
2) Mid-year population estimate.
3) Age 65 for men, 60 for women.

Chart 1.2   Estimated population by age and sex, 1994

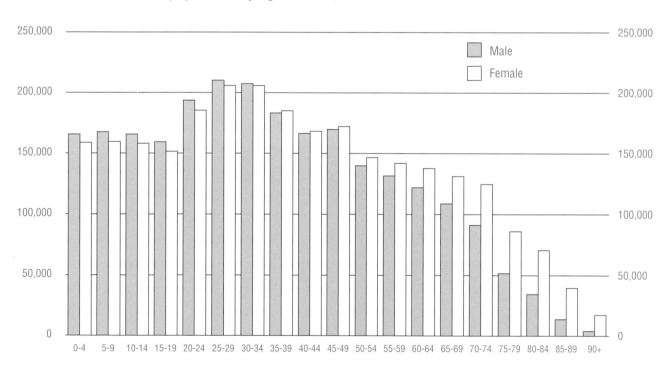

Source: General Register Office (Scotland)

11

Table 1.7 Death rates, by age and sex, 1951-1994

Age	Per 1,000 population										
	1951	1961	1971	1981	1988	1989	1990	1991	1992	1993	1994
Persons											
0	37.9	26.8	20.2	11.4	8.2	8.6	8.0	7.2	6.8	6.4	6.1
1-4	1.7	1.1	0.7	0.5	0.4	0.4	0.4	0.4	0.4	0.4	0.3
5-9	0.8	0.4	0.4	0.2	0.2	0.1	0.1	0.2	0.2	0.2	0.1
10-14	0.5	0.3	0.4	0.3	0.2	0.2	0.3	0.2	0.2	0.2	0.2
15-24	1.2	0.7	0.7	0.7	0.7	0.7	0.6	0.7	0.6	0.6	0.7
25-34	2.0	1.1	1.0	0.9	0.9	0.9	0.9	0.8	0.9	0.9	0.9
35-44	3.3	2.7	2.3	2.1	1.9	1.7	1.8	1.7	1.7	1.7	1.7
45-54	8.3	7.2	7.0	6.4	5.3	5.0	4.9	4.8	4.8	4.7	4.4
55-64	20.4	19.2	17.4	16.3	15.2	15.1	14.2	13.7	13.3	13.4	12.8
65-74	50.3	45.8	41.0	39.4	36.0	37.0	35.3	34.8	34.5	35.4	33.3
75-84	126.0	112.1	92.4	86.0	80.2	84.5	79.4	78.2	77.8	83.6	76.0
85+	279.0	247.2	202.2	192.2	178.6	194.0	177.5	175.9	182.9	194.3	174.6
Male											
0	43.5	30.6	22.6	12.3	9.5	10.1	9.1	8.8	7.8	7.3	6.6
1-4	1.8	1.2	0.8	0.6	0.5	0.5	0.5	0.4	0.4	0.4	0.3
5-9	0.9	0.6	0.4	0.3	0.2	0.1	0.2	0.3	0.2	0.2	0.2
10-14	0.5	0.4	0.5	0.3	0.3	0.3	0.3	0.2	0.2	0.2	0.3
15-24	1.3	1.0	1.1	1.0	1.0	1.0	1.0	0.9	1.0	0.9	1.0
25-34	2.1	1.4	1.2	1.2	1.2	1.1	1.2	1.1	1.3	1.2	1.3
35-44	3.6	3.2	2.8	2.7	2.4	2.1	2.2	2.2	2.1	2.1	2.0
45-54	10.4	9.1	8.7	8.2	6.9	6.1	6.1	6.1	6.0	6.0	5.4
55-64	26.4	26.1	23.3	21.3	19.6	19.2	17.8	17.3	17.0	17.2	16.2
65-74	59.0	59.4	56.7	52.5	47.3	48.4	46.2	45.8	44.5	45.8	42.9
75-84	140.0	131.5	118.6	114.8	104.1	109.0	103.9	101.0	101.0	107.3	97.9
85+	298.4	275.8	236.2	229.9	213.8	229.9	203.9	202.1	225.9	226.6	206.0
Female											
0	33.2	22.8	17.6	10.4	6.8	7.1	6.9	5.4	5.7	5.5	5.5
1-4	1.6	0.9	0.6	0.4	0.3	0.4	0.3	0.4	0.4	0.4	0.2
5-9	0.6	0.3	0.3	0.2	0.1	0.1	0.1	0.1	0.1	0.2	0.1
10-14	0.5	0.3	0.3	0.2	0.1	0.2	0.2	0.2	0.1	0.2	0.1
15-24	1.2	0.4	0.3	0.3	0.3	0.4	0.3	0.4	0.3	0.3	0.3
25-34	1.9	0.8	0.7	0.6	0.5	0.6	0.5	0.6	0.6	0.6	0.6
35-44	3.0	2.2	1.9	1.5	1.4	1.4	1.4	1.3	1.3	1.3	1.4
45-54	6.3	5.5	5.4	0.7	3.8	3.9	3.7	3.6	3.7	3.5	3.5
55-64	15.6	13.4	12.4	12.0	11.3	11.5	10.9	10.5	10.0	10.0	9.7
65-74	43.5	36.7	30.1	29.9	27.6	28.4	27.1	26.4	26.7	27.3	25.9
75-84	115.6	100.3	79.5	71.8	67.4	71.3	66.2	65.8	65.3	70.5	63.9
85+	267.9	232.9	188.9	181.1	168.2	183.4	169.5	167.8	170.1	184.3	164.8

Source: General Register Office (Scotland)

Table 1.8 Expectation of life, by sex and selected age, 1861-1994[1]

Period	Expectation of life at									
	Birth		Age 1		Age 15		Age 45		Age 65	
	Males	Females	Males	Females	Males	Females	Males	Females	Males	Females
1861-1870	40.3	43.9	45.6	47.5	42.3	44.5	22.7	24.5	10.8	11.6
1891-1900	44.7	47.4	51.1	52.7	44.3	46.2	22.2	24.2	10.5	11.5
1930-1932	56.0	59.5	60.7	63.1	50.4	42.7	25.1	27.3	11.0	12.6
1950-1952	64.4	68.7	66.2	69.9	53.1	56.7	25.5	29.1	11.4	13.2
1960-1962	66.3	72.0	67.3	72.7	53.9	59.1	25.8	30.5	11.5	14.2
1970-1972	67.3	73.7	67.8	73.9	54.3	60.3	26.2	31.5	11.6	15.4
1980-1982	69.1	75.3	69.0	75.1	55.4	61.4	27.1	32.4	12.3	16.1
1988	70.5	76.7	70.1	76.2	56.4	62.4	28.2	33.4	13.0	16.7
1989	70.6	76.1	70.3	75.7	56.6	61.9	28.2	32.9	12.7	16.3
1990	71.7	76.9	70.8	76.4	57.1	62.6	28.8	33.6	13.1	16.8
1991	71.4	77.1	71.0	76.6	57.3	62.8	29.0	33.8	13.3	17.0
1992	71.5	77.2	71.1	76.7	57.3	62.9	29.0	33.8	13.3	16.9
1993	71.4	76.9	70.9	76.3	57.2	62.5	28.8	33.5	13.1	16.5
1994	72.1	77.6	71.6	77.1	57.8	63.2	29.6	34.2	13.7	17.3

Source: General Register Office (Scotland)

(1)   The single year data have been extracted from GRO(S) Annual Abridged Life Tables.

Table 1.9   **Number of localities and usually resident population in localities by size of locality, 1991**[1]

Region/Islands area	Size of locality									
	Under 1,000		1,000-9,999		10,000-99,999		100,000 and over		Total	
	Number	Population	Number	Population	Number	Population	Number	Population	Number	Population
Scotland	**155**	**113,375**	**363**	**1,171,392**	**81**	**1,860,252**	**4**	**1,412,303**	**603**	**4,557,322**
Borders	8	4,993	15	42,881	2	29,565	-	-	25	77,439
Central	13	9,692	24	78,195	8	164,114	-	-	45	252,001
Dumfries & Galloway	7	5,167	16	52,844	2	43,484	-	-	25	101,495
Fife	11	8,688	41	131,606	6	181,730	-	-	58	322,024
Grampian	21	16,231	53	162,491	3	50,544	1	188,931	78	418,197
Highland	21	15,420	30	79,601	2	51,625	-	-	53	146,646
Lothian	10	7,226	35	128,400	10	165,329	1	401,910	56	702,865
Strathclyde	35	25,820	117	402,619	43	1,073,860	1	662,954	196	2,165,253
Tayside	12	8,704	24	66,201	5	100,001	1	158,508	42	333,414
Orkney	-	-	2	8,359	-	-	-	-	2	8,359
Shetland	8	5,502	2	8,392	-	-	-	-	10	13,894
Western Isles	9	5,932	4	9,803	-	-	-	-	13	15,735

Source: 1991 Census (Provisional classification of localities)

(1)   The above table contains one locality split by Local Government boundaries.
Harthill-Lothian Region population. 334. Strathclyde Region population 1,163
Each part of these areas is counted as an individual locality within the resident Region and therefore the total number of localities is 602.

Chart 1.3   Economically Active Population: means of transport to work, 1991

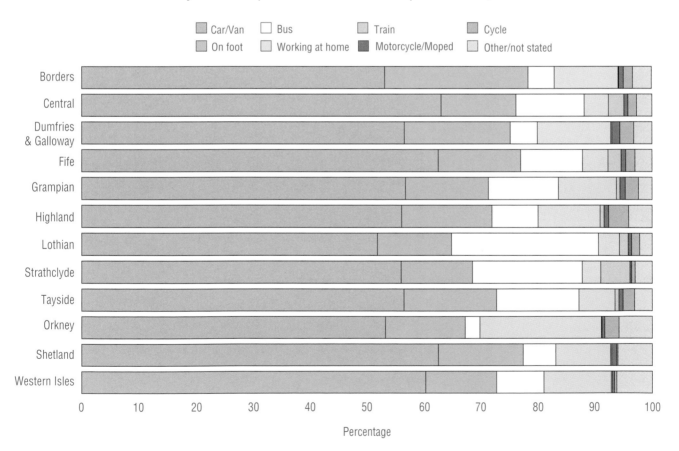

Source: General Register Office (Scotland)

Table 1.10   Population in localities and rural areas, 1991[1]

Region/Islands area	Households usually resident	Persons usually resident
Scotland		
Total	**2,020,050**	**4,998,567**
Localities	**1,813,478**	**4,446,297**
Rural	**206,572**	**552,270**
Borders		
Total	**43,243**	**103,881**
Localities	30,774	72,446
Rural	12,469	31,435
Central		
Total	**105,793**	**267,492**
Localities	96,545	242,309
Rural	9,248	25,183
Dumfries and Galloway		
Total	**59,070**	**147,805**
Localities	38,997	96,328
Rural	20,073	51,477
Fife		
Total	**137,041**	**341,199**
Localities	126,128	312,693
Rural	10,913	28,506
Grampian		
Total	**200,292**	**503,888**
Localities	163,893	403,073
Rural	36,399	100,815
Highland		
Total	**79,212**	**204,004**
Localities	51,237	131,226
Rural	27,975	72,778
Lothian		
Total	**304,382**	**726,010**
Localities	293,247	696,021
Rural	11,135	29,989
Strathclyde		
Total	**903,339**	**2,248,706**
Localities	863,981	2,140,344
Rural	39,358	108,362
Tayside		
Total	**160,645**	**383,848**
Localities	138,349	325,303
Rural	22,296	58,545
Orkney Islands		
Total	**7,695**	**19,612**
Localities	3,391	8,359
Rural	4,304	11,253
Shetland Islands		
Total	**8,368**	**22,522**
Localities	3,226	8,392
Rural	5,142	14,130
Western Isles		
Total	**10,970**	**29,600**
Localities	3,710	9,803
Rural	7,260	19,797

Source: 1991 Census General Register Office for Scotland

(1)   Localities with fewer than 1,000 usual residents are included in the Rural category.
(2)   Provisional data in SES4 has been superseded by this final data.

land

2 land

2.1   This section deals with statistics of land area and land use.

GEOLOGICAL MAP OF SCOTLAND

2.2   Map 2.1(a) is a simplified geological map provided by the Scottish Office Development Department.

LAND AREA

2.3   Ordnance Survey figures for land area and inland waters are shown in table 2.1. Data for the length of coastline and urban areas were obtained from the Scottish Office Development Department (SODD). The coastline includes developed and underdeveloped mainland coastline. Urban areas are derived from the areas of 'settlement' defined as continuously built up areas, separated by a gap of more than 1km, that had 500 or more resident population at the time of the 1981 Census. It is realised that the reform of Local Government will result in the requirement for a new table to be published, and this will be included in the next publication.

NATIONAL SOIL INVENTORY

2.4   The Macaulay Land Use Research Institute (MLURI), holds a National Soil Inventory, comprising descriptions of site characteristics and soil profiles located at every 5 km intersect of the National Grid, and soil analytical data for every 10km intersect. The descriptions follow standard notation and include information on parent material, soil drainage, degree of erosion, etc. The analytical data cover standard analyses (eg particle size analysis, exchangeable cations, pH, carbon content, etc.) and also special analyses that include information on aqua regia extractable heavy metals like nickel (Ni) and lead (Pb). Examples of these datasets are given as maps 2.2(a)(lead) and 2.2(b)(soil). These analytical datasets provide a unique baseline against which to measure and monitor changes in environmental quality over time. For example, changes in soil pH may reflect long term soil acidification; changes in heavy metal content, for example lead, may reflect changes in pollution climates (lead might be expected to stabilise as a result of the use of lead-free petrol).

The National Soil Inventory is particularly valuable for strategic resource assessments. It has been, and is being used in studies of soil pollution, most recently in studies of potential for sewage sludge utilisation in Scotland where a 15 fold increase in sludge volumes applied to land is envisaged by the year 2000 because of the EU Urban Waste Water Treatment Directive. A rule-based land suitability classification gas been applied to the National Soil Inventory and this has been used to derive estimates of suitable land on a Region by region basis (map 2.2(c)). This has enabled an objective appraisal of the Regional Council disposal strategies. It should also be noted that considerable differences in land suitability will remain after the formation of the three new Scottish Water Authorities in April 1996 (table 2.3).

THE LAND COVER OF SCOTLAND

2.5   A census of land cover in Scotland, based on the interpretation of specially flown aerial photography, has provided information on the relative importance of different vegetation types. It shows that over 50% of the country is covered by semi-natural vegetation, of which heather moorland (8.7%) and peatland (8.4%) are the most extensive single cover types. A further 22.3% of the total land area has mosaics with these two vegetation types. Woodland cover is predominantly coniferous plantation which, including recent planting, accounts for some 11.7%. This is broadly similar to the areas with arable agriculture (11.2%) and improved grassland (13.0%). A more comprehensive summary appears in table 2.2(a) and (b), and map 2.1(b).

The land cover of Scotland data relates to a 1988 baseline and they have been extensively used by Scottish Office Departments, including Scottish Natural Heritage as basis for strategic planning, (eg in relation to the Cairngorm Working Party), and the Forestry Commission which is using the data as part of the new Woodland Inventory. It is intended that the census be repeated to provide an indication of land cover changes at a national level.

AGRICULTURE

2.6   Map 2.3(a) outlines climatic guidelines for agriculture.

2.7   The Scottish Agricultural Census of main holdings, is carried out in June each year, whereby the Scottish Office Agriculture, Environment and Fisheries Department (SOAEFD) provides information on farm tenure, crop area, livestock and manpower.

A questionnaire is sent to all farm holdings, provided they meet certain criteria - the main ones being:-

a.   that the Standard Gross Margin (SGM) - which is a measure of the business size of the holding - is not less than one European Size Unit.

b.   that the area of the holding is at least one hectare.

In 1994, over 32,500 of the 50,000 holdings in Scotland were included in the annual census (the remainder were minor holdings) tables 2.4 to 2.6.

2.8   The "net losses from agricultural land" figures (table 2.7) are from the June Census and show the reasons for any changes in the areas of the holdings. The "Five Year Set-aside Scheme" (table 2.8) is an EC initiative introduced in 1988 whereby farmers receive annual payments to take land currently used for arable crops out of production for a specified length of time.

2.9   The pesticide usage section of the Scottish Agricultural Science Agency (SASA) undertakes regular surveys of pesticide usage as apart of a UK programme. Surveys on arable crops have been carried out in 1974, 1977, 1982, 1988, 1990, 1992 and 1994. Table 2.10 shows the use of different groups of pesticides on arable crops between 1990 and 1994, whilst 2.11 shows the use on cereals, potatoes and oilseed rape in 1994. Detailed results are presented in a SOAEFD series of Survey Reports covering pesticide usage in Scotland that include all field crops and various stored products, and are available from SASA on request.

2.10   Map 2.3(b) and table 2.12 are based on the agricultural land capability classification devised by MLURI and adopted by SOAEFD on 1 July 1987. The agricultural capability of the 7 classes is as follows;

Class	Production Capability
1	Very wide range of crops
2	Wide range of crops
3.1	Moderate range of crops - above average
3.2	Moderate range of crops - average
4	Narrow range of crops
5	Used as improved grassland
6	Use only as rough grazing
7	Very limited agricultural value

2.11   Information on Forestry (maps 2.4 and 2.5(a) and (b) and tables 2.13 to 2.20) is provided by the Forestry Commission and MLURI. Map 2.4 and table 2.13 are based on MLURI forestry capability classification. The classification descriptions are as follows:

Class	Flexibility for growth and management of tree crops
F1	Excellent
F2	Very good
F3	Good
F4	Moderate
F5	Limited
F6	Very limited
F7	Unsuitable

2.12   From 1 April 1992, the Forestry Commission re-organised to make a clear distinction between its regulatory and grant aiding function as a Government department (carried out by the Forestry Authority) and the management of the Commission's forest estate (carried out by Forest Enterprise which is now a trading body acting as executive agency of the Commission). Maps 2.5(a) and (b) are based on Forestry Commission records of Forestry Commission planted land and privately owned planted land covered by grant schemes, and on Ordnance Survey records. The census of woodland and non-woodland trees is carried out at intervals of approximately 15 years. Tables 2.18 and 2.19 are from the 1980 Census which involved a detailed survey of woodland areas in Scotland (excluding Orkney, Shetland and the Western Isles). A new survey is currently underway from which revised information will become available. Table 2.20 shows the areas of land acquired and disposed of by the Forestry Commission in each of the last ten financial years.

PLANNING APPLICATIONS AND APPEALS

2.13   Tables 2.21 to 2.25 give information on the number of planning applications and certain appeals submitted to the Secretary of State for Scotland under the Town and Country Planning legislation. The main types of appeal are against decisions by planning authorities on applications for planning permission or advertisement consent, and against enforcement notices served by planning authorities. Although appeals are submitted to the Secretary of State, the great majority are decided by Reporters from the Scottish Office Inquiry Reporter's Unit acting under delegated powers.

ROAD LENGTHS

2.14   Information on road lengths (tables 2.26 and 2.27) is obtained from annual returns by Highway Authorities (Regional and Islands Councils). Information on traffic volume is obtained from Department of Transport traffic estimates.

INDUSTRIAL SITES AND LAND

2.15   The Industrial Sites Register (map 2.6 and tables 2.29 to 2.30) is compiled by SODD from annual returns completed by Regional and Islands Councils and is designed to monitor industrial land supply. It deals with (a) land allocated in development plans for industrial use, (b) land not allocated for industrial use but which is secure in terms of planning permission, (c) industrial land in Enterprise Zones and Special Planning Zones.

HOUSING LAND SUPPLY

2.16   Housing Land Supply and new dwellings completed (map 2.7 and tables 2.31 and 2.32) are monitored annually by SODD through the Housing Land Annual Returns made by the Planning Authorities and New Town Development Corporations. These returns were last published for 1990, and HLAR has not operated since then. The returns published to 1990 cover all land likely to be developed for housing, measured by the potential number of dwellings on each site. Not all the sites may be immediately available because of physical conditions or infrastructure provision. Also the marketability of some of the sites may be constrained by their location, size and quality.

2.17   Information on new dwellings completed (tables 2.33 and 2.34) is provided by the Housing Statistics Unit, SODD. Further details are available in their series of bulletins "Housing Trends in Scotland".

VACANT AND DERELICT LAND

2.18   The Scottish Vacant and Derelict Land Survey provides information from local Authorities on:
a. derelict sites
b. vacant sites in urban areas (ie areas with a population of 2,000 or more)
c. vacant sites within 1 km of the edge of urban areas

Tables 2.35 and 2.36 give results from the 1994 survey. Information from that survey has also been published in a SODD commentary.

PRODUCTION OF MINERALS AND AGGREGATES

2.19   Tables 2.37, 2.38 (a) and (b) are from the Central Statistical Office (CSO) publication "Business Monitor" PA1007. Table 2.39 is from the "Survey of Aggregate Working in Scotland: 1993; Collated Results and Commentary", published by SODD in May 1995. CSOs carry out an annual survey of all mineral production in the UK. Other statistical information on minerals is available from the annual British Geological Survey publication "United Kingdom Minerals Yearbook". Map 2.8 is from SODD's report for 1993.

WASTE COLLECTION, DISPOSAL AND REGULATION

2.20   Tables 2.40 to 2.44 and charts 2.6 to 2.8 are derived from responses to the Hazardous Waste Inspectorate's Annual Survey "Waste Collection, Disposal and Regulation Statistics" of District and Island Councils. Some provisional statistics for 1991 were published in the second Hazardous Waste Inspectorate Scotland Report (August 1993), but where appropriate, the opportunity has been taken in this publication to update these figures using a verification exercise.

2.21   A revised format has been adopted for table 2.40 using a different database to that used in previous editions of "Scottish Environment Statistics". Comparisons in numbers of licences and resolutions with the previous versions may not, therefore, be appropriate.

2.22   Maps 2.9(a) and (b) show the distribution, by size and location, of all local authority and private sector landfill sites that were reported as being operational in 1995.

2.23   Tables 2.43 and 2.44 show the types of waste collected for recycling and the origin of such waste, respectively.

2.24   Table 2.45 on bottle bank sites and the amount of glass collected was supplied by the British Glass Manufacturers Confederation, and is compiled from returns made to them by District Councils and United Glass Limited, of Alloa, Clackmannanshire.

Map 2.1a Simplified geological map of Scotland (see notes, paragraph 2.2)

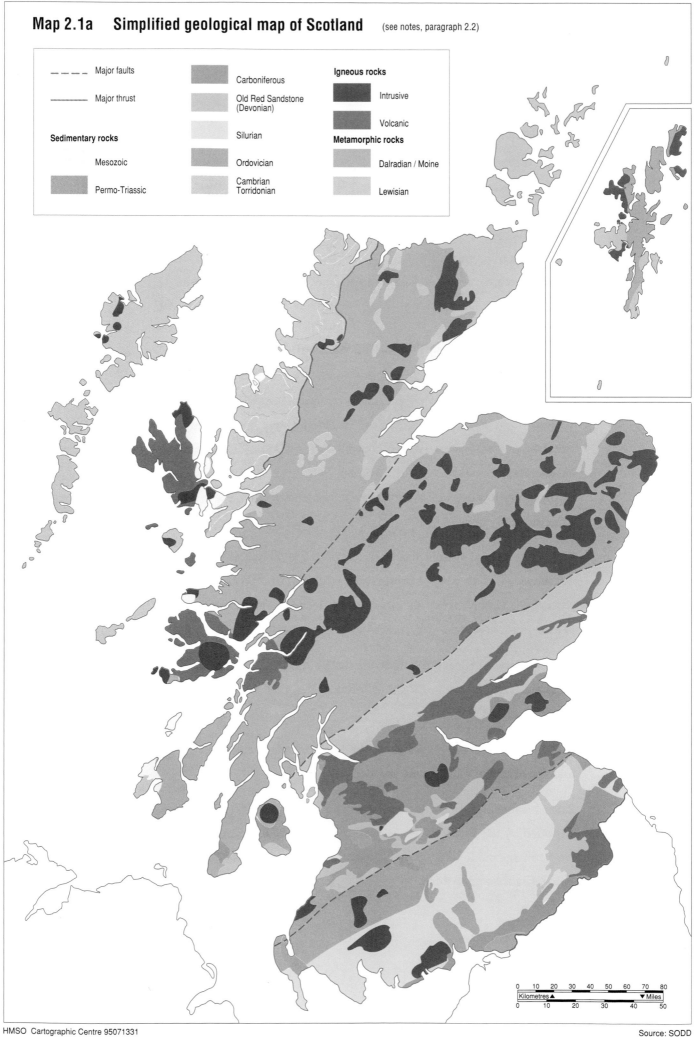

Legend:

- – – – – Major faults
- ——— Major thrust

Sedimentary rocks
- Mesozoic
- Permo-Triassic
- Carboniferous
- Old Red Sandstone (Devonian)
- Silurian
- Ordovician
- Cambrian Torridonian

Igneous rocks
- Intrusive
- Volcanic

Metamorphic rocks
- Dalradian / Moine
- Lewisian

Kilometres ▲ 0 10 20 30 40 50 60 70 80
▼ Miles 0 10 20 30 40 50

HMSO Cartographic Centre 95071331

Source: SODD

Table 2.1 **Land area[1], inland water[1], coastline[2] and urban area[3], by region and district[4]**

Region/district	Total area (km²)	Land area (km²)	Inland water (km²)	Total mainland coastline (km)	Developed mainland coastline (km)	Undeveloped mainland coastline (km)	Urban area (km²)
Scotland	**78,783**	**77,080**	**1,703**	**3,906**	**478**	**3,428**	**2,370**
Borders	**4,698**	**4,670**	**28**	**32**	**2**	**30**	**49**
Berwickshire	880	876	4	32	2	30	10
Ettrick & Lauderdale	1,366	1,355	11	-	-	-	18
Roxburgh	1,548	1,540	8	-	-	-	13
Tweeddale	904	899	5	-	-	-	8
Central	**2,700**	**2,627**	**73**	**27**	**13**	**14**	**139**
Clackmannan	161	160	1	4	-	4	24
Falkirk	294	291	3	23	13	10	72
Stirling	2,245	2,176	69	-	-	-	43
Dumfries and Galloway	**6,425**	**6,370**	**55**	**350**	**24**	**326**	**83**
Annandale & Eskdale	1,563	1,553	9	24	1	23	36
Nithsdale	1,441	1,433	8	36	4	32	23
Stewartry	1,691	1,671	20	99	3	96	14
Wigtown	1,730	1,713	17	191	16	175	9
Fife	**1,319**	**1,308**	**11**	**170**	**93**	**77**	**164**
Dunfermline	307	302	5	40	27	14	61
Kirkcaldy	251	248	2	28	23	6	57
North East Fife	761	758	3	101	44	57	47
Grampian	**8,751**	**8,707**	**44**	**295**	**57**	**238**	**264**
Aberdeen City	186	184	2	17	5	12	75
Banff & Buchan	1,533	1,528	5	118	25	93	37
Gordon	2,221	2,214	7	23	1	93	37
Kincardine & Deeside	2,567	2,550	17	56	7	50	34
Moray	2,244	2,231	13	80	19	61	75
Highland	**26,136**	**25,304**	**832**	**1,906**	**65**	**1,841**	**195**
Badenoch & Strathspey	2,366	2,317	49	-	-	-	15
Caithness	1,806	1,776	30	157	3	154	29
Inverness	2,911	2,789	122	44	5	40	28
Lochaber	4,648	4,468	180	398	13	385	14
Nairn	425	422	3	14	3	12	4
Ross & Cromarty	5,173	4,976	197	635	34	601	47
Skye & Lochalsh	2,730	2,691	39	222	3	219	15
Sutherland	6,077	5,865	212	436	5	431	43
Lothian	**1,770**	**1,756**	**14**	**99**	**39**	**60**	**288**
East Lothian	717	713	4	67	21	46	52
Edinburgh City	264	261	3	26	17	9	135
Midlothian	361	358	3	-	-	-	34
West Lothian	428	423	5	6	1	5	66
Strathclyde	**13,773**	**13,529**	**244**	**938**	**166**	**772**	**854**
Argyll & Bute	6,613	6,497	116	693	25	668	63
Bearsden & Milngavie	37	36	1	-	-	-	19
Clydebank	36	35	1	2	2	-	13
Clydesdale	1,332	1,322	10	-	-	-	24
Cumbernauld & Kilsyth	105	103	2	-	-	-	19
Cumnock & Doon Valley	805	800	5	-	-	-	20
Cunninghame	885	878	7	47	28	19	69
Dumbarton	526	472	54	79	70	9	47
East Kilbride	286	285	1	-	-	-	21
Eastwood	118	115	3	-	-	-	19
Glasgow City	201	198	3	-	-	-	178
Hamilton	133	131	2	-	-	-	33
Inverclyde	162	158	4	29	20	9	34
Kilmarnock & Loudoun	375	373	2	-	-	-	28
Kyle & Carrick	1,338	1,317	21	79	20	59	57
Monklands	168	164	4	-	-	-	36
Motherwell	174	172	2	-	-	-	60
Renfrew	313	307	6	9	2	8	79
Strathkelvin	166	164	2	-	-	-	37
Tayside	**7,643**	**7,502**	**141**	**89**	**20**	**69**	**180**
Angus	2,045	2,031	14	50	5	45	42
Dundee City	236	235	1	24	16	8	54
Perth & Kinross	5,362	5,236	126	15	-	15	84
Orkney Islands	**1,010**	**976**	**34**	..	..	..	**14**
Shetland Islands	**1,470**	**1,433**	**37**	..	..	..	**16**
Western Isles	**3,087**	**2,898**	**189**	..	..	..	**124**

Source:Ordnance Survey/SODD

[1] At 1985.
[2] At 1983. Total mainland coastline excludes island authority areas, and smaller islands. The mainland coastline of the Orkney Islands, the Shetland Islands and the Western Isles total 944 km, 1,369 km and 1,813 km, respectively. In addition, coastline of smaller islands totals 817 km in Highland Region and 1,344 km in Strathclyde Region. Developed and undeveloped coastline figures are for mainland only.
[3] At 1981 census. See introductory notes, paragraph 2.3 for definition.
[4] Figures may not sum to total due to rounding.

Map 2.1b   Land Cover of Scotland, 1995

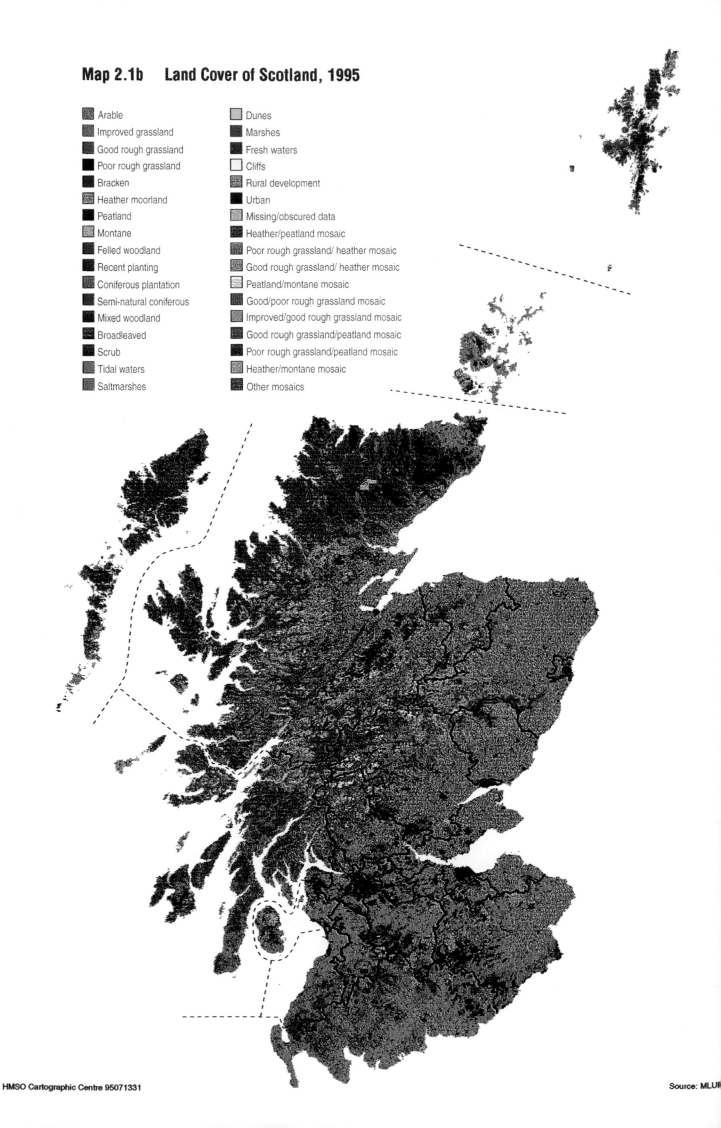

Arable
Improved grassland
Good rough grassland
Poor rough grassland
Bracken
Heather moorland
Peatland
Montane
Felled woodland
Recent planting
Coniferous plantation
Semi-natural coniferous
Mixed woodland
Broadleaved
Scrub
Tidal waters
Saltmarshes

Dunes
Marshes
Fresh waters
Cliffs
Rural development
Urban
Missing/obscured data
Heather/peatland mosaic
Poor rough grassland/ heather mosaic
Good rough grassland/ heather mosaic
Peatland/montane mosaic
Good/poor rough grassland mosaic
Improved/good rough grassland mosaic
Good rough grassland/peatland mosaic
Poor rough grassland/peatland mosaic
Heather/montane mosaic
Other mosaics

Source: MLU

Table 2.2(a) Land cover summary, Scotland[(1)(2)], 1988 — Km²

Cover Types	Single Feature area	Single Feature %	features in mosaics primary	features in mosaics secondary	Estimated total cover[(3)]
Open Countryside					
Arable	8,826.9	11.2	18.1	10.1	8,841.8
Improved grassland	10,281.1	13.0	1,086.2	230.1	11,024.9
Good rough grassland	2,472.2	3.1	1,995.2	2,847.3	4,808.2
Poor rough grassland	2,011.0	2.6	1,735.3	3,371.8	4,400.9
Bracken	117.3	0.1	201.3	752.1	538.9
Heather moorland	6,881.5	8.7	13,685.9	4,572.6	16,922.1
Peatland	6,600.2	8.4	3,661.1	11,308.2	13,320.1
Montane	1,604.5	2.0	1,202.2	346.9	2,464.6
Rock and cliffs	348.1	0.4	46.7	98.2	415.4
Woodland					
Felled woodland	299.8	0.4	13.6	5.0	310.0
Recent planting	3,092.0	3.9	94.7	110.7	3,193.1
Coniferous plantation	6,142.1	7.8	85.5	29.5	6,205.2
Semi-natural coniferous	75.0	0.1	4.1	14.8	83.4
Mixed woodland	854.5	1.1	17.1	27.1	875.6
Broadleaved	1,024.3	1.3	39.4	49.3	1,067.7
Scrub	74.4	0.1	8.6	82.3	112.5
Wet Ground					
Fresh waters	1,532.0	1.9	-	9.7	1,535.0
Marshes	127.9	0.2	8.2	72.0	161.6
Saltmarshes	60.4	0.1	0.6	1.8	61.5
Dunes	193.1	0.2	55.7	43.7	244.0
Tidal waters	27.3	-	-	-	27.3
Developed					
Rural development	470.3	0.6	50.0	4.2	502.0
Urban	1,444.8	1.8	1.0	1.3	1,445.9
Other					
Missing photography/obscured land	256.0	0.3	1.5	23.1	266.1
Subtotal	**54,816.7**	**69.5**			
Mosaics of types above	24,011.8	30.5	24,011.8	24,011.8	
National Total	**78,828.5**	**100.0**			**78,828.5**

Source: MLURI

1) Area in square kilometres to 1 decimal place.
2) The totals shown may not match the totals of the columns due to rounding.
3) This estimate is based on the assumption that where a cover type is the primary feature in a mosaic it accounts for 60% of the mosaic area and where it appears as a secondary feature it accounts for 40%. These estimates are therefore very crude and only appear as a guide to the extent of cover types within single features and mosaics combined.

Table 2.2(b) Significant Mosaics, Scotland 1988 — Km²

Mosaics	Area	Percent
Heather moorland and Peatland	12,370.9	15.7
Poor rough grassland and Heather moorland	3,230.0	4.1
Good rough grassland and Heather moorland	1,452.9	1.8
Peatland and Montane	935.5	1.2
Good rough grassland and Poor rough grassland	848.0	1.1
Improved grassland and Good rough grassland	814.8	1.0
Good rough grassland and Bracken	660.9	0.8
Poor rough grassland and Peatland	634.0	0.8
Heather moorland and Montane	539.0	0.7
Sub Total	**21,486.9**	**27.3**
Remaining mosaics	**2,524.9**	**3.2**
Mosaics of summary cover types	**24,011.8**	**30.5**

Source: MLURI

Table 2.3 Proposed Scottish Water Authorities 1996

Proposed Water Authority	Area estimates (square kilometres	Projected sludge volumes (tonnes dry solids)	Ratio of volume of sludge to land available	Percentage of land required annually *
North	7,597	39,000	5.1	1.0
East	4,176	36,200	8.7	1.7
West	4,550	66,900	14.7	2.9

Source: MLURI

* Application rate of 5 tds/hectare/annum

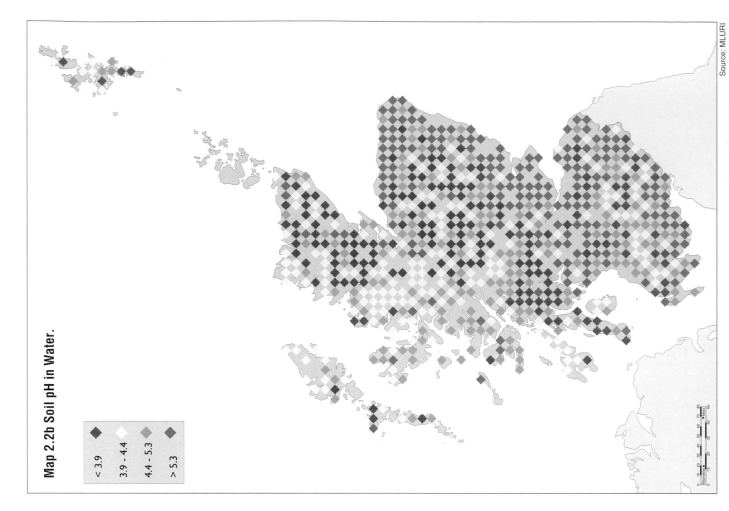

Map 2.2b Soil pH in Water.

◆	< 3.9
◇	3.9 - 4.4
◆	4.4 - 5.3
◆	> 5.3

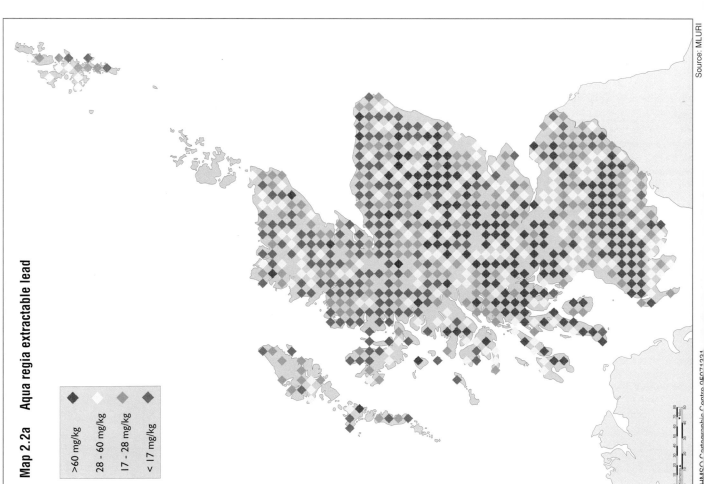

Map 2.2a   Aqua regia extractable lead

◆	>60 mg/kg
◇	28 - 60 mg/kg
◆	17 - 28 mg/kg
◆	< 17 mg/kg

Source: MLURI

HMSO Cartographic Centre 05071321

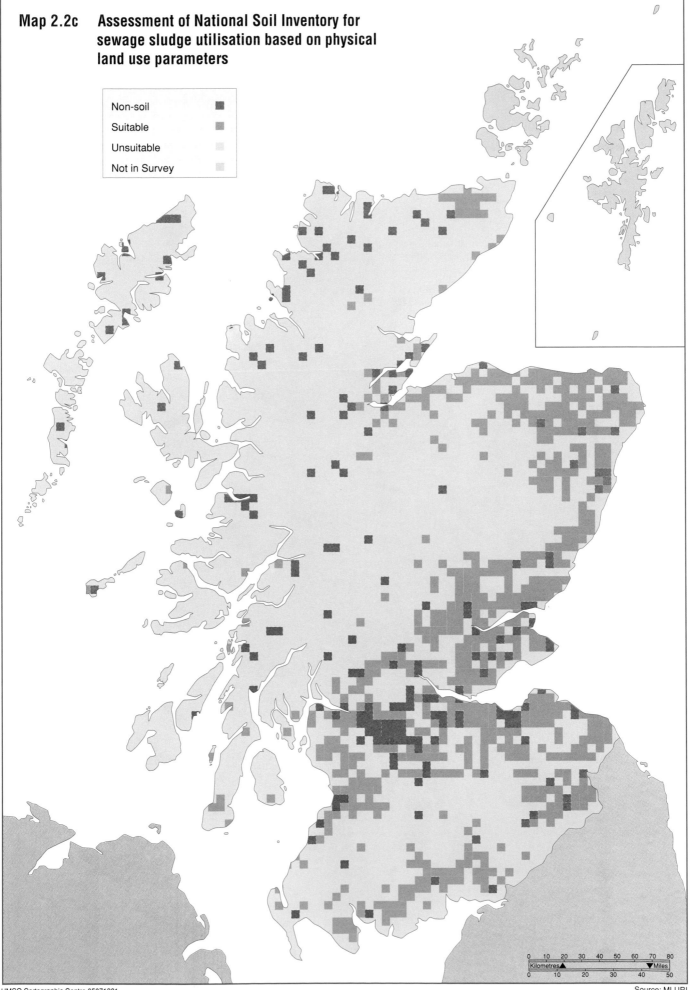

Map 2.2c   Assessment of National Soil Inventory for
            sewage sludge utilisation based on physical
            land use parameters

Non-soil
Suitable
Unsuitable
Not in Survey

0 10 20 30 40 50 60 70 80
Kilometres▲   ▼Miles
0   10   20   30   40   50

HMSO Cartographic Centre 95071331

Source: MLURI

Map 2.3a   Assessment of Climatic Factors in Land Capability for Agriculture in Scotland

Very minor or no climatic restraints

Minor climatic restraints

Moderate climatic restraints

Moderately severe climatic restraints

Severe climatic restraints

Very severe climatic restraints

Extremely severe climatic restraints

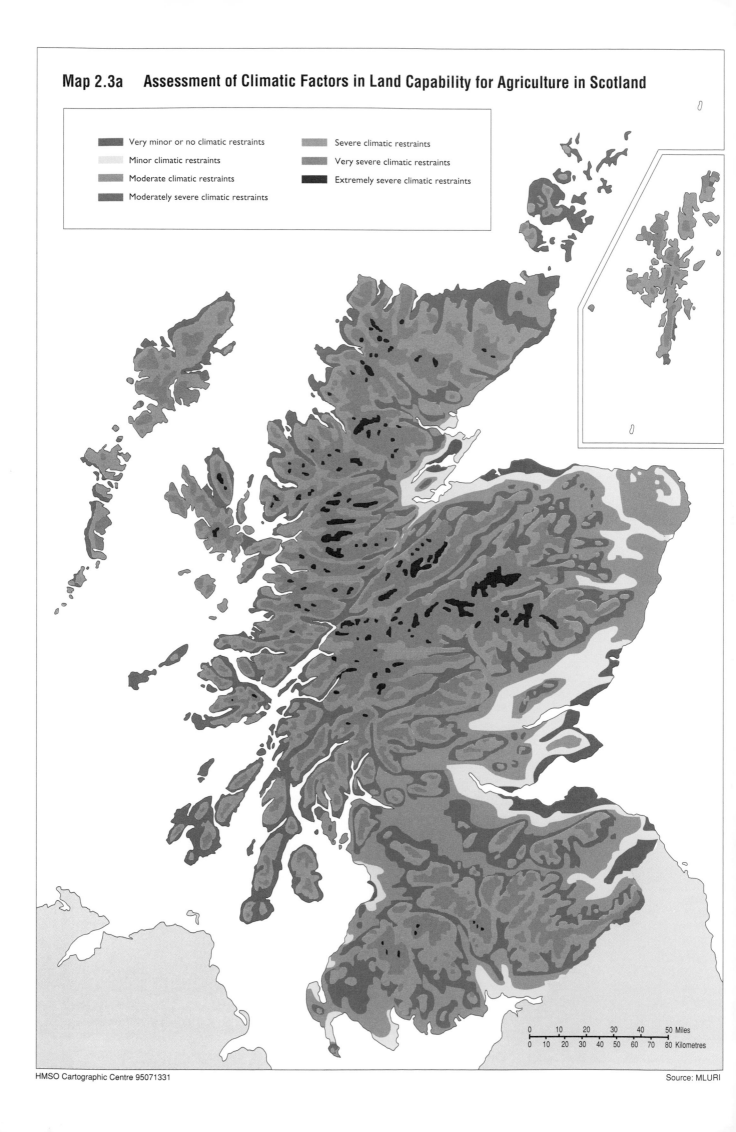

0   10   20   30   40   50 Miles

0   10   20   30   40   50   60   70   80 Kilometres

HMSO Cartographic Centre 95071331

Source: MLURI

Table 2.4 Area under crops, 1985-1994[1][2]

thousand hectares

	1985	1986	1987	1988	1989	1990	1991	1992	1993	1994
Total agricultural area	5,988	5,967	5,955	5,925	5,903	5,890	5,858	5,885	5,859	5,840
Rough grazing[3]	4,172	4,145	4,113	4,081	4,051	4,033	4,006	4,009	3,962	3,904
Crop and grass	1,704	1,709	1,722	1,719	1,717	1,717	1,711	1,728	1,734	1,752
Crops and fallow	669	668	675	670	652	638	628	637	644	637
Wheat	82	89	104	99	108	111	110	122	109	105
Triticale[4]	...	...	2	1	1	1	1	1	1	1
Barley	416	418	388	390	362	338	329	311	276	262
Oats and mixed grain	29	28	29	36	35	30	28	27	25	28
Rape for oilseed	23	22	45	42	36	45	50	57	60	70
Peas for combining	15	10	13	9	5	4	3	4	4	2
Potatoes intended for seed	20	18	17	17	17	16	15	15	15	15
ware	13	12	12	12	11	11	12	12	12	12
Turnips and swedes for stockfeeding	36	34	32	31	30	27	23	22	20	18
Other crops for stockfeeding	16	16	14	13	12	12	11	11	10	9
Vegetables for human consumption	8	9	8	9	10	11	11	11	10	11
Soft fruit	3	3	3	3	3	3	3	2	2	2
Other crops	2	2	2	2	2	2	3	5	5	3
Fallow	5	7	7	7	19	26	28	37	97	6
Total grass	1,035	1,042	1,047	1,049	1,065	1,079	1,084	1,091	1,089	1,114
Grass less than 5 years old										
For mowing	230	219	214	203	203	207	198	196	192	187
Not for mowing	225	218	210	213	211	201	197	189	184	186
Grass more than 5 years old										
For mowing	113	114	118	117	121	128	127	132	139	140
Not for mowing	467	491	506	516	531	542	561	573	575	602

Source: SOAEFD

.. Data not collected.
(1) Figures may not sum to total due to rounding.
(2) 1987 et seq on new threshold basis.
(3) Includes common grazing.
(4) Triticale is a cereal developed from wheat and rye.

Table 2.5 Crops, grass and rough grazing, by region, 1994[1]

thousand hectares

	Scotland	North West				North East	South East				South West		
		Shetland	Orkney	Western Isles	Highland	Grampian	Tayside	Fife	Lothian	Borders	Central	Strathclyde	Dumfries & Galloway
Crops, Grass and Rough Grazing	5,074	65	80	55	1,589	612	607	93	119	365	189	873	427
Rough Grazing	3,323	49	29	45	1,433	223	392	7	32	179	132	596	206
Grass	1,114	15	46	9	114	193	80	28	33	105	41	250	200
Cereals	396	-	4	-	27	118	75	36	35	53	10	20	16
Oilseed Rape	70	-	-	-	3	28	18	7	4	7	2	-	1
Other crops and bare fallow	172	-	1	1	12	50	43	16	14	21	4	6	4

Source: SOAEFD

- = less than half the final digit ie less than ½ hectare.

1) At the June census, table excludes common grazing and woodland and other land on farms.

Chart 2.1   Crops, grass and rough grazing, 1994

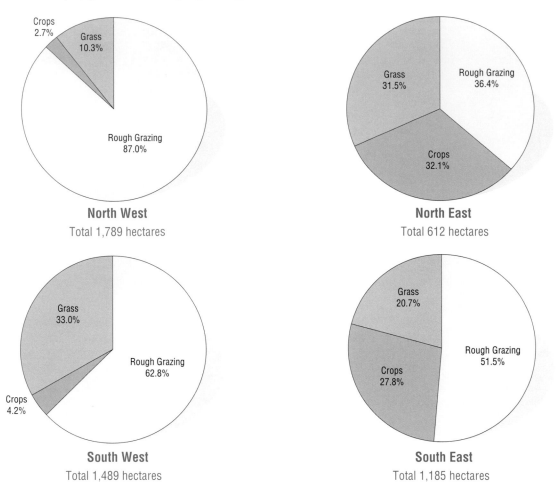

Crops
2.7%
Grass
10.3%
Rough Grazing
87.0%

North West
Total 1,789 hectares

Grass
31.5%
Rough Grazing
36.4%
Crops
32.1%

North East
Total 612 hectares

Grass
33.0%
Rough Grazing
62.8%
Crops
4.2%

South West
Total 1,489 hectares

Grass
20.7%
Rough Grazing
51.5%
Crops
27.8%

South East
Total 1,185 hectares

Source: SOAEFD

Chart 2.2   Distribution of agricultural units, percentages by size, groups and region, 1994

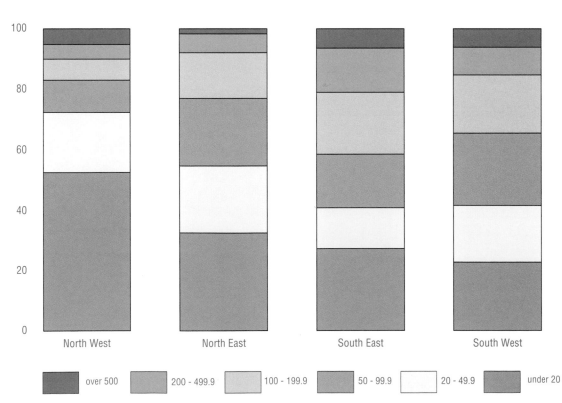

over 500	200 - 499.9	100 - 199.9	50 - 99.9	20 - 49.9	under 20

North West   North East   South East   South West

Source: SOAEFD

Table 2.6   Distribution of agricultural units, by size groups and region 1994[1]

number

Size (hectares)	Scotland	North West				North East	South East				South West		
		Shetland	Orkney	Western Isles	Highland	Grampian	Tayside	Fife	Lothian	Borders	Central	Strathclyde	Dumfries & Galloway
Total	32,513	1,309	1,342	1,634	4,758	6,648	2,909	1,071	1,153	1,766	1,100	5,747	3,076
0.1 - 0.9	496	9	12	41	124	109	29	27	18	15	7	66	39
1 - 1.9	1,240	28	24	193	264	246	101	61	45	36	30	148	64
2 - 4.9	3,273	141	98	485	641	642	252	112	160	114	84	407	137
5 - 9.9	2,804	259	87	400	539	528	180	62	94	103	60	342	150
10 - 19.9	3,302	249	232	317	636	649	186	64	93	138	99	462	177
20 - 49.9	6,070	348	445	120	864	1,478	441	129	167	199	212	1,161	506
50 - 99.9	6,031	147	255	26	531	1,475	594	226	189	221	252	1,432	683
100 - 199.9	4,925	72	134	23	398	997	599	271	212	322	191	915	791
200 - 499.9	2,736	39	41	15	335	410	333	107	138	420	79	464	355
500 and over	1,636	17	14	14	426	114	195	12	37	198	86	349	174

Source: SOAEFD

1) At the June agricultural census.

Table 2.7   Net losses of agricultural land, 1988/89-1993/94[1]

hectares

	1988/89	1989/90	1990/91	1991/92	1992/93	1993/94
Roads, Housing, Industry[2]	485.3	583.7	544.0	649.5	733.9	791.3
Recreation	259.0	332.8	360.6	415.9	197.0	677.3
Mineral Workings	803.6	914.8	766.0	95.9	197.5	24.3
Electricity and Water	147.1	2.0	158.8	9.1	0.4	2.7
Service Depts	1.4	1.6	0.7	0.0	0.0	13.0
Forestry[2]	14,503.4	16,406.8	9,887.2	6,967.2	8,244.3	5,907.3
Other	698.3	402.8	311.9	320.4	156.9	3,488.9
Total	**16,898.1**	**18,644.5**	**12,029.2**	**8,458.0**	**9,530.0**	**10,904.8**

Source: SOAEFD

1) Year is from June to June.
2) The figures for losses to roads, housing and industry for 1989/90 and 1990/91 and those for losses to forestry in 1990/91 have been amended from the last volume.

Table 2.8   Land set-aside under the five year set aside scheme by type, 1988-1994[1]

hectares

	Number of Holdings	Area				
		Fallow	Woodland	Farm woodland scheme	Non-agricultural use	Total
1988 Programme	369	10,829.84	93.94	64.84	461.38	11,450.00
1988 & 1989 Prog	517	16,807.09	218.21	190.19	652.51	17,868.00
1988 - 1990 Prog	645	20,111.33	900.47	316.03	955.17	22,283.00
1988 - 1991 Prog	736	21,078.02	1,118.11	426.44	1,893.55	24,516.12
1988 - 1992 Prog	630	20,433.10	1,083.90	413.39	1,835.61	23,766.00
1988 - 1993 Prog	313	9,612.14	509.89	194.47	863.50	11,180.00
1988 - 1994 Prog*	193	4,804.40	628.37	96.55	380.19	5,909.51

Source: SOAEFD

1) Cumulative figures over the period shown.
*Provisional

Table 2.9 Estimated fertiliser use on crops and grass, 1988-1994[1]

Kilograms per hectare

	1988	1989	1990	1991	1992	1993	1994
Nitrogen	129	118	122	117	116	119	118
Phosphate	45	45	43	40	43	41	43
Potash	47	51	50	47	48	47	46

Source: SOAEFD

(1) Excludes Orkney, Shetland and Western Isles.

Table 2.10 Trends in pesticide usage on all arable crops[1], 1990, 1992 and 1994

	1990		1992		1994	
	Total hectares treated with active ingredients	Total tonnes of active ingredients	Total hectares treated with active ingredients	Total tonnes of active ingredients	Total hectares treated with active ingredients	Total tonnes of active ingredients
Area grown (hectares)	550,110		543,240		491,316	
All pesticides	4,446.800	6,348.0	4,768,029	5,244.8	4,218,563	6,947.9
Seed dressings	695,575	48.2	883,652	74.5	982,576	154.5
Insecticides	234,303	32.7	204,388	20.4	221,423	24.3
Molluscicides	18,073	3.7	33,088	6.9	24,744	6.5
Fungicides	1,873,805	1,004.2	1,907,244	784.6	1,499.626	678.2
Herbicides and desiccants	1,236,509	4,988.0	1,216,736	4,081.8	1,190,725	5,828.7
Growth regulators	388,535	271.2	432,921	276.7	299,238	199.0

Source: SASA

(1) Refers to cereal crops (barley, wheat and oats), potatoes and oilseed rape.

Table 2.11 Usage of pesticides on arable crops, 1994

	Cereals[1]		Potatoes		Oilseed Rape	
	Total hectares treated with active ingredients	Total tonnes of active ingredients	Total hectares treated with active ingredients	Total tonnes of active ingredients	Total hectares treated with active ingredients	Total tonnes of active ingredients
Area grown (hectares)	395,286		26,411		69,619	
All pesticides	3,250,033	1,039.8	506,981	5,660.8	461,549	247.3
Seed dressings	779,010	112.5	24,599	24.2	178,967	17.8
Insecticides	51,010	9.8	128,371	11.9	42,042	2.6
Molluscicides	17,025	4.9	2,764	0.5	4,955	1.1
Fungicides	1,095,294	336.0	254,259	159.0	150,073	183.2
Herbicides and desiccants	1,012,461	383.3	96,330	5,406.6	81,934	38.8
Growth regulators	295,233	193.4	427	1.8	3,578	3.8

Source: SASA

(1) Refers to barley, wheat and oats.

Table 2.12   **Areas of land capability for agricultural classes**[1] **by region**   Km²

| | Land Classifications | | | | | | | | | | Total[2] |
	1	2	3.1	3.2	4	5	6	7	Built-up Area	Not Surveyed	
Scotland	41	1,070	3,368	7,350	8,587	13,828	38,533	2,547	1,901	1,837	78,859
Borders	5	160	535	427	798	1,356	1,356	5	33	19	4,692
Central	-	11	51	362	297	475	1,269	27	127	84	2,700
Dumfries & Galloway	-	13	135	713	1,150	1,761	2,481	58	71	64	6,427
Fife	-	129	404	371	103	120	30	-	132	32	1,320
Grampian	-	123	491	3,110	1,454	1,367	1,551	517	131	44	8,761
Highland	-	78	181	543	1,320	3,933	17,389	1,423	233	906	25,877
Lothian	28	222	413	170	255	318	126	2	224	20	1,774
Strathclyde	-	14	225	857	2,038	2,404	7,338	112	773	323	14,057
Tayside	8	321	933	795	589	1,131	3,173	344	168	176	7,645
Orkney	-	-	-	-	496	218	241	9	3	31	998
Shetland	-	-	-	-	40	354	1,030	22	-	30	1,476
Western Isles	-	-	-	-	47	392	2,549	28	6	110	3,132

Source: MLURI

(1)   For definition of agricultural land capability classes see notes, paragraph 2.11.

(2)   Figures may not sum to total due to rounding.

Table 2.13   **Areas of land capability for forestry classes**[1] **by region**   Km²

	F1	F2	F3	F4	F5	F6	F7	Built-up	Total
Scotland	747	4,069	6,207	10,217	13,536	19,061	21,678	1,565	77,080
Borders	189	354	631	771	1,186	1,211	300	28	4,670
Central	32	403	231	489	333	563	489	87	2,627
Dumfries & Galloway	30	534	872	1,471	2,046	1,141	222	54	6,370
Fife	23	451	481	194	41	25	1	92	1,308
Grampian	27	147	580	2,956	2,127	1,415	1,332	123	8,707
Highland	70	402	591	945	3,068	9,064	11,101	63	25,304
Lothian	36	427	310	303	273	151	20	236	1,756
Strathclyde	38	665	1,057	2,289	3,599	3,416	1,699	766	13,529
Tayside	302	686	1,454	799	863	1,447	1,850	101	7,502
Orkney	-	-	-	-	-	101	868	7	976
Shetland	-	-	-	-	-	76	1,352	5	1,433
Western Isles	-	-	-	-	-	451	2,444	3	2,898

Source: MLURI

(1)   For definition of forestry classes see notes, paragraph 2.12.

Chart 2.3   Agricultural Capability Classes

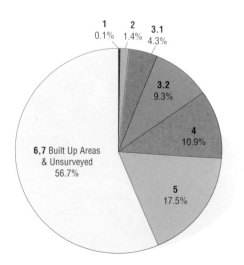

Chart 2.4   Forestry Land Capability

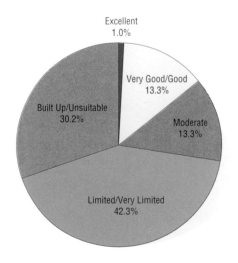

Source: MLURI

33

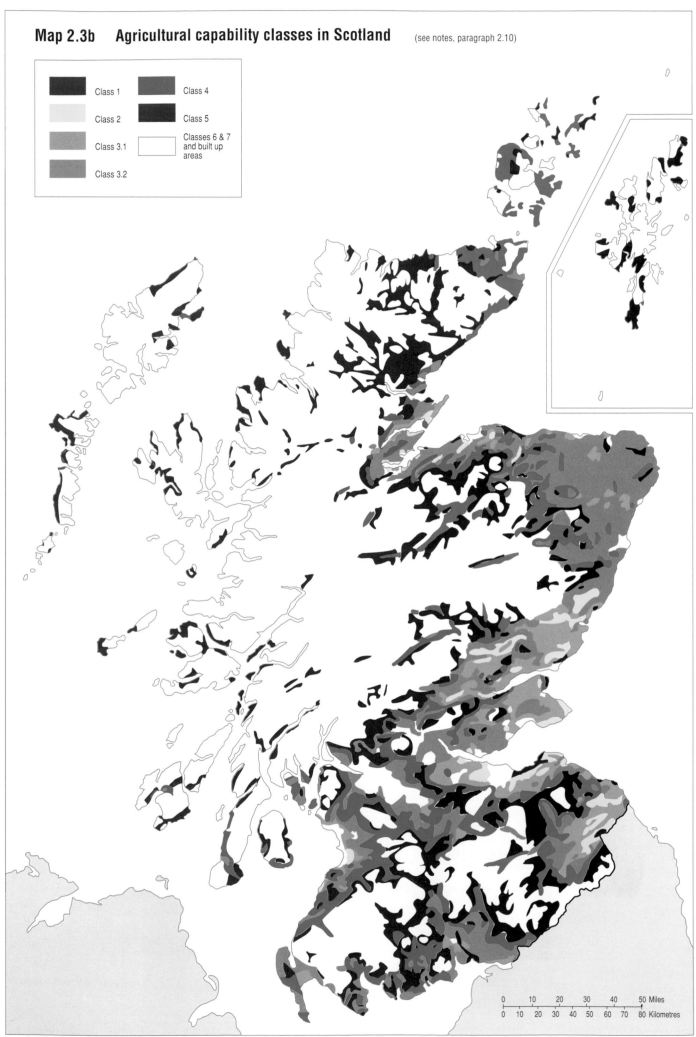

Map 2.3b Agricultural capability classes in Scotland (see notes, paragraph 2.10)

Class 1
Class 2
Class 3.1
Class 3.2
Class 4
Class 5
Classes 6 & 7 and built up areas

0   10   20   30   40   50 Miles
0 10 20 30 40 50 60 70 80 Kilometres

Source: MLURI

Map 2.4 Forestry capability classes in Scotland (see notes, paragraph 2.11)

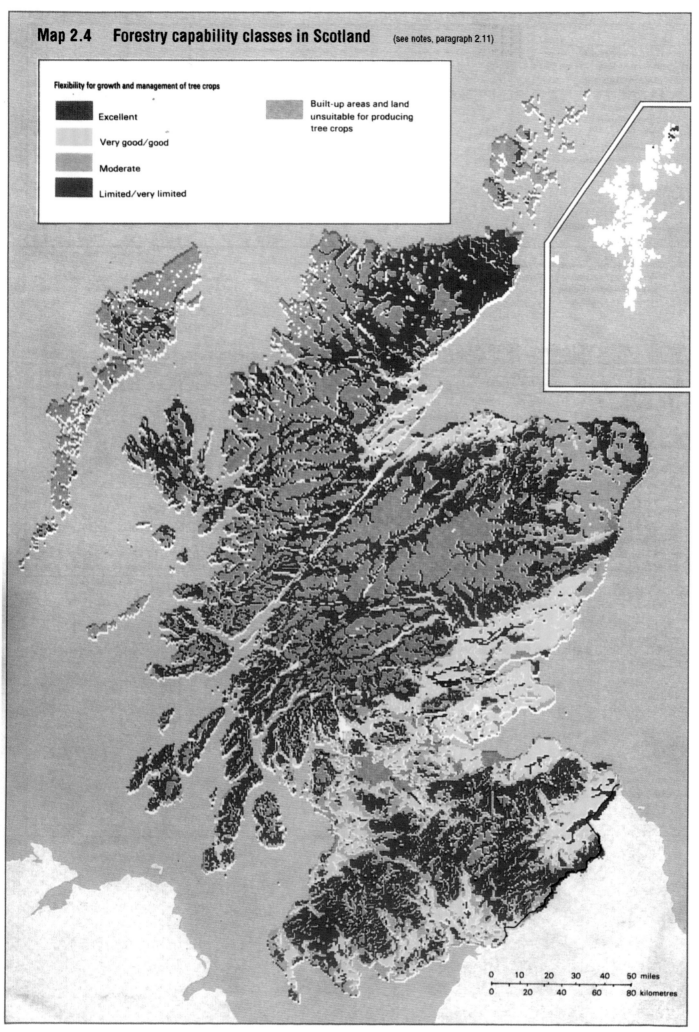

Flexibility for growth and management of tree crops

- Excellent
- Very good/good
- Moderate
- Limited/very limited
- Built-up areas and land unsuitable for producing tree crops

| 0 | 10 | 20 | 30 | 40 | 50 miles |
| 0 | 20 | 40 | 60 | 80 kilometres |

HMSO Cartographic Centre 95071331

Source: MLURI

Table 2.14 Forestry, 1984-1995[1]

thousand hectares

	1984	1985	1986	1987	1988	1989	1990	1991	1992	1993	1994	1995
Forestry Commission												
Total area	760	742	732	729	728	726	723	720	718	709	695	688
Plantation area	519	517	517	520	523	525	517	516	515	509	495	488
Conifers	515	513	513	516	519	521	512	510	509	503	489	482
Broadleaves	4	4	4	4	4	4	5	6	6	6	6	6
Awaiting planting	33	29	25	23	18	15	10	9	5	5	3	2
Other land[2]	208	196	210	186	187	186	196	196	198	195	197	173
Area planted[3]	10.4	7.2	7.4	8.4	8.1	7.8	7.6	7.1	6.5	6.2	4.5	4.3
Plantable land acquired (net)	2.7	0.7	0.7	1.6	1.5	1.3	-	2.5	1.3	0.1	0.3	0
Private Woodlands												
Plantation area	410	430	451	470	492	510	522	533	542	553	571	587
Conifers	338	358	378	396	418	435	444	452	458	465	477	488
Broadleaves	72	72	73	74	74	75	78	81	84	88	94	100
Scrub and cleared woodland	66	65	65	65	67	65	65	65	65	65	65	65
Area planted[3]	15.1	15.3	18.8	18.9	22.9	24.7	13.5	13.4	13.0	13.4	13.5	15.6

Source: Forestry Commission

(1) All figures are as at year ending 31 March.
(2) Includes non-forest land and areas retained chiefly for amenity purposes.
(3) New planting and restocking.

Table 2.15 Planting, 1984-1994[1]

hectares

	1985	1986	1987	1988	1989	1990	1991	1992	1993	1994	1995
Forestry Commission											
New Planting											
Conifers	4,735	3,997	4,845	4,320	3,671	3,563	3,275	2,651	2,098	1,150	739
Broadleaves	42	41	221	297	243	224	191	223	215	139	96
Re-stocking											
Conifers	2,429	3,292	3,107	3,145	3,561	3,486	3,453	3,358	3,425	2,908	3,101
Broadleaves	16	71	212	382	283	298	211	270	425	346	413
Private Woodlands[2]											
New Planting											
Conifers	14,008	17,047	16,781	20,113	20,882	9,204	7,923	7,285	5,925	4,608	7,556
Broadleaves	127	245	439	1,084	1,551	2,284	2,640	2,540	3,889	4,572	5,021
Re-stocking											
Conifers	1,055	1,375	1,281	1,212	1,591	1,132	1,670	2,042	1,876	2,540	2,152
Broadleaves	122	184	266	448	657	852	1,170	1,168	1,733	1,774	916

Source: Forestry Commission

(1) All figures are as at year ending 31 March.
(2) Areas for which Forestry Commission grants were paid. In addition a small amount of planting is carried out each year without grant aid.

Table 2.16 Volume of timber harvested, 1980, 1988-1994

thousand cubic metres

	Calendar year							
	1980	1988	1989	1990	1991	1992	1993	1994
Total	1,540	2,200	2,285	2,315	2,365	2,505	3,100	3,380
Forestry Commission	980	1,410	1,505	1,490	1,670	1,750	1,865	1,925
Private Woodlands	560	790	780	825	745	755	1,235	1,455
Conifers								
Total	**1,440**	**2,110**	**2,195**	**2,230**	**2,285**	**2,445**	**3,050**	**3,310**
Forestry Commission	980	1,410	1,505	1,490	1,620	1,750	1,860	1,925
Private Woodlands	460	700	690	740	665	695	1,190	1,385
Broadleaves								
Total	**100**	**90**	**90**	**85**	**80**	**60**	**50**	**70**
Forestry Commission	-	-	-	-	-	-	-	-
Private Woodlands	100	90	90	85	80	60	50	70

Source: Forestry Commission

Map 2.5a   Forest Enterprise Regional and Forest District Boundaries

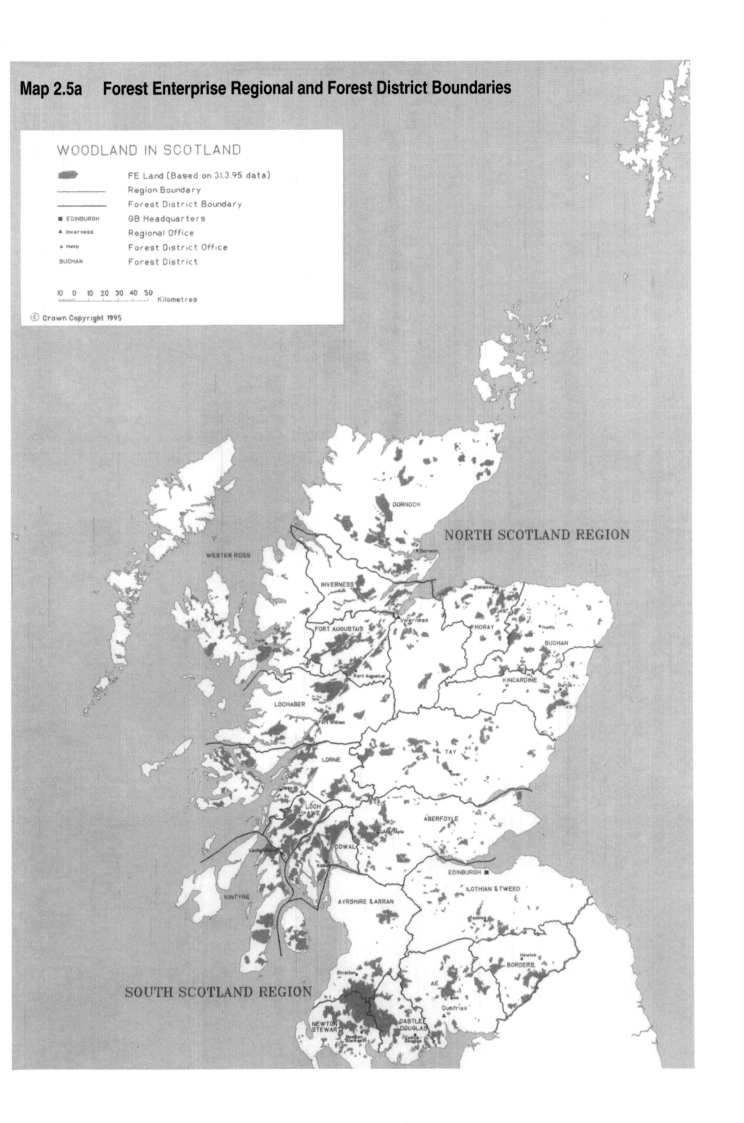

WOODLAND IN SCOTLAND

FE Land (Based on 31.3.95 data)
Region Boundary
Forest District Boundary
■ EDINBURGH   GB Headquarters
▲ Inverness   Regional Office
● Huntly   Forest District Office
BUCHAN   Forest District

10 0 10 20 30 40 50
Kilometres

© Crown Copyright 1995

NORTH SCOTLAND REGION

SOUTH SCOTLAND REGION

Map 2.5b   Forestry Authority National and Conservancy Boundaries

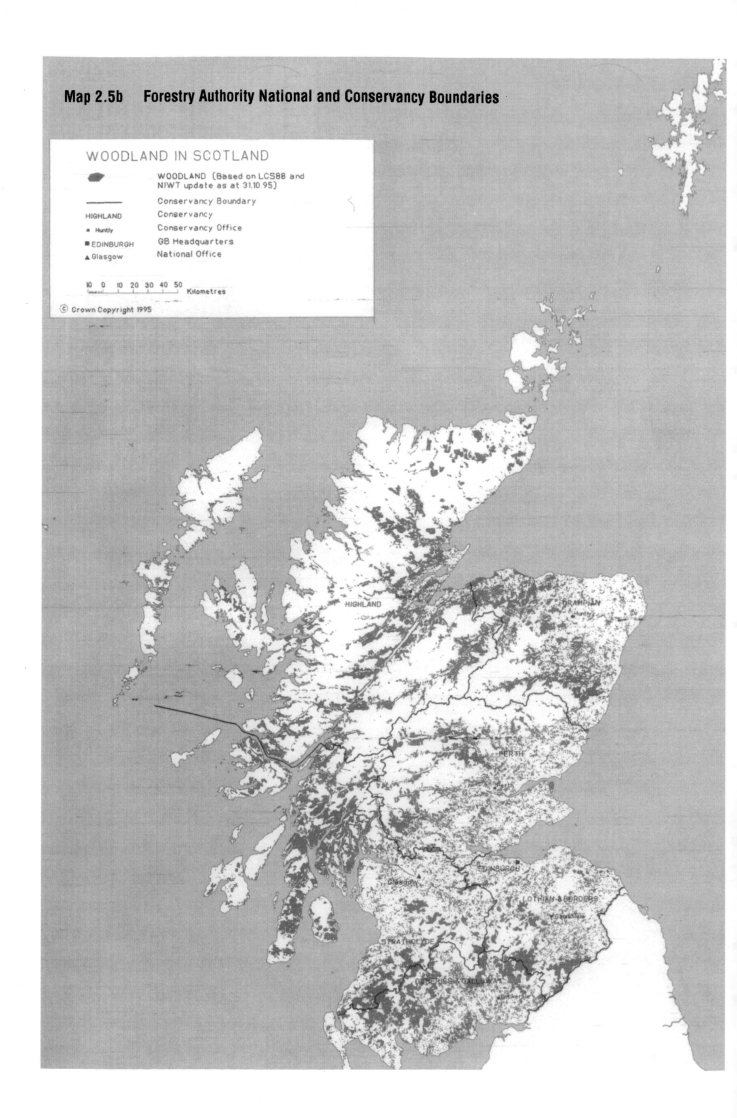

WOODLAND IN SCOTLAND

WOODLAND (Based on LCS88 and NIWT update as at 31.10.95)

——— Conservancy Boundary

HIGHLAND   Conservancy

• Huntly   Conservancy Office

■ EDINBURGH   GB Headquarters

▲ Glasgow   National Office

10 0 10 20 30 40 50 Kilometres

© Crown Copyright 1995

Table 2.17 Woodland area 1947, 1965 and 1980[1]

	1947	1965	1980
Estimated area of woodland 0.25 hectares and over[2]	530,000	657,000	920,000
Woodland density per cent of land area	7.2	9.0	12.6

Source: Forestry Commission

[1] Excludes island authorities.
[2] An allowance has been added for woods between 0.25 and 2.00 ha for the 1947 results and between 0.25 and 0.40 ha for the 1965 results to bring the 3 census results to a common base.

Table 2.18 Forest types, by area and ownership, 1980[1]

thousand hectares

	Forestry Commission		Private Woodland		Total		Per cent of total woodland area
	Area	Per cent of total	Area	Per cent of total	Area	Per cent of total	
Total	**497.8**	**54**	**422.1**	**46**	**919.0**	**100**	**100**
Total productive forest	489.0	58	353.2	42	842.2	100	91
Mainly coniferous	485.0	63	281.4	37	766.4	100	83
Mainly broadleaved	4.0	5	71.8	95	75.8	100	8
Scrub	**2.7**	**4**	**57.8**	**96**	**60.5**	**100**	**7**
Cleared	**6.1**	**35**	**11.1**	**65**	**17.2**	**100**	**2**

Source: Forestry Commission

[1] Excludes islands authorities.

Table 2.19 Area of productive forest, by principal species, ownership and planting year classes, 1980[1]

per cent

	Area(ha)	Ownership		Planting Year Classes				
		Forestry Commission	Private Woodland	Pre-1900	1901-20	1921-40	1941-60	1961-80
Total	**489,027**	**100**	**100**	**100**	**100**	**100**	**100**	**100**
Total conifers	**484,840**	**99**	**80**	**36**	**58**	**83**	**93**	**98**
Scots pine	61,299	12	24	30	37	30	26	8
Corsican pine	2,640	1	<1	<1	<1	1	1	<1
Lodgepole pine	82,497	17	6	-	<1	1	8	18
Sitka spruce	256,066	52	31	<1	1	20	31	59
Norway spruce	32,500	7	6	<1	4	15	11	4
European larch	5,222	1	3	3	10	6	2	1
Jap/hybrid larch	32,417	7	6	<1	2	6	11	5
Douglas fir	6,438	1	1	1	1	2	2	1
Other conifers	4,472	1	<1	<1	<1	1	1	1
Mixed conifers	1,829	<1	2	1	2	1	1	1
Total broadleaves	**4,187**	**1**	**20**	**64**	**42**	**17**	**7**	**2**
Oak	1,242	1	4	23	12	2	<1	<1
Beech	563	<1	3	16	2	1	<1	<1
Sycamore	327	<1	3	6	6	2	1	<1
Ash	149	<1	1	3	1	2	<1	<1
Birch	801	<1	4	<1	8	6	3	<1
Poplar	23	<1	<1	<1	<1	<1	<1	<1
Sweet chestnut	1	<1	<1	<1	<1	<1	<1	<1
Elm	5	<1	1	4	3	1	<1	<1
Other broadleaves	177	<1	1	1	2	2	1	<1
Mixed broadleaves	899	<1	3	11	7	2	1	<1

Source: Forestry Commission

Excludes islands authorities. Figures may not sum to total because of rounding.

Table 2.20 Areas of land acquired and disposed of by the Forestry Commission, 1984/85-1994/95

hectares

	1984-85	1985-86	1986-87	1987-88	1988-89	1989-90	1990-91	1991-92	1992-93	1993-94	1994/95
Acquisitions											
Area of plantable land	687	635	2,281	1,635	1,690	425	2,601	1,444	89	349	197
Area of woodland	0	26	47	3	27	1	18	10	0	6	9
Area of other land	150	55	1,242	79	386	46	351	368	2	16	94
Total area acquired	**837**	**716**	**3,570**	**1,717**	**2,103**	**472**	**2,970**	**1,822**	**91**	**371**	**300**
Disposals											
Area of Forestry Land	7,671	4,055	2,674	1,622	1,716	2,339	1,223	3,088	4,930	12,105	682
Area of other land	10,688	6,500	3,546	1,697	2,570	2,281	3,531	429	3,507	357	462
Total area sold	**18,359**	**10,555**	**6,220**	**3,359**	**4,286**	**4,620**	**4,754**	**3,517**	**8,437**	**12,462**	**7,280**

Source: Forestry Commission

Table 2.21 Statement of planning applications, 1984-1994

	1984	1985	1986	1987	1988	1989	1990	1991	1992	1993[1]	199
Planning Applications	38,745	38,218	39,317	41,096	44,107	46,168	48,892	47,917	47,721	57,429	22,18
Granted	35,437	34,432	35,664	37,559	40,269	41,527	43,436	43,078	43,347	52,835	20,20
Refused	3,308	3,786	3,653	3,537	3,838	4,641	5,456	4,839	4,374	4,594	1,98
Of which:											
Industrial Applications	1,759	1,951	5,850	6,589	6,819	6,399	6,652	6,500	5,542	5,981	2,07
Granted	1,667	1,826	5,289	5,997	6,240	5,877	6,105	5,941	5,060	5,471	1,88
Refused	92	125	561	592	579	522	547	559	482	510	19
Applications for Listed Building Consent	1,724	1,925	1,782	2,021	1,767	1,708	1,820	1,953	2,075	2,566	1,31
Granted	1,510	1,707	1,603	1,860	1,620	1,561	1,601	1,765	1,877	2,347	1,20
Refused	214	218	179	161	147	147	219	188	198	219	10
Applications to Display Advertisements	3,271	3,191	3,358	3,638	3,862	3,589	3,424	2,916	2,825	3,360	1,64
Granted	2,733	2,591	2,838	3,152	3,278	2,979	2,747	2,431	2,424	2,943	1,38
Refused	538	600	520	486	584	610	677	485	401	417	25

(1) The statistics cover a period of 15 months instead of the usual 12 ie 1/1/93 to 31/3/94

Source: Planning Division, SODD

Table 2.22 Planning applications and appeals by region, 1993[1]

	Planning Applications			Planning Appeals		
	Granted	Refused	Total	Received	Withdrawn	Decided
Scotland	52,835	4,594	57,429	914	89	764
Borders	1,710	101	1,811	33	-	21
Central	2,667	224	2,891	60	8	53
Dumfries & Galloway	2,478	150	2,628	28	3	14
Fife	3,772	272	4,044	66	8	59
Grampian	9,622	1,024	10,646	152	8	135
Highland	5,300	299	5,599	61	3	50
Lothian	5,983	534	6,517	122	17	73
Strathclyde	15,135	1,477	16,612	296	29	285
Tayside	4,600	472	5,072	84	13	67
Orkney	423	17	440	3	-	-
Shetland	662	19	681	7	-	5
Western Isles	483	5	488	2	-	2

Source: Planning Division/Inquiry Reporters Unit, SODD

(1) The statistics cover a period of 15 months instead of the usual 12 ie 1/1/93 to 31/3/94.

Table 2.23 Planning appeals, 1984-1994

	1984	1985	1986	1987	1988	1989	1990	1991	1992	1993	199
Appeals received	794	877	1,036	1,022	1,204	1,514	1,664	1,740	1,424	1,311	1,31
Planning permission	566	606	723	724	764	959	1,137	1,130	1,022	917	86
Enforcement notice	112	117	151	135	183	180	204	191	143	153	16
Advertisement[1]	109	138	142	148	168	252	307	399	177	142	17
Others[2]	7	16	19	15	89	123	16	20	14	99	11
Appeals withdrawn	201	189	203	233	241	210	273	211	227	165	16
Planning permission	118	123	107	120	147	125	173	119	125	86	9
Enforcement notice	48	46	69	84	58	53	55	47	56	37	3
Advertisement[1]	34	17	22	23	12	13	41	38	40	20	2
Others[2]	1	3	5	6	24	19	4	7	6	22	2
Appeals decided	590	706	751	825	968	1,042	1,427	1,365	1,211	1,060	91
Planning permission	396	510	546	589	637	704	967	942	893	764	64
Enforcement notice	77	67	90	83	121	108	147	112	107	94	10
Advertisement[1]	112	123	102	139	146	151	304	299	199	139	10
Others[2]	5	6	13	14	64	79	9	12	12	63	6

Source: Inquiry Reporters Unit, SODD

(1) The figures for advertisement appeals for 1984 onwards include appeals against discontinuance notices and enforcement notices served under the Control of Advertisement Regulations.
(2) The "others" category covers appeals against section 63 (waste land) notices, certificates of alternative development, tree enforcement notice appeals, established use certificates and determinations as to whether planning permission is required. From 1987 this category also includes appeals arising from applications for listed building consent and against listed building enforcement notices.

Table 2.24 Planning appeal decisions, 1993[1]

	Number of appeals decided	of which					
		Decided by Reporters		Decided by written submissions		Sustained	
		Number	%	Number	%	Number	%
Planning permission	755	739	97.9	663	87.8	269	35.6
Enforcement notice	91	86	94.5	73	80.2	29	31.9
Advertisement[2]	139	139	100.0	137	98.5	24	17.3
Listed Building	54	48	88.9	4.8	88.9	20	37.0
Others[3]	7	3	42.8	5	71.4	2	28.6

Source: Inquiry Reporters Unit, SODD

(1) The figures in this table exclude a small number of appeals which were dismissed for procedural reasons at an early stage in the process.
(2) and (3) See footnotes (1) and (2) of table 2.25.

Table 2.25 Time taken to decide planning permission appeals[1], 1986-1993

	Decided by reporters				Decided by Secretary of State				All appeals	
Year	On basis of written submissions		After a public inquiry		On basis of written submissions		After a public inquiry			
	Number	Weeks	Number	Weeks	Number	Weeks	Number	Weeks	Number	Weeks
1986	396	26	103	37	24	47	19	59	542	29
1987	471	27	84	39	23	47	11	65	589	29
1988	518	27	90	45	19	42	9	91	636	28
1989	600	26	84	41	6	42	12	99	702	27
1990	842	23	104	39	2	56	12	114	960	24
1991	831	21	78	37	5	81	9	68	942	24
1992	807	27	69	37	1	60	9	57	886	28
1993	663	25	76	38	4	72	10	83	753	26

Source: SODD

(1) The figures in weeks are median times.

Table 2.26   **Road lengths, in non-built up areas, by region and class, 1994**   Kilometres

	Trunk (M & A Roads)		Principal (M & A Roads)		Non-principal (B & C)		Unclassified	Total
	Dual[1]	Single	Dual[1]	Single	Dual	Single		
Scotland	818	2,196	177	6,192	54	15,614	11,660	36,709
Borders	3	165	-	403	-	1,313	862	2,746
Central	79	98	1	259	2	498	301	1,238
Dumfries & Galloway	69	278	-	454	-	1,764	1,384	3,949
Fife	46	69	7	234	11	455	276	1,098
Grampian	76	236	2	726	1	2,878	2,225	6,144
Highland	26	660	-	1,523	-	2,225	2,074	6,508
Lothian	72	91	55	253	-	799	385	1,655
Strathclyde	273	497	111	1,095	40	2,942	1,781	6,740
Tayside	173	102	-	588	-	1,669	1,170	3,701
Orkney	-	-	-	153	-	363	344	860
Shetland	-	-	-	186	-	373	385	944
Western Isles	-	-	-	318	-	336	472	1,127

Source: SOEID

[1]   Includes motorway slip roads.

Table 2.27   **Road lengths in built-up areas by region and class, 1994**   Kilometres

	Trunk (A Roads)		Principal (A Roads)		Non-principal (B & C)		Unclassified	Total
	Dual	Single	Dual	Single	Dual	Single		
Scotland	26	188	164	1,080	50	1,896	12,232	15,636
Borders	-	17	-	32	-	49	228	326
Central	-	10	3	78	1	110	672	874
Dumfries & Galloway	-	15	1	52	-	79	299	445
Fife	-	11	3	70	4	147	1,007	1,243
Grampian	3	26	13	121	3	234	1,228	1,627
Highland	1	44	2	93	2	170	638	949
Lothian	1	6	10	117	10	194	1,745	2,083
Strathclyde	15	56	120	375	29	716	5,407	6,716
Tayside	6	3	13	113	2	172	863	1,173
Orkney	-	-	-	7	-	4	83	93
Shetland	-	-	-	8	-	10	34	52
Western Isles	-	-	-	14	-	13	29	56

Source: Road Directorate, SOEID

Table 2.28   **Traffic on major roads by road class and vehicle type, 1993, from traffic estimates produced by the Department of Transport**

Ownership	Cars	Two wheeled motor vehicles	Buses	Light goods vehicles	Heavy goods vehicles	All motor vehicles	Pedal cycles	All vehicle traffic
Million vehicle kilometres								
All motorways[1]	2,616	8	33	301	391	3,348	-	3,348
Trunk A roads - non built up	5,644	34	71	600	850	7,200	7	7,207
Trunk A roads - built up	577	3	9	61	55	706	2	708
Principal A roads - non built up	4,746	36	82	545	415	5,824	16	5,840
Principal A roads - built up	4,553	31	134	458	280	5,457	26	5,482
Total: all major roads	**18,136**	**111**	**330**	**1,966**	**1,991**	**22,534**	**50**	**22,584**
Percentage of all vehicles								
All motorways[1]	78.1	0.2	1.0	9.0	11.7	100.0	-	100.0
Trunk A roads - non built up	78.3	0.5	1.0	8.3	11.8	99.9	0.1	100.0
Trunk A roads - built up	81.6	0.4	1.3	8.6	7.8	99.8	0.2	100.0
Principal A roads - non built up	81.3	0.6	1.4	9.3	7.1	99.7	0.3	100.0
Principal A roads - built up	83.0	0.6	2.5	8.4	5.1	99.5	0.5	100.0
Total: all major roads	**80.3**	**0.5**	**1.5**	**8.7**	**8.8**	**99.8**	**0.2**	**100.0**
Percentage of all major roads								
All motorways[1]	14.4	6.9	10.1	15.3	19.6	14.9	-	14.8
Trunk A roads - non built up	31.1	30.8	21.6	30.5	42.7	32.0	13.9	31.9
Trunk A roads - built up	3.2	2.8	2.8	3.1	2.8	3.1	3.3	3.1
Principal A roads - non built up	26.2	31.9	24.8	27.7	20.8	25.8	32.1	25.9
Principal A roads - built up	25.1	27.7	40.7	23.3	14.1	24.2	50.7	24.3
Total: all major roads	**100.0**	**100.0**	**100.0**	**100.0**	**100.0**	**100.0**	**100.0**	**100.0**

Source: Road Directorate, SOEID

[1]   All motorways include trunk motorways and the Glasgow urban motorway.

Table 2.29 Industrial sites and land, by region 1991-1993[1]

Region	1991		1992		1993		1994	
	Number of sites	Area (hectares)	Number of sites	Area (hectares)	Number of sites	Area (hectares)	Number of sites	Area (hectares)
Scotland	**966**	**7,435**	**964**	**7,471**	**1,033**	**8,044**	**7,044**	**7,951**
Borders	21	42	26	58	57	78	57	78
Central	24	454	23	399	25	421	29	352
Dumfries & Galloway	28	125	33	148	34	154	32	154
Fife	63	668	65	632	53	527	55	532
Grampian	110	562	114	528	128	591	130	580
Highland	121	2,042	121	2,042	118	2,042	120	2,048
Lothian	88	733	93	811	112	957	113	1,161
Strathclyde	401	1,873	370	1,949	374	2,356	369	2,079
Tayside	87	336	96	308	109	320	115	369
Orkney	4	11	4	7	4	9	4	9
Shetland	17	587	17	587	17	587	17	587
Western Isles	2	2	2	2	2	3	2	3

Source: Planning Services, SODD

(1) Figures may not sum to total due to rounding.

Table 2.30 Ownership, existing and proposed use of industrial sites and land, 1993[1]

Ownership	Number of sites	Area (hectares)	Proposed Use	Number of sites	Area (hectares)	Existing Use	Number of sites	Area (hectares)
Total	**1,033**	**8,044**	**Total**	**1,033**	**8,044**	**Total**	**1,033**	**8,044**
Private	489	4,641	Industrial or business	870	4,237	Brownfield	457	1,403
Local Authority	317	1,774	Industrial	31	74	Greenfield	467	4,088
SDA	101	645	Business	51	419	Prime agriculture	31	1,140
New Towns	51	517	Single User	24	745	Other	77	1,444
Nationalised Industry	19	322	Specialist User	37	2,417	Unknown	1	1
Crown	2	6	Science park	8	117			
HIDB	31	71	Other	12	35			
Other	16	51						
Unknown	7	19						

Source: Planning Services, SOEnD

(1) Figures may not sum to total due to rounding.

Table 2.31 Housing land supply, 1989

Region/Islands area	Private sector		Number of public sector[1]	Number of tenure unknown	Number of total potential dwellings
	number	per cent with planning permission			
Scotland	**143,109**	**60.65**	**35,389**	**31,218**	**209,736**
Borders	2,890	58.51	1,507	-	4,397
Central	9,610	59.53	943	449	11,200
Dumfries & Galloway	2,528	99.17	1,637	3,833	7,998
Fife	8,878	49.10	2,848	548	12,274
Grampian	14,518	64.40	5,383	2,838	22,579
Highland	11,038	59.71	2,517	376	13,931
Lothian	21,664	49.10	4,867	1,374	27,905
Strathclyde	60,582	62.21	12,354	17,746	90,862
Tayside	10,256	73.05	2,232	2,975	15,463
Orkney Islands	262	86.26	207	-	469
Shetland Islands	679	48.90	602	50	1,331
Western Isles	204	96.08	292	1,029	1,525

Source: Planning Services, SODD

(1) Public sector includes Local Authority, Housing Associations, New Towns and Government Departments.

Table 2.32 Housing land supply 1990

Region/Islands area	Private sector		Number of public sector[1]	Number of tenure unknown	Number of total potential dwellings
	number	per cent with planning permission			
Scotland	**141,663**	**62.4**	**34,127**	**26,002**	**201,792**
Borders	3,485	60.5	1,465	-	4,950
Central	8,950	64.0	904	727	10,581
Dumfries & Galloway	3,241	96.3	1,505	3,586	8,332
Fife	8,372	48.5	2,288	540	11,200
Grampian	13,962	59.3	4,674	2,766	21,402
Highland	12,600	65.5	2,625	376	15,601
Lothian	22,729	49.1	4,673	1,312	28,714
Strathclyde	57,915	65.7	12,862	13,525	84,302
Tayside	9,354	73.1	2,261	2,186	13,801
Orkney Islands	346	91.0	148	-	494
Shetland Islands	437	67.5	451	50	938
Western Isles	272	97.1	271	934	1,477

Source: Planning Services, SODD

(1) See note (1) to 2.32(a).

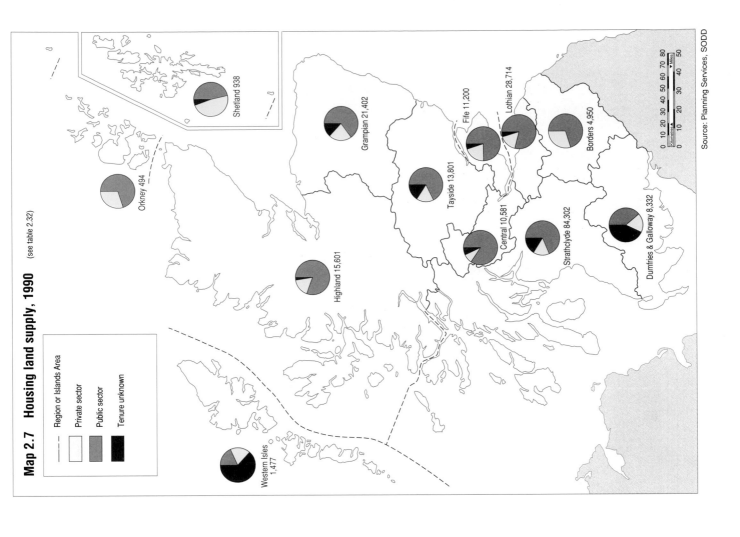

Map 2.7 Housing land supply, 1990 (see table 2.32)

Legend:
- Region or Islands Area
- Private sector
- Public sector
- Tenure unknown

Shetland 938

Orkney 494

Grampian 21,402

Fife 11,200

Lothian 28,714

Borders 4,950

Tayside 13,801

Central 10,581

Highland 15,601

Strathclyde 84,302

Dumfries & Galloway 8,332

Western Isles 1,477

0 10 20 30 40 50 60 70 80 Kilometres
0 10 20 30 40 50 Miles

Source: Planning Services, SODD

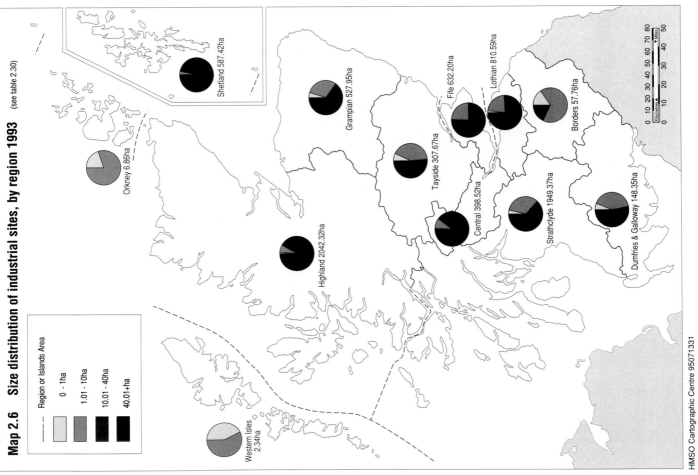

Map 2.6 Size distribution of industrial sites, by region 1993 (see table 2.30)

Legend:
- Region or Islands Area
- 0 - 1ha
- 1.01 - 10ha
- 10.01 - 40ha
- 40.01+ha

Shetland 587.42ha

Orkney 6.86ha

Grampian 527.95ha

Fife 632.20ha

Lothian 810.59ha

Borders 57.76ha

Tayside 307.67ha

Central 398.52ha

Highland 2042.32ha

Strathclyde 1949.37ha

Dumfries & Galloway 148.35ha

Western Isles 2.34ha

0 10 20 30 40 50 60 70 80 Kilometres
0 10 20 30 40 50 Miles

HMSO Cartographic Centre 95071331

Table 2.33   New dwellings completed, 1989-1994

| | Private sector[1] | Housing association[2] | Public authorities | | | | Total |
			Local authority[3]	New town[3]	Scottish Homes[4]	Government Departments	
1989	16,287	1,620	1,474	409	400	-	20,190
1990	16,455	1,430	1,046	720	157	69	19,877
1991	15,502	1,920	1,016	550	166	-	19,154
1992	14,373	1,975	703	276	37	-	17,364
1993	17,688	1,677	502	456	-	-	20,323
1994	17,813	1,255	514	113	-	-	19,695

Source: Housing Statistics Unit, SODD

(1)   Includes estimates for outstanding returns.
(2)   Provisional figures as data is under review.
(3)   Returns are incomplete.
(4)   Individual region figures are unavailable.

Table 2.34   New dwellings completed, 1994

| | Private sector[1] | Housing association[2] | Public authorities | | | | Total |
			Local authority[3]	New town[3]	Scottish Homes[4]	Government Departments	
Scotland	**17,813**	**1,255**	**514**	**113**	**-**	**-**	**19,695**
Borders	220	-	-	-	-	-	220
Central	956	172	-	-	-	-	1,128
Dumfries & Galloway	428	-	99	-	-	-	527
Fife	1,298	64	-	-	-	-	1,362
Grampian	2,770	137	68	-	-	-	2,975
Highland	1,030	83	156	-	-	-	1,269
Lothian	2,802	183	26	-	-	-	3,011
Strathclyde	6,779	452	75	113	-	-	7,419
Tayside	1,272	150	78	-	-	-	1,500
Orkney	-	-	-	-	-	-	-
Shetland	97	-	12	-	-	-	109
Western Isles	161	14	-	-	-	-	175

Source: Housing Statistics Unit, SODD

(1)   Scotland total includes estimates for outstanding returns.
(2)   Provisional figures as data is under review.
(3)   Returns are incomplete.
(4)   Individual region figures are unavailable due to outstanding returns.

Table 2.35   Previous uses of vacant and derelict land[1], 1994

| Previous Use | Derelict Land | | | Vacant Land | | | Total Vacant and Derelict Land | | |
	Area (ha)	% of area	No. of Sites	Area (ha)	% of area	No. of Sites	Area (ha)	% of area	No. of Sites
Agriculture	399	4	175	1,321	26	509	1,720	12	684
Forestry/Woodland	30	0	18	24	0	19	54	0	37
Community & Health	420	5	92	292	6	67	712	5	159
Defence	478	5	27	111	2	19	589	4	46
Education	35	0	30	115	2	84	151	1	114
Passive Open Space	21	0	24	198	4	157	218	2	181
Recreation & Leisure[2]	132	1	65	109	2	107	242	2	172
Manufacturing	1,242	14	281	511	10	167	1,752	12	448
Other General Industry[3]	156	2	75	95	2	116	252	2	191
Mineral Activity	4,210	47	748	188	4	29	4,398	31	777
Offices	1	0	5	5	0	16	6	0	21
Residential	156	2	238	257	5	345	413	3	583
Retailing	18	0	28	22	0	54	40	0	82
Storage	126	1	67	72	1	68	197	1	135
Transport	627	7	285	316	6	163	943	7	448
Utility Services	43	0	20	8	0	15	51	0	35
Wholesale Distribution	13	0	5	5	0	7	17	0	12
Business Class	1	0	3	1	-	2	2	0	5
Other	132	1	56	191	4	128	323	2	184
Unknown	773	9	429	1,242	24	1,252	2,015	14	1,681
Total	**9,012**	**100**	**2,671**	**5,082**	**100**	**3,323**	**14,094**	**100**	**5,995**

Source: SODD

(1)   Figures may not sum due to rounding.
(2)   Excluding passive open space.
(3)   Excluding manufacturing.

Table 2.36 **Scottish Vacant and Derelict Land Survey; type and owner of site by region[1], 1994**

	Derelict		Vacant		Total	
	Area (hectares)	Number of sites	Area (hectares)	Number of sites	Area (hectares)	Number of sites
Scotland	**9,012**	**2,671**	**5,082**	**3,324**	**14,094**	**5,995**
Public	2,745	604	2,133	1,259	4,879	1,863
Private	3,692	1,160	1,604	955	5,296	2,115
Mixed	645	234	492	274	1,137	508
Unknown	1,930	673	853	836	2,783	1,509
Borders	**49**	**48**	**26**	**37**	**75**	**85**
Public	12	9	6	7	18	16
Private	36	39	19	29	55	68
Mixed	0	0	1	1	1	1
Unknown	0	0	0	0	0	0
Central	**296**	**100**	**379**	**239**	**675**	**339**
Public	163	33	224	120	387	153
Private	29	13	55	20	83	33
Mixed	14	1	14	8	28	9
Unknown	91	53	86	91	177	144
Dumfries and Galloway	**309**	**38**	**59**	**27**	**368**	**65**
Public	13	5	6	7	18	12
Private	118	3	45	3	163	6
Mixed	4	3	1	3	4	6
Unknown	175	27	8	14	183	41
Fife	**656**	**119**	**48**	**66**	**703**	**185**
Public	460	16	21	15	482	31
Private	23	27	4	23	27	50
Mixed	26	11	4	4	30	15
Unknown	146	65	18	24	165	89
Grampian	**256**	**161**	**219**	**157**	**474**	**318**
Public	40	27	30	27	70	54
Private	66	33	114	71	180	104
Mixed	8	10	32	12	41	22
Unknown	141	91	42	47	184	138
Highland	**315**	**233**	**498**	**276**	**813**	**509**
Public	71	40	111	77	182	117
Private	192	109	324	152	516	261
Mixed	23	39	55	29	78	68
Unknown	29	45	7	18	37	63
Lothian	**1,528**	**296**	**685**	**254**	**2,213**	**550**
Public	699	81	270	87	969	168
Private	321	109	74	58	394	167
Mixed	45	11	134	12	179	23
Unknown	464	95	207	97	671	192
Strathclyde	**5,100**	**1,546**	**2,840**	**2,059**	**7,940**	**3,605**
Public	1,084	355	1,275	822	2,359	1,177
Private	2,829	776	876	514	3,705	1,290
Mixed	510	151	218	186	728	337
Unknown	677	264	471	537	1,148	801
Tayside	**492**	**116**	**300**	**181**	**791**	**297**
Public	196	33	181	89	377	122
Private	74	43	72	67	147	110
Mixed	15	7	33	18	48	25
Unknown	206	33	13	7	219	40
Orkney	**10**	**11**	**15**	**23**	**26**	**34**
Public	8	5	3	5	11	10
Private	2	5	12	16	14	21
Mixed	0	1	1	1	1	2
Unknown	0	0	0	1	0	1
Shetland	**2**	**2**	**0**	**0**	**2**	**2**
Public	0	0	0	0	0	0
Private	2	2	0	0	2	2
Mixed	0	0	0	0	0	0
Unknown	0	0	0	0	0	0
Western Isles	**0**	**1**	**15**	**5**	**15**	**6**
Public	0	0	6	3	6	3
Private	0	1	9	2	9	3
Mixed	0	0	0	0	0	0
Unknown	0	0	0	0	0	0

Source: Planning Services, SODD

(1)   Figures may not add to total due to rounding.

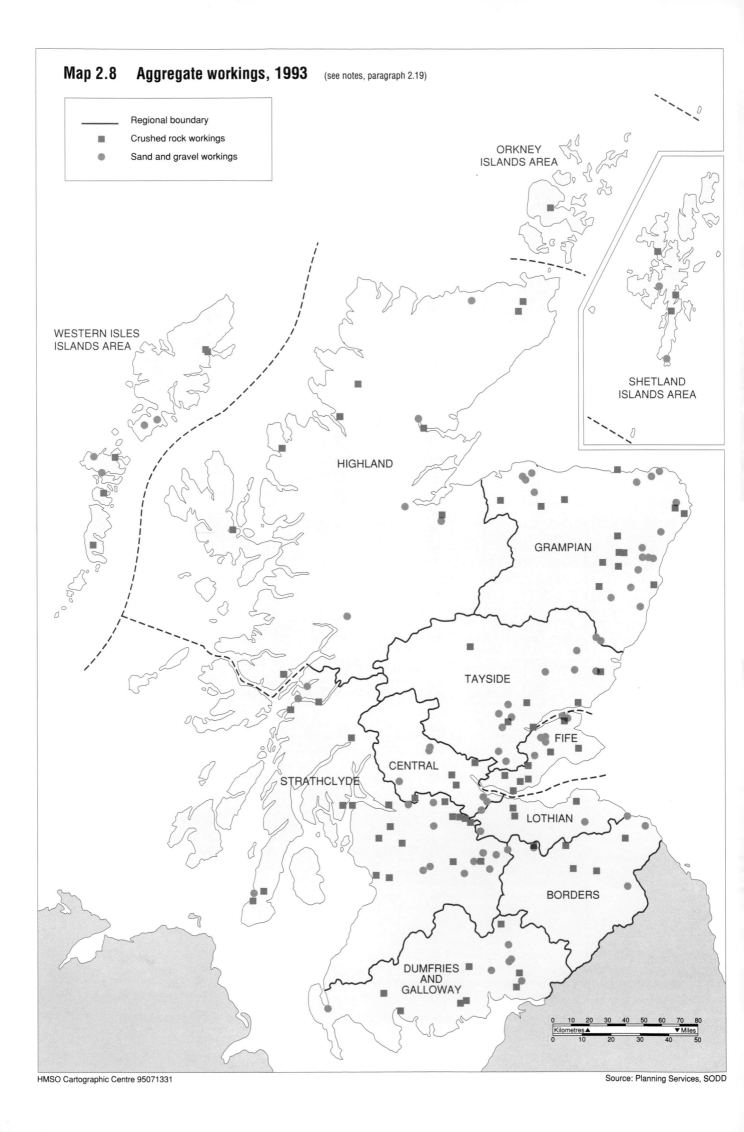

Map 2.8 Aggregate workings, 1993 (see notes, paragraph 2.19)

Regional boundary
■ Crushed rock workings
● Sand and gravel workings

ORKNEY
ISLANDS AREA

SHETLAND
ISLANDS AREA

WESTERN ISLES
ISLANDS AREA

HIGHLAND

GRAMPIAN

TAYSIDE

FIFE

CENTRAL

LOTHIAN

STRATHCLYDE

BORDERS

DUMFRIES
AND
GALLOWAY

0 10 20 30 40 50 60 70 80
Kilometres ▲   ▼ Miles
0   10   20   30   40   50

HMSO Cartographic Centre 95071331

Source: Planning Services, SODD

Table 2.37   **Mineral production, 1989-1993** [1]   thousand tonnes

Mineral	1989	1990	1991	1992	1993
Clay and shale	1,695	884	686	664	622
Limestone [2]	1,865	1,778	2,018	1,410	1,432
Igneous rock	19,020	19,280	19,588	20,064	20,806
Sandstone	1,918	1,834	1,555	1,658	1,716
Sand and gravel	12,004	12,634	12,226	11,774	11,359
Industrial sands	563	536	553	526	511
Talc	15	15	11	5	5
Peat [3]	-	-	357	423	380

Source: Central Statistical Office

(1)   Scotland has over this period produced other minerals eg Barytes, fire clay, lead, silver, gold, zinc and honestone but for confidentiality reasons production is not disclosed. However apart from Barytes and fire clay these minerals are usually only produced in small amounts..

(2)   Includes dolomite used for constructional purposes.

(3)   Production figures for peat (thousand cubic metres) have only been collected since 1991.

Table 2.38(a)   **Mineral production by region, 1992**   thousand tonnes

Region/Islands area	Clay and shale	Limestone	Igneous Rock	Sandstone	Sands and gravel	Industrial sands	Talc	Peat [5]
Scotland	**664**	**1,410**	**20,064**	**1,658**	**11,774**	**526**	**5**	**423**
Borders	17	-	1,198	-	589	-	-	10
Central	80	1	936	-	450	-	-	**
Dumfries and Galloway	36	(1)	300	**	918	-	-	**
Fife	**	1	1,719	2	1,148	462 [4]	-	-
Grampian	-	126 [2]	1,634	172	1,929	-	-	64
Highland	-	96	5,420	217	1,167	(4)	-	28
Lothian	**	1,186 [1]	1,256	-	774	62 [3]	-	47
Strathclyde	285	(1)	6,168	197	3,336	(3)	-	**
Tayside	-	(2)	986	-	1,397	-	-	-
Islands	-	-	447	**	66	2	5	4+

Source: Central Statistical Office

**   Withheld to avoid disclosure.

+   Additional production undisclosed.

(1)   Production in Dumfries and Galloway and Strathclyde included in Lothian figure.

(2)   Production in Grampian included in Tayside figure.

(3)   Production in Strathclyde included in Lothian figure.

(4)   Production in Highland included in Fife figure.

(5)   Thousand cubic metres.

Table 2.38(b)   **Mineral production by region, 1993**   thousand tonnes

Region/Islands area	Clay and shale	Limestone	Igneous Rock	Sandstone	Sands and gravel	Industrial sands	Talc	Peat [2]
Scotland	**622**	**1,432**	**20,806**	**1,716**	**11,359**	**511**	**5**	**380**
Borders	27	-	1,132	-	472	-	-	21
Central	171	-	887	-	326+	-	-	**
Dumfries and Galloway	19	(1)	324	**	1,041	-	-	**
Fife	**	-	1,598	2	1,221	349	-	-
Grampian	-	136	1,543	202	1,876	-	-	60+
Highland	-	79+	5,450	196	1,173	107	-	**
Lothian	95+	1,216 [1]	1,424	-	629	**	-	30
Strathclyde	150	(1)	7,065	**	3,263	**	-	101
Tayside	**	(1)	877	-	1,285	-	-	-
Islands	-	-	506	**	5+	**	5	5+

Source: Central Statistical Office

**   Withheld to avoid disclosure.

(1)   Production in Dumfries and Galloway, Tayside and Strathclyde included in Lothian figure.

+   Additional production undisclosed.

(2)   Thousand cubic metres.

Table 2.39 **Total production of aggregates, reserves and maximum years supply, by region 1993**

million tonnes

Region/Islands Area	Crushed Rock			Sand & Gravel		
	Production[1]	Estimated reserves[2]	Maximum years supply at 1993 production	Production[1]	Estimated reserves[2]	Maximum years supply at 1993 production
Borders	1.052	14.735	14	0.274	3.340	12
Central	1.095	34.100	31	0.777	12.836	17
Dumfries and Galloway	1.798	19.894	11	0.603	1.499	2
Fife	1.886	24.976	13	1.145	16.544	14
Grampian	1.330	89.532	67	1.626	24.515	15
Highland	5.531	439.566	79	0.620	4.268	7
Lothian	1.329	39.470	30	0.250	1.190	5
Strathclyde	5.737	135.798	24	2.624	31.710	12
Tayside	0.791	30.310	38	1.161	3.421	3
Islands	0.279	13.870	50	0.015	0.55	36

Source: 1993 Scottish Aggregates Survey

(1) Production figures include aggregate and non-aggregate uses and are the total for which estimates of reserves are given in the survey returns.

(2) Figures for crushed rock reserves exclude some 100 million tonnes mainly in Strathclyde, Grampian, Borders and Fife and some 10 million tonnes of sand and gravel reserves mainly in Lothian, Dumfries and Galloway, Tayside and Grampian, under planning permission and held for future use; these are considered uncertain sources of supply.

Table 2.40 **Waste Disposal: Site Category Table for all licences and resolutions in force as at 31/12/93**

	Total	Site Category											
		Baling	Compaction	Incin-eration	Mineshaft/ Borehole	Pulver-isation	Scrap-yard	Storage	Transfer Station	Treatment	Landfill	Civic Amenity	Recycling Centre
No of Licences	775	1	3	16	2	1	109	8	148	24	458	0	5
No of Resolutions	279	9	8	6	0	6	0	1	18	0	177	50	4
Totals	1,054	10	11	22	2	7	109	9	166	24	635	50	9

Source: Environmental Affairs Group SOAEFD

Table 2.41 **Controlled, and Special Waste Arisings, 1993**

	Controlled Waste Arisings[1] (million tonnes)	Special Waste Arisings (tonnes)		
		Total	Retained in Scotland	Exported outwith Scotland
1990	10.23	94,000	64,000	30,000
1991	11.92	95,300	41,900	53,400
1992	13.96	98,200	49,600	48,600
1993	15.46	111,000	68,000	43,000

Source: Environmental Affairs Group SOAEFD

(1) Figures take into account inconsistencies in the quantities of waste reported as being transferred between Scottish districts.

Table 2.42   Total Controlled and Special Waste Arisings in Scotland, 1993

	1,000 tonnes	% of total
Total Controlled Waste[1]		
Arising in Scotland	15,200	98.32
Imported from England, Wales and Northern Ireland	257	1.66
Imported from outwith UK	3	0.02
Total arisings	**15,460**	**100**
Total Controlled Waste[1]		
Retained in Scotland	15,225	98.48
Exported to England, Wales and Northern Ireland	105	0.68
Exported outwith UK (for recycling)	130	0.84
Total arisings	**15,460**	**100**
Total Special Waste		
Arising in Scotland	100	90.09
Imported from England, Wales and Northern Ireland	8	7.21
Imported from outwith UK	3	2.70
Total special waste arisings	**111**	**100**

Source: Environmental Affairs Group SOAEFD

(1)   Figures take into account inconsistencies in the quantities of waste reported as being transferred between Scottish districts.

Table 2.43   Waste collected for recycling by type of waste, 1993

Type of Waste	Total Amount (tonnes) collected for recycling by:		Total Amount for Recycling	% of Total
	Public Sector	Private Sector		
Paper/Board	45,380	69,860	115,240	23.01
Glass	22,440	11,040	33,480	6.69
Ferrous Metals	8,340	178,600	186,940	37.33
Aluminium	800	4,460	5,260	1.05
Other Non-Ferrous Metals	460	20,100	20,560	4.10
Cars	3,930	29,590	33,520	6.69
Plastics	210	2,430	2,640	0.53
Textiles	620	1,790	2,410	0.48
Oils	340	22,980	23,320	4.66
CFCs	-	-	-	-
Batteries	30	1,010	1,040	0.21
Tyres	50	7,700	7,750	1.55
Miscellaneous	5,910	62,680	68,590	13.70
Total	**88,510**	**412,240**	**500,750**	**100**

Source: Environmental Affairs Group SOAEFD

Table 2.44   Waste collected for recycling, by origin of waste, 1993

Collected for recycling by:	Tonnes of waste collected from					
	Households	Commercial Premises	Industrial Premises	Civic Amenity Sites Recycling Centres, and Council Collection Banks	Voluntary Organisations	Sum
Public Sector	31,240	21,210	3,500	29,850	2,700	88,500
						-
Private Sector	19,050	114,730	275,800	2,000	650	412,220
						-
Total	**50,290**	**135,940**	**279,300**	**31,840**	**3,350**	**500,720**
						-
% of Total	10	27.1	55.8	6.4	0.7	100

Source: Environmental Affairs Group SOAEFD

Chart 2.5   Disposal routes for Controlled Waste, 1993

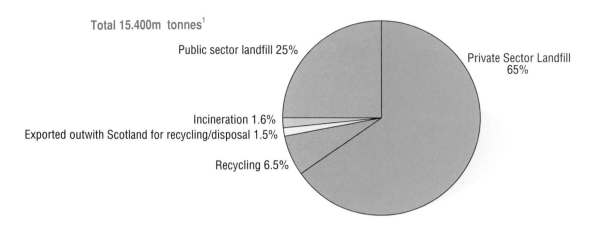

Total 15.400m tonnes[1]

Public sector landfill 25%

Private Sector Landfill
65%

Incineration 1.6%
Exported outwith Scotland for recycling/disposal 1.5%

Recycling 6.5%

Chart 2.6   Disposal routes for Special Waste, 1993

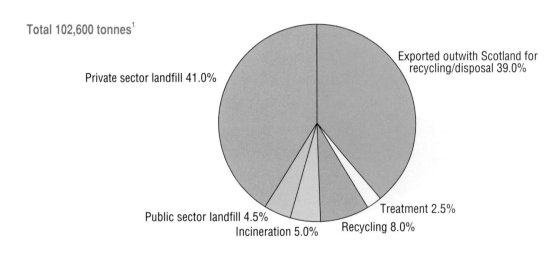

Total 102,600 tonnes[1]

Private sector landfill 41.0%

Exported outwith Scotland for
recycling/disposal 39.0%

Public sector landfill 4.5%

Incineration 5.0%

Recycling 8.0%

Treatment 2.5%

Chart 2.7   Controlled, and Special Waste Arisings in Scotland, 1993

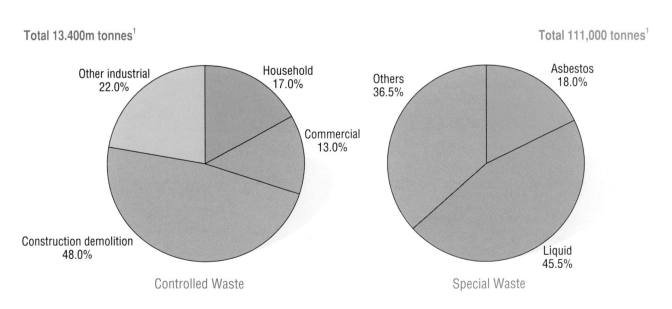

Total 13.400m tonnes[1]

Total 111,000 tonnes[1]

Other industrial
22.0%

Household
17.0%

Commercial
13.0%

Construction demolition
48.0%

Controlled Waste

Others
36.5%

Asbestos
18.0%

Liquid
45.5%

Special Waste

NOTE : Special Waste is a subset of Controlled Waste
[1] Reported figures

Source: Hazardous Waste Inspectorate, SODD

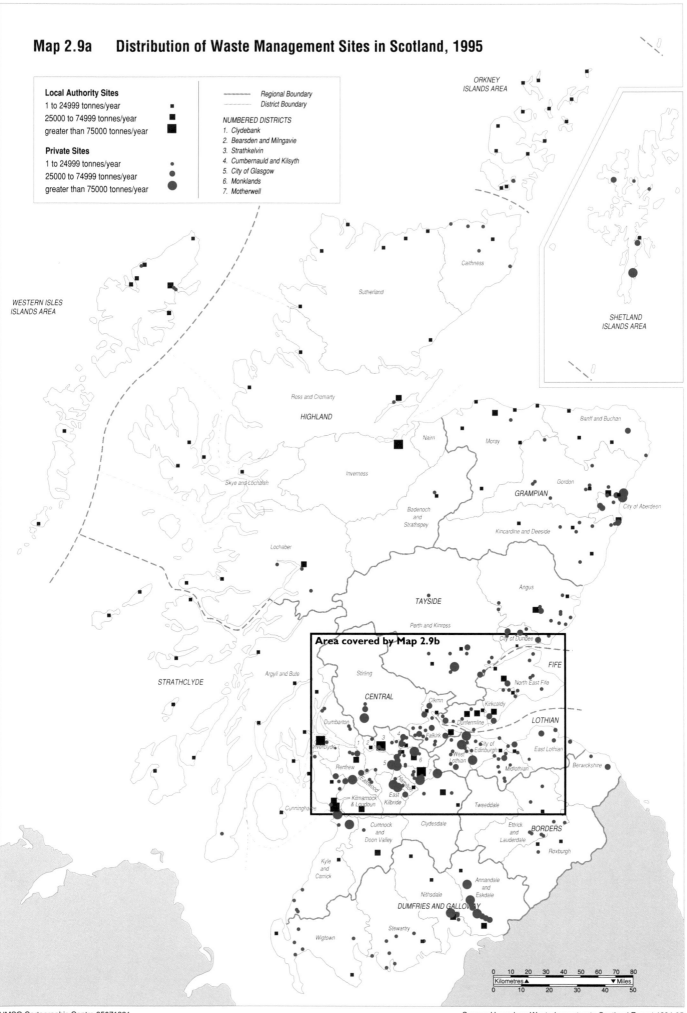

Map 2.9a   Distribution of Waste Management Sites in Scotland, 1995

Local Authority Sites
- 1 to 24999 tonnes/year
- 25000 to 74999 tonnes/year
- greater than 75000 tonnes/year

Private Sites
- 1 to 24999 tonnes/year
- 25000 to 74999 tonnes/year
- greater than 75000 tonnes/year

— — — Regional Boundary
- - - - District Boundary

NUMBERED DISTRICTS
1. Clydebank
2. Bearsden and Milngavie
3. Strathkelvin
4. Cumbernauld and Kilsyth
5. City of Glasgow
6. Monklands
7. Motherwell

ORKNEY
ISLANDS AREA

WESTERN ISLES
ISLANDS AREA

SHETLAND
ISLANDS AREA

Caithness

Sutherland

Ross and Cromarty

HIGHLAND

Nairn

Moray

Banff and Buchan

Gordon

GRAMPIAN

City of Aberdeen

Skye and Lochalsh

Inverness

Badenoch
and
Strathspey

Kincardine and Deeside

Lochaber

TAYSIDE

Perth and Kinross

Angus

City of Dundee

Area covered by Map 2.9b

FIFE

Argyll and Bute

Stirling

CENTRAL

Clkmn

North East Fife

Kirkcaldy

LOTHIAN

STRATHCLYDE

Dumbarton

Dunfermline

Falkirk

City of
Edinburgh

East Lothian

1 2 3 4

Inverclyde

5

6

West
Lothian

Midlothian

Berwickshire

Renfrew

7

Eastwood

Hmltn

East
Kilbride

Kilmarnock
& Loudoun

Cunninghame

Tweeddale

Ettrick
and
Lauderdale

BORDERS

Roxburgh

Cumnock
and
Doon Valley

Clydesdale

Kyle
and
Carrick

Nithsdale

Annandale
and
Eskdale

DUMFRIES AND GALLOWAY

Wigtown

Stewartry

| 0 | 10 | 20 | 30 | 40 | 50 | 60 | 70 | 80 |
Kilometres ▲   ▼ Miles
| 0 | 10 | 20 | 30 | 40 | 50 |

Source: Hazardous Waste Inspectorate Scotland Report 1994-95

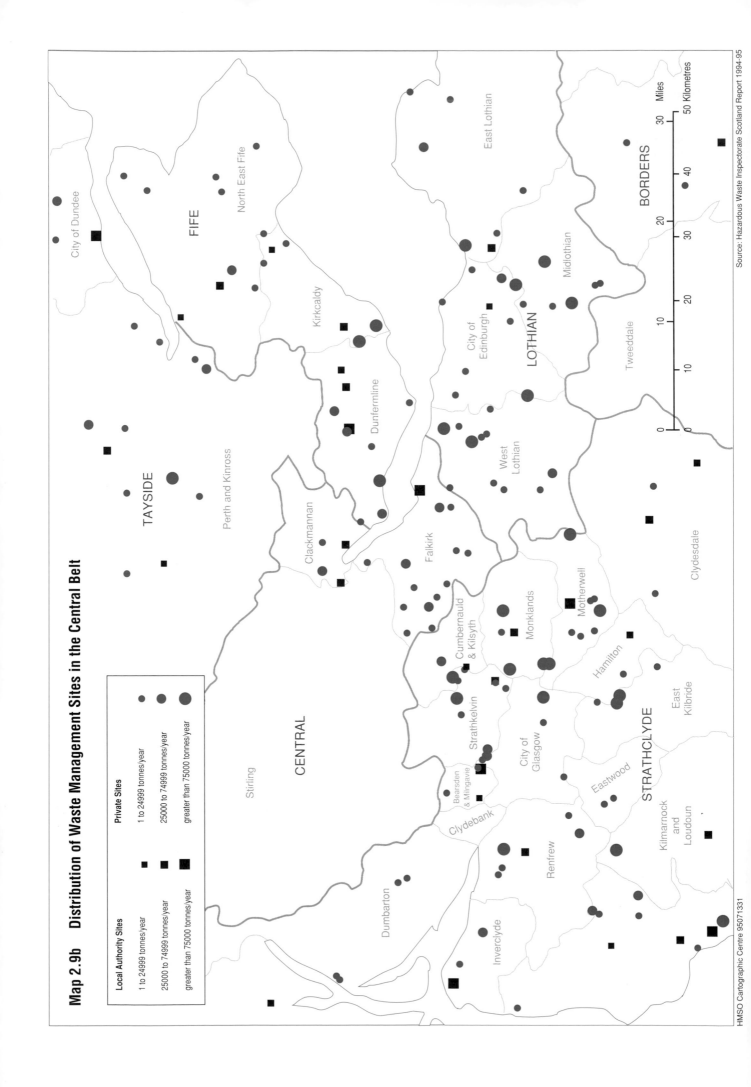

Map 2.9b   Distribution of Waste Management Sites in the Central Belt

Local Authority Sites

1 to 24999 tonnes/year

25000 to 74999 tonnes/year

greater than 75000 tonnes/year

Private Sites

1 to 24999 tonnes/year

25000 to 74999 tonnes/year

greater than 75000 tonnes/year

Source: Hazardous Waste Inspectorate Scotland Report 1994-95

HMSO Cartographic Centre 95071331

Table 2.45   Bottle bank sites and glass collected, by region 1990-1994[1]

	1990	1991	1992	1993	1994
Scotland					
Number of sites	3,051	3,363	3,309	3,966	4,034
Public	630	701	868	1,055	1,131
Commercial	2,421	2,662	2,441	2,911	2,903
Tonnage collected	17,873	22,204	23,144	25,918	29,356
Kilograms per person	4.24	4.40	4.59	5.04	5.81
Borders					
Number of sites	79	80	88	119	96
Public	48	37	36	50	37
Commercial	31	43	52	69	59
Tonnage collected	671	794	760	735	914
Kilograms per person	6.58	7.78	7.34	7.09	8.82
Central					
Number of sites	357	354	472	519	513
Public	38	30	49	77	91
Commercial	319	324	423	442	422
Tonnage collected	1,364	1,442	1,694	1,772	2,427
Kilograms per person	5.01	5.31	6.23	6.51	8.92
Dumfries & Galloway					
Number of sites	64	83	150	164	168
Public	50	48	50	62	70
Commercial	14	35	100	102	98
Tonnage collected	436	630	713	861	863
Kilograms per person	2.97	4.29	4.81	5.81	5.82
Fife					
Number of sites	580	607	529	551	578
Public	116	114	136	131	134
Commercial	464	493	393	420	444
Tonnage collected	2,013	2,291	2,351	2,588	2,628
Kilograms per person	5.86	6.65	6.80	7.48	7.6
Grampian					
Number of sites	594	654	673	835	886
Public	80	130	150	132	151
Commercial	514	524	523	703	735
Tonnage collected	3,559	4,115	4,904	5,097	5,317
Kilograms per person	5.74	8.09	9.69	10.07	10.51
Highland					
Number of sites	272	276	232	214	232
Public	27	31	44	62	72
Commercial	245	245	188	152	160
Tonnage collected	1,235	1,498	1,733	1,516	1,866
Kilograms per person	6.16	7.42	8.48	5.01	9.14
Lothian					
Number of sites	281	280	136	231	273
Public	85	73	94	176	187
Commercial	196	207	42	55	86
Tonnage collected	2,616	2,761	2,692	3,362	3,653
Kilograms per person	3.51	3.69	3.59	4.48	4.87
Strathclyde					
Number of sites	528	512	489	749	694
Public	153	189	244	289	301
Commercial	375	323	245	460	393
Tonnage collected	4,102	5,681	4,642	6,100	7,086
Kilograms per person	1.76	2.45	2.00	2.65	3.07
Tayside					
Number of sites	296	517	540	574	583
Public	33	49	65	71	80
Commercial	263	468	475	503	503
Tonnage collected	1,877	2,992	3,655	3,747	4,402
Kilograms per person	4.77	7.63	9.28	9.51	11.17

Source: The British Glass Manufacturers Confederation

(1)   Records for some regions are incomplete

recreation

3 recreation

3.1   This chapter contains information on recreation activities in Scotland. It deals with sports and leisure activities and trends in tourism.

TOURISM: ACCOMMODATION

3.2   Figures in table 3.1 are derived from returns made by the Area Tourist Boards, District Councils and the private sector to the Scottish Tourist Board (STB) and the Accommodation Occupancy Survey, a sample survey conducted by System Three Scotland Ltd. The figures in table 3.2 also come from this survey. The Tourist Board areas are compiled as follows:

Aberdeen:	City of Aberdeen
Ayrshire:	Ayrshire Tourist Board
Borders:	Scottish Borders
Dundee Area:	Angus, City of Dundee, St Andrews and North East Fife
Forth Valley Area:	Forth Valley, Dunfermline District Council, Kirkcaldy District Council
Greater Glasgow Area:	Clyde Valley, Greater Glasgow, East Kilbride
Highland and Islands Enterprise Area:	All Tourist Boards and Tourist Organisations within the Highlands and Islands Enterprises' administrative area.
Loch Lomond Area:	Loch Lomond, Stirling and the Trossachs
Dumfries and Galloway:	Dumfries and Galloway Region
	Perthshire: Perthshire
Rural North East:	Banff and Buchan, Gordon, Kincardine and Deeside, Moray

The numbers of hotels, bedrooms and bed spaces are taken from the STB's database of hotels registered with the Board. As registration is voluntary, these statistics do not cover all hotels - only those which are registered.

3.3   Tables 3.3 and 3.4, chart 3.1 and map 3.1 were provided by the Scottish Youth Hostels Association (SYHA). In table 3.3, junior members are those aged under 18 and senior members are all those above that age. The areas covered by SYHA districts are as follows:

Aberdeen: Grampian Region, Badenoch and Strathspey, Nairn, Inverness, Ross and Cromarty, Sutherland and Caithness District, Orkney and Shetland

Dundee: Tayside Region and North East Fife District Edinburgh: Lothian and Borders Region, Falkirk, Clackmannan, Dunfermline and Kirkcaldy District

Glasgow: City of Glasgow, Clydebank, Bearsden and Milngavie, Strathkelvin, Cumbernauld and Kilsyth, Monklands, Motherwell, Hamilton, Lanark, East Kilbride, Eastwood, Renfrew, Inverclyde, Dumbarton, Argyll and Bute, Stirling, Lochaber and Skye and Lochalsh Districts, Western Isles.

South West: Dumfries and Galloway Region, Kyle and Carrick, Cumnock and Doon Valley, Kilmarnock and Loudon and Cunninghame Districts.

LEISURE AND SPORTING ACTIVITIES

3.4 Country Parks and Regional Parks provide the focus for informal countryside recreation around Scotland's main centres of population. Most of the 36 Country Parks (table 6.4) are well established and attract over 14 million visitors annually. Visitor numbers are collated by Scottish Natural Heritage (table 3.5). The four Regional Parks in Scotland also provide opportunities for outdoor recreation and access to the wider countryside, at the same time maintaining existing land uses (table 6.5).

3.5 Table 3.6 shows statistics for visitors to gardens that are open to the public. The data is based on the visitor attractions survey undertaken each year by the Scottish Tourist Board in an attempt to determine trends in the tourism market. Map 3.2 shows the distribution of golf courses in Scotland.

3.6 Table 3.7 is derived from the Forestry Commission's Annual Reports. In addition to the facilities indicated in table 3.7, there is increasing recreation potential in the Commission's forests as they mature, and also because of improved forest design, management and conservation practices.

3.7   The Mountaineering Council of Scotland is the national body for mountaineering in Scotland. The organisation aims to foster and promote interest in mountaineering as well as providing technical knowledge and education. Membership is open to all mountaineering clubs on payment of an annual membership fee, and there are also facilities for individual membership (table 3.9).

3.8   Tables 3.10 and 3.11 are derived from the Scottish Mountaineering Club Journal that publishes details of accidents on Scottish mountains. Hypothermia is defined as core body temperature being below 35 degrees centigrade. Hyperthermia is defined as abnormally high body temperature.

Table 3.1 Number of hotels, bedroom and bedspace occupancy, by Tourist Board Area, 1993[1]

Tourist Board Area[2]	Total number of hotels[3]	Number of bedrooms						Total number of bedspaces	Accommodation Occupancy Survey[4]	
		5-9	10-25	26-50	51-100	101+	No details		Bedroom Occupancy Annual Average (%)	Bedspace Occupancy Annual Average (%)
Scotland	**2,398**	**927**	**925**	**222**	**125**	**67**	**132**	**97,856**	**57**	**44**
Aberdeen	72	17	29	7	10	8	1	6,556	66	51
Ayrshire	149	22	44	8	4	3	8	4,512	50	37
Borders	89	44	29	5	1	1	9	2,304	59	51
Dumfries and Galloway	187	101	72	7	6	1	0	5,089	52	44
Dundee Area	145	51	62	10	3	3	16	5,217	53	32
Edinburgh Area	213	74	87	21	13	15	3	12,457	68	50
Forth Valley Area	87	25	37	14	3	3	5	2,854	59	36
Greater Glasgow Area	182	36	70	28	12	15	21	12,270	64	44
HIE Area[5]	799	301	331	81	45	11	30	28,321	50	43
Loch Lomond Area	130	49	46	11	13	3	8	5,522	61	42
Perthshire	179	73	67	20	10	3	6	7,225	62	50
Rural North East	166	74	51	10	5	1	25	6,556	48	38

Source: Scottish Tourist Board

1) The table only covers hotels with 5 or more bedrooms.
2) See introductory notes, paragraph 8.2 for description of Tourist Board Areas.
3) "Hotel" refers to hotels, motels, and inns but not guesthouses which are registered with STB.
4) Sample size is a minimum of 250 hotels each month in any given year.
5) Highlands and Islands Enterprise.

Table 3.2 Self-catering accommodation and caravan and camping sites' occupancy rates, 1994

Month	Self-catering accommodation						Touring caravan & camping parks
	Occupancy of property (percentage)				Properties occupied by overseas visitors %	Average length of stay (weeks)	Pitch occupancy %
	Total	Houses[1]	Chalets	Caravans[2]			
April	48	54	48	28	4	1.9	14
May	61	69	65	34	4	3.0	25
June	71	72	79	57	6	2.8	31
July	79	81	87	67	12	3.2	49
August	85	87	90	78	9	4.3	53
September	73	75	75	65	5	2.9	24
October	64	69	63	44	4	2.6	12

Source: Scottish Tourist Board

1) Includes cottages, flats and bungalows.
2) Holiday hire static caravans.

Table 3.3 Membership of Scottish Youth Hostels Association 1994[1][2]

SYHA District	Family Members		Junior Members		Senior Members		Total	
	Male	Female	Male	Female	Male	Female	Male	Female
Scotland	**2,203**	**1,770**	**1,499**	**1,074**	**15,009**	**11,635**	**18,712**	**14,479**
Aberdeen	277	245	213	142	1,941	1,510	2,431	1,897
Dundee	177	151	137	74	1,241	1,023	1,555	1,248
Edinburgh	790	622	470	376	5,144	4,079	6,404	5,077
Glasgow	768	608	531	364	5,753	4,317	7,052	5,289
South West	191	144	148	118	930	706	1,269	968

Source: Scottish Youth Hostels Association

1) Excludes life members.
2) See introductory notes, paragraph 8.3 for description of SYHA administrative areas.

Table 3.4 **Overnight stays in Scottish Youth Hostels Association accommodation, by region, 1989-1993[1]**

Region/Islands Area	Number of hostels in 1993[2]	Number of overnight stays				
		1989	1990	1991	1992	1993
Scotland	**84**	**596,094**	**629,009**	**629,932**	**633,817**	**609,504**
Borders	6	16,749	17,706	15,977	18,599	19,570
Central	5	38,292	45,293	32,950	36,005	46,769
Dumfries and Galloway	3	5,290	6,137	5,725	5,617	5,682
Fife	1	3,095	2,783	2,340	3,221	3,142
Grampian	5	27,063	27,112	33,757	32,728	30,258
Highland	31	254,924	269,146	265,820	261,074	243,330
Lothian	2	78,801	79,719	84,331	83,614	85,919
Strathclyde	13	122,477	127,831	135,919	140,322	128,528
Tayside	4	27,257	29,704	28,503	27,762	25,962
Orkney	6	11,871	12,308	12,266	12,087	10,010
Shetland	1	3,250	3,563	2,724	2,706	-
Western Isles	7	7,168	7,707	9,620	10,082	10,334

Source: Scottish Youth Hostels Association

(1) Figures include adopted hostels.
(2) Figures include 11 adopted hostels.

Chart 3.1 Scottish Youth Hostel Accommodation: visitors by country of origin, 1983 and 1993 [1]

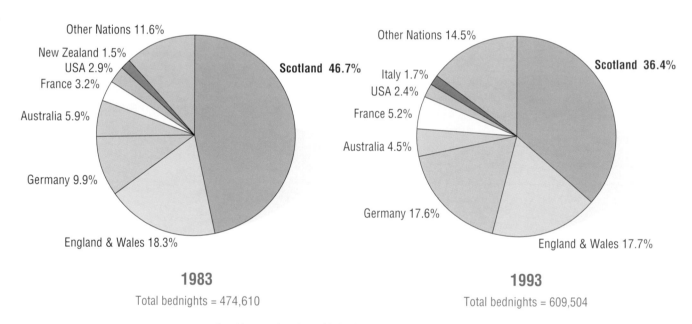

1983
Other Nations 11.6%
New Zealand 1.5%
USA 2.9%
France 3.2%
Australia 5.9%
Germany 9.9%
England & Wales 18.3%
Scotland 46.7%
Total bednights = 474,610

1993
Other Nations 14.5%
Italy 1.7%
USA 2.4%
France 5.2%
Australia 4.5%
Germany 17.6%
England & Wales 17.7%
Scotland 36.4%
Total bednights = 609,504

Countries named are those with the highest number of visitors in year.

(1) Figures may not sum due to rounding

Source: Scottish Youth Hostels Association

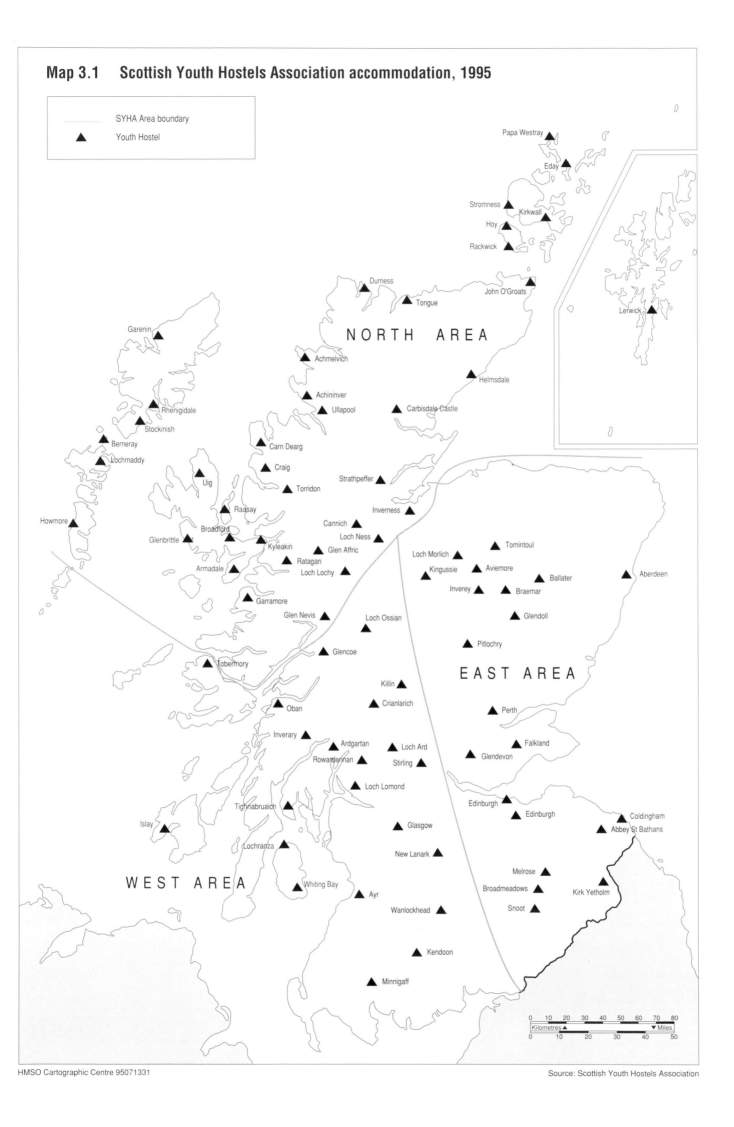

Map 3.1 Scottish Youth Hostels Association accommodation, 1995

SYHA Area boundary
▲ Youth Hostel

Papa Westray
Eday
Stromness
Kirkwall
Hoy
Rackwick

Durness
Tongue
John O'Groats

NORTH AREA

Garenin
Achmelvich
Helmsdale
Achininver
Ullapool
Carbisdale Castle

Rhenigidale
Stockinish
Berneray
Lochmaddy

Carn Dearg
Craig
Strathpeffer

Uig
Torridon
Inverness

Raasay
Cannich
Loch Ness

Howmore
Broadford
Glen Affric
Tomintoul

Glenbrittle
Kyleakin
Loch Morlich
Kingussie
Aviemore
Ballater
Aberdeen

Ratagan
Inverey
Braemar

Armadale
Loch Lochy

Garramore
Glendoll

Glen Nevis
Loch Ossian
Pitlochry

Glencoe

Tobermory

EAST AREA

Killin

Oban
Crianlarich
Perth

Inverary
Ardgartan
Loch Ard
Falkland

Rowardennan
Stirling
Glendevon

Loch Lomond

Tighnabruaich
Edinburgh
Edinburgh
Coldingham

Islay
Abbey St Bathans

Glasgow

Lochranza
New Lanark

Melrose

WEST AREA
Broadmeadows
Kirk Yetholm

Whiting Bay
Snoot

Ayr

Wanlockhead

Kendoon

Minnigaff

Lerwick

0 10 20 30 40 50 60 70 80
Kilometres ▲
▼ Miles
0 10 20 30 40 50

Source: Scottish Youth Hostels Association

Table 3.5　Scottish Country Parks - Annual Visitor Figures, 1990-92

Name of Park	1990	1991	1992
Aden	186,906	205,955	207,907
Almondell/Calderwood	110,000	160,000	135,000
Balloch	270,000	295,000	250,000
Balmedie	100,000	110,000	150,000
Beecraigs	400,000	394,000	401,000
Bonaly	52,000	50,000	55,328
Brodick Castle	66,915	69,492	63,513
Calderglen	260,000	400,000	225,000
Camperdown/Templeton	600,000	500,000	550,000
Castle Semple	250,000	232,500	230,311
Chatelherault	300,000	278,346	254,553
Clatto	90,000	90,787	90,525
Craigtoun	95,000	115,744	105,355
Crombie	44,742	45,750	49,477
Culzean	365,000	385,781	353,204
Dean Castle	100,000	100,000	200,000
Drumpellier	363,000	462,925	575,000
Eglinton	35,871	37,550	88,602
Forfar Loch	263,231	230,623	129,371
Gartmore Dam	16,000	84,144	127,080
Gleniffer Braes	400,000	400,000	400,000
Haddo	150,000	190,000	155,000
Haughton House	17,000	26,000	104,000
Hillend	160,000	160,000	347,412
John Muir	200,000	262,833	279,904
Lochore Meadows	400,000	420,000	357,000
Monikie	180,000	180,733	147,209
Mugdock	220,000	280,000	255,000
Muiravonside	100,000	107,622	115,000
Muirshiel	45,000	42,000	39,708
Palacerigg	120,000	125,000	125,000
Pollok	900,000	900,000	750,000
Polkemmet	347,846	328,322	286,000
Strathclyde	6,452,808	6,493,749	6,500,000
Townhill	No record	25,000	47,000
Vogrie	45,000	130,000	209,052
Total	**13,706,319**	**14,319,856**	**14,358,511**

Source: Scottish Natural Heritage

Table 3.6　Gardens open to the public with over 10,000 visitors, 1991-1994[1][2]

Name of Property	Total number of visitors			
	1991	1992	1993	1994
Royal Botanic Garden, Edinburgh	765,909	662,489	787,107	788,119
Glasgow Botanic Garden	350,000[2]	350,000[2]	350,000[2]	350,000[2]
Inverewe Garden, near Gairloch	144,993	130,468	128,008	120,931
Threave Garden, Castle Douglas	71,984	63,729	58,575	55,618
Bells Cherrybank Garden, Perth	45,000	46,129	32,103	38,500
Younger Botanic Garden, near Dunoon	38,876	34,035	35,725	34,633
Logan Botanic Garden, Stranraer	35,004	32,358	33,706	33,728
Pitmedden Garden, Pitmedden	26,919	23,567	23,700	22,300
Greenbank, Glasgow	21,574	22,713	17,615	22,375
Branklyn Garden, Perth	18,869	18,869	15,230	17,521
Priorwood Garden, Melrose	14,555	13,407	14,719	17,846

Source: Scottish Tourist Board

(1)　In 1992, 1989-1991 figures given for comparison purposes.
(2)　Estimated figures.

Table 3.7　Forestry Commission public recreational facilities, 1983-1995[1]

	1983	1984	1985	1986	1987	1988	1989	1990	1991	1992	1993	1994	1995
Camping and caravan sites[2]	9	9	9	9	8	8	8	9	9	9	10	9	9
Picnic places	134	134	125	148	168	168	185	189	193	200	182	188	179
Forest walks and forest nature trails	239	235	180	199	292	292	246	259	274	289	315	319	320
Visitor centres	9	6	6	6	7	8	8	8	9	9	9	10	11
Arboreta and forest gardens	5	5	5	4	5	4	4	2	3	3	4	4	4
Forest drives	2	2	2	2	2	2	2	2	3	4	4	5	5
Forest cabins and holiday houses	84	83	84	84	87	85	71	67	67	67	67	67	67

Source: Forestry Commission

(1)　At 31 March.

(2)　Figures do not include sites leased to the Caravan Club, Camping Club of Great Britain and Northern Ireland, or those set aside for youth camping or facilities for caravan rallies.

Map 3.2   Golf Courses, 1995

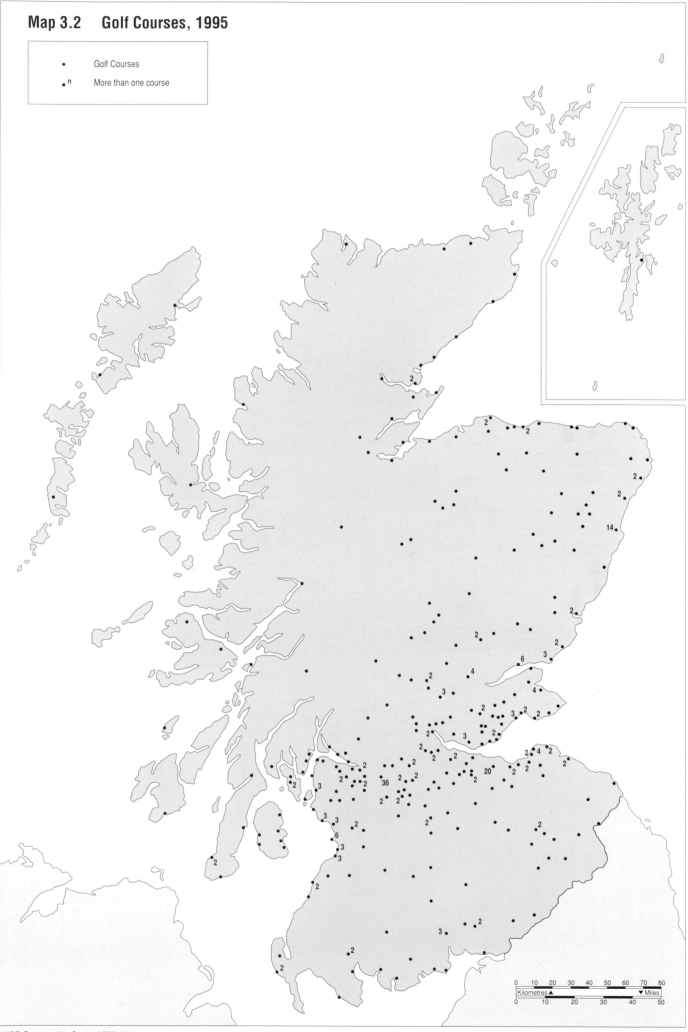

- Golf Courses
- n   More than one course

Source: Scottish Tourist Board

Table 3.8   Skiing developments, 1995

Region	Ski Centre	Lifts/Tows	Capacity[1]
Grampian	Cairngorm	17	6,000
Grampian	Lecht	10	2,500
Highland	Aonach Mor	7	3,000
Highland	Glencoe	5	1,200
Tayside	Glenshee	24	5,400

(1)   Approximate skiers daily.

Source: SODD

Table 3.9   Clubs affiliated to the Mountaineering Council of Scotland by region, 1991-1994

	1991	1992	1993	1994
Scotland	107	116	121	130
Borders	4	4	2	3
Central	11	10	11	9
Dumfries and Galloway	1	1	-	9
Fife	14	14	12	11
Grampian	9	9	23	12
Highland	8	9	11	8
Lothian	18	18	8	17
Strathclyde	24	28	16	35
Tayside	9	12	30	10
Orkney	-	0	0	0
Shetland	-	0	0	0
Western Isles	-	1	1	0
National[1]	9	10	7	9
Associate members			-	7

(1)   Clubs with no obvious regional base eg Ladies Scottish Climbing Club.

Source: Mountaineering Council of Scotland

Table 3.10   Scottish mountain accidents, 1988-1993

	Casualties					Incidents									Number of man-hours spent
	Injuries	Exhaustion, exposure, hypothermia, hyperthermia	Illness	Total casualties		Actual rescue		Other callouts				Total incidents	Non-mountaineering		
	Number	Number	Number	Number	of which deaths	Incidents with casualties	Cragfast	Separated	Lost	Overdue or benighted	False alarms		Animal rescues	Incidents	
1988	121	34	10	165	25	131	18	7	13	24	16	219	-	14	22,782
1989	130	15	13	158	25	141	8	15	12	25	14	215	3	11	22,560
1990	122	34	11	167	29	147	19	14	14	37	21	254	4	18	19,207
1991	217	23	20	260	44	235	22	13	28	46	10	354	1	10	-
1992	164	26	16	206	43	194	20	11	13	45	14	297	4	7	-
1993	194	15	24	235	62	215	20	16	13	46	7	317	5	15	-

Source: Mountain Rescue Committee of Scotland

Table 3.11   Scottish mountain accidents by area, 1994

Area	Casualties					Incidents							Non-mountaineering	
	Injuries	Exhaustion, exposure, hypothermia, hyperthermia	Illness	Total casualties		Actual rescue		Other callouts				Total incidents		
	Number	Number	Number	Number	of which deaths	Incidents with casualties	Cragfast	Separated	Lost	Overdue or benighted	False alarms		Animal rescues	Incidents
Scotland	157	29	22	234	45	209	25	19	12	42	10	317	3	19
Northern Highlands	16	5	2	23	3	18	2	4	1	6	3	34	1	1
Western Highlands	12	-	2	14	3	11	-	1	1	3	1	17	-	1
Ben Nevis	17	6	2	25	6	24	7	1	1	1	-	34	-	1
Glencoe[1]	27	2	-	29	5	28	7	-	2	4	2	43	-	-
Other Central Highlands	28	3	1	32	4	29	5	1	3	5	2	46	1	1
Cairngorms	34	4	5	44	6	76	1	3	2	8	-	56	-	4
Southern Highlands	2	2	6	35	9	3	2	6	-	4	2	43	1	5
Skye	12	1	-	13	6	1	1	1	-	2	-	12	-	2
Islands[2]	5	1	-	6	1	6	-	-	-	1	-	7	-	1
Southern Uplands	4	5	4	13	2	13	-	2	2	8	-	25	-	3

(1)   Including Buachaille.
(2)   Other than Skye.

Source: Mountain Rescue Committee of Scotland

atmosphere

4 atmosphere

4.1   Data for tables 4.1 to 4.8, maps 4.1a and b and 4.2a and b were supplied by the Meteorological Office (Edinburgh). Site details of climatological stations in these tables are as follows:

	Height above mean sea level(m)	Height correction to temperature
Aberdeen (Craibstone)	102	0.6
Dundee (Mayfield)	45	0.3
Edinburgh (Blackford Hill)	134	0.8
Royal Botanical Gardens (from 1992)	26	0.2
Glasgow (Abbotsinch)	5	0.0
Auchincruive (Strathclyde)	48	0.3
Bowhill (Selkirk)	168	1.0
Braemar	339	2.0
Dumfries	49	0.3
Inverness	4	0.0
Lerwick	82	0.5
Stornoway	15	0.1
Wick	36	0.2

There was a change of site at Glasgow Airport from Renfrew to Abbotsinch in May 1966 and 1951/80 averages have been calculated using the combined data. From 1992 the site in Edinburgh has been the Royal Botanic Gardens.

4.2   The temperature maps 4.1(a) and (b) are based on observations of temperatures from about 150 stations in Scotland for the 30 year period 1941 to 1970. For some stations, data for shorter periods or incomplete records have been weighted to give estimated values for the full 30 year period. Mean daily temperature is obtained from the arithmetic mean of the mean daily maximum and mean daily minimum. The altitude correction for maps of mean temperature is 0.6C per 100m above mean sea level.

ELECTRICITY GENERATING STATIONS

4.3   Map 4.3 supplied by Electrical Review, shows electricity generating stations in Scotland. Stations north of the boundary line are owned by Scottish Hydro-Electric, except for the nuclear power station at Dounreay, which is owned by the United Kingdom Atomic Energy Authority. Those south of the boundary are owned by Scottish Power - excluding the nuclear power stations at Hunterston and Torness which are owned by Scottish Nuclear and the nuclear power station at Chapelcross, owned by British Nuclear Fuels.

AIR QUALITY STANDARDS AND GUIDELINES

4.4   Map 4.4 shows the location of sites in the DoE UK automatic urban and rural monitoring networks in Scotland. In the UK, air quality for sulphur dioxide, smoke, nitrogen dioxide, ozone and lead is regulated by EC Directives. In addition, the World Health Organisation has issued air quality guidelines for a number of pollutants. In 1991, the Secretary of State for the Environment established the Expert Panel on Air Quality Standards (EPAQS) to provide recommended air quality standards for the UK. This panel has now recommended standards for a number of pollutants discussed in this Digest, and the Government is currently considering these recommendations. A summary of all these air quality standards and guidelines is given in tables 4.19 and 4.20 (a)-(f).

In addition, in order to describe air quality on a daily basis, the Department of the Environment has specified air quality bands of VERY GOOD, GOOD, POOR, and VERY POOR, for nitrogen dioxide, sulphur dioxide, and ozone. Information on air quality, on an hourly basis, is now provided on the air quality information line (0800 556677).

LEAD AND OTHER ELEMENTS

4.5   Lead is a trace element which is emitted into the environment by the consumption of leaded petrol, by the burning of coal and from metal works. Concentrations can accumulate in the environment and in the body, and can affect health, particularly in children. A range of trace elements, including lead, is monitored at two sites in Scotland: Motherwell and Glasgow. Data for lead, iron, and zinc are given in table 4.9. Concentrations of lead are generally decreasing, as a result of the increased use of unleaded petrol, and concentrations at both sites are well below the EC Directive limit value and the WHO guideline concentration.

Tropospheric Ozone

4.6   Tropospheric ozone should not be confused with the stratospheric ozone layer, which protects the earth against harmful ultra-violet radiation. The troposphere is the lowest layer of the atmosphere, and although some ozone occurs here naturally, concentrations can be enhanced by reactions between pollutants which arise from human activity. Ozone can also reduce crop yield, cause damage to natural vegetation, contribute to acid rain formation, and damage some man made materials such as paints, elastomers and fabrics.

AEA Technology's National Environmental Technology Centre is responsible for managing a national network of ozone monitoring stations in rural areas in the UK. The main objectives of the network are to provide a broad picture of the spatial and temporal variation of ozone concentrations, and to aid the assessment of the impact of this pollutant on sensitive areas. The results from the stations in Scotland are summarised in table 4.10. In October 1992, an urban monitoring station in Edinburgh was established by DoE as part of the Automatic Urban Monitoring Network. Ozone measurements at this site are also presented in table 4.10. Under a continuing programme of quality control checking of data and international intercomparisons of primary standards, some retrospective re-scaling of UK rural ozone data has been necessary. Rural ozone measurements carried out from April 1991 to March 1993 have been re-scaled upwards by approximately 5%. Data presented in this table are derived from the corrected dataset.

Nitrogen Dioxide

4.7   Nitric Oxide and Nitrogen dioxide are gases formed in combustion processes, both from the nitrogen present in fuel and by the oxidation of nitrogen in air. High concentrations of nitrogen dioxide can affect the respiratory system, reduce plant growth, contribute to acid deposition, and play a part in the formation of tropospheric ozone. Hourly average concentrations of nitrogen oxide are monitored at 3 sites in Scotland: Strath Vaich (a rural site in Highland Region); Glasgow and Edinburgh (as part of the Automatic Urban Monitoring Network.) A summary of data from these sites is given in table 4.11.

An extensive survey of NO_2 concentration measurements, with diffusion tube samplers, has been established in the UK in a collaborative programme between the DoE and local authorities. The main aims of the survey are to identify areas of the UK which may require additional monitoring to ensure compliance with the EC Directive on NO_2 concentrations and to determine trends in NO_2 concentrations throughout the UK from a long running survey with a consistent siting and operational methodology. Results for sites in Scotland located at the kerbsides of busy roads are shown in map 4.12 and corresponding results for sites in intermediate and urban background areas are shown in map 4.13. At intermediate and urban background sites in Scotland the maximum annual average concentration of 23ppb was recorded in Glasgow. The overall average concentration for urban areas in Scotland was 13ppb. At kerbside locations, the overall average for Scotland was 22ppb and the maximum average concentration of 47ppb was also recorded in Glasgow.

SULPHUR DIOXIDE

4.8   Sulphur dioxide is released by the combustion of sulphur containing fuels such as coal, smokeless fuel, and oil. Sulphur dioxide, particularly in combination with smoke, can cause temporary breathing problems for some people. This pollutant is also one of the principal contributors to acid rain. Hourly average concentrations are measured at 2 sites in Scotland: Strath Vaich and Edinburgh. A summary of the data from these sites is given in table 4.12. In addition, daily smoke and sulphur dioxide measurements are made at 40 sites in Scotland, to determine compliance with the EC Directive for these pollutants. Map 4.5 shows the annual average SO_2 concentration in air in ppb, averaged over 20-20km grid squares containing one or more monitoring sites, for the period April 1993 to March 1994.

CARBON MONOXIDE

4.9   Carbon monoxide is primarily formed as a result of incomplete combustion of petrol in motor vehicles. It is toxic at high concentrations and affects physical co-ordination, vision and judgement. Carbon monoxide is measured in both Glasgow and Edinburgh, and the results are summarised in table 4.13.

FINE PARTICLES

4.10   Particles in the size range which can penetrate the human thorax are generally called the thoracic fraction (often referred to as PM_{10}) because the size fraction is defined in relation to particles of aerodynamic diameter 10mm). Recent studies have identified this particle size as significant in relation to effects on human health. Measurements of the thoracic particle size fraction are undertaken at the Edinburgh site and the data are presented in table 4.14.

SMOKE CONTROL ORDERS AND CLEAN AIR GRANTS

4.11   Under the Clean Air Act 1993, local authorities are empowered to make smoke control orders prohibiting the emission of smoke from buildings, including dwellings, in any part of their district. They can also give grants to householders to help them pay for new boilers and fires in newly-declared smoke control zones. Details of orders and grants made in 1993/94 are shown in table 4.15

PRECIPITATION COMPOSITION MONITORING NETWORK

4.12   The Department of the Environment funds a national precipitation composition monitoring programme, co-ordinated by the National Environmental Technology centre. The mean concentrations of the major ions in precipitation observed in 1993 are listed in table 4.21.

WET DEPOSITED ACIDITY

4.13   The annual mean non-marine sulphate concentration in 1993 is shown in map 4.8. The mean concentrations are larger in southern and eastern Scotland than in north western Scotland because precipitation in the north-west is mainly associated with airflow from the Atlantic and does not contain high levels of pollutants from the UK or Europe. The distribution of wet deposition, however, is determined largely by the variation in total rainfall and is largest in the south-west Highlands.

4.14   Additional information on acid deposition can be found in the report of the Review Group on Acid Rain, Acid Deposition in the United Kingdom, 1986-88 available from the Department of the Environment, Publication Sales Department. Results from the monitoring network are published annually by the National Environmental Technology Centre, Culham, Oxfordshire. (eg Acid Deposition in the UK 1993, Report AEA/CS/16419029/001).

CRITICAL LOAD FOR SOILS

4.15   The critical load is an estimate of the maximum quantity of acidifying factors which can be absorbed by the soil without adverse changes in soil functions occurring. Empirical maps, showing the distribution of critical loads of soils, and where they have been exceeded (maps 4.10 and 4.11) have been produced by the Macaulay Land Use Research Institute (MLURI). The compilation of the maps is part of ongoing research into the development and application of critical load work as an aid to policy formulation on emission abatement and indicative forestry strategy in Scotland.

CONTRAVENTIONS OF AIR POLLUTION ACTS AND NOISE COMPLAINTS

4.16   Tables 4.16 - 4.18 are derived from the Annual Report on Environmental Health in Scotland for 1992-1993, published by the Royal Environmental Health Institute of Scotland. The information summarises the situation in 48 of the 56 district councils, comprising 95 per cent of the population of Scotland.

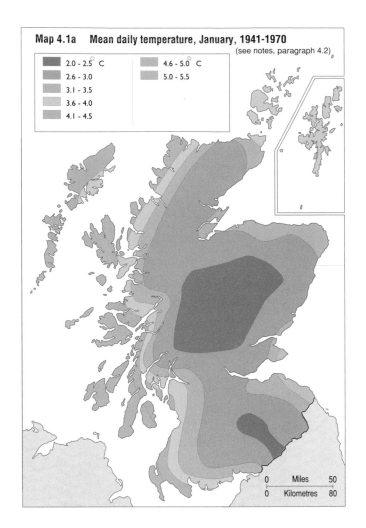

Map 4.1a   Mean daily temperature, January, 1941-1970

(see notes, paragraph 4.2)

- 2.0 - 2.5 °C
- 2.6 - 3.0
- 3.1 - 3.5
- 3.6 - 4.0
- 4.1 - 4.5
- 4.6 - 5.0 °C
- 5.0 - 5.5

| 0 | Miles | 50 |
| 0 | Kilometres | 80 |

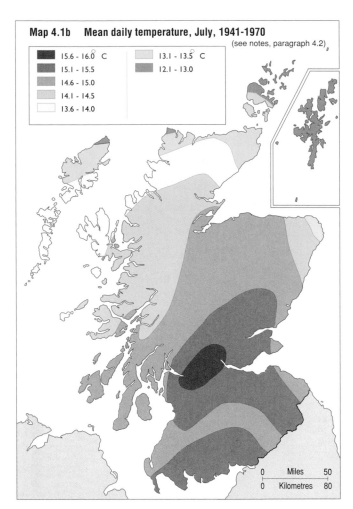

Map 4.1b   Mean daily temperature, July, 1941-1970

(see notes, paragraph 4.2)

- 15.6 - 16.0 °C
- 15.1 - 15.5
- 14.6 - 15.0
- 14.1 - 14.5
- 13.6 - 14.0
- 13.1 - 13.5 °C
- 12.1 - 13.0

| 0 | Miles | 50 |
| 0 | Kilometres | 80 |

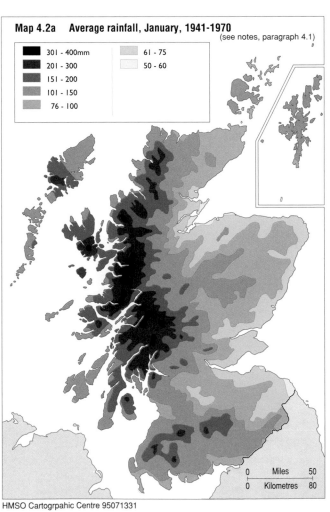

Map 4.2a   Average rainfall, January, 1941-1970

(see notes, paragraph 4.1)

- 301 - 400mm
- 201 - 300
- 151 - 200
- 101 - 150
- 76 - 100
- 61 - 75
- 50 - 60

| 0 | Miles | 50 |
| 0 | Kilometres | 80 |

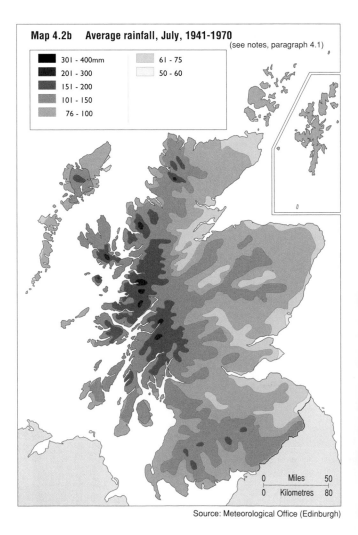

Map 4.2b   Average rainfall, July, 1941-1970

(see notes, paragraph 4.1)

- 301 - 400mm
- 201 - 300
- 151 - 200
- 101 - 150
- 76 - 100
- 61 - 75
- 50 - 60

| 0 | Miles | 50 |
| 0 | Kilometres | 80 |

HMSO Cartogrpahic Centre 95071331

Source: Meteorological Office (Edinburgh)

Table 4.1 Mean daily temperature, 1951-1994[1][2][3]

degrees celsius

	Yearly average	Jan	Feb	Mar	Apr	May	June	July	Aug	Sept	Oct	Nov	Dec
Aberdeen													
1951/80 averages	7.7	2.7	2.6	4.3	6.2	8.7	11.8	13.2	13.1	11.5	9.1	5.2	3.6
1991	8.1	2.5	1.9	5.9	6.4	9.5	10.3	14.7	15.1	11.9	8.9	5.4	4.5
1992	7.9	3.9	4.5	5.5	6.7	10.5	13.3	13.5	12.6	11.1	6.3	5.2	3.0
1993	7.6	3.7	5.5	5.4	7.1	8.5	11.9	12.8	12.5	10.6	7.3	4.3	1.9
1994	8.1	3.1	1.9	4.9	6.3	7.9	12.6	14.7	13.2	11.3	8.3	7.9	4.3
Dundee													
1951/80 averages	8.6	2.9	3.2	5.1	7.5	10.2	13.3	14.8	14.4	12.5	9.7	5.6	3.9
1991	8.9	2.5	3.1	6.3	7.6	11.3	11.5	16.1	16.3	12.9	9.4	5.8	4.3
1992	8.9	3.7	5.3	6.5	7.9	11.5	15.0	14.7	13.7	11.8	6.7	5.7	3.3
1993	..	4.4	6.3	5.9	..	9.8	13.5	14.4	13.6	11.4	7.7	3.9	3.2
1994	9.0	3.5	2.6	5.9	7.3	9.5	13.8	15.6	14.6	12.2	9.3	8.7	5.0
Edinburgh[4]													
1951/80 averages	8.5	3.2	3.1	4.9	7.2	10.0	13.0	14.4	14.3	12.5	9.8	5.8	4.3
1991	8.5	2.7	2.5	6.5	7.3	10.7	11.5	15.4	15.7	10.0	9.1	5.7	4.8
1992	8.9	3.7	5.3	6.7	8.1	12.0	14.7	14.9	13.9	11.9	6.7	6.3	3.5
1993	8.6	5.0	6.3	6.4	8.0	9.9	13.3	14.3	13.9	11.5	7.3	4.1	3.7
1994	9.1	3.9	2.7	6.1	7.3	9.7	13.3	15.5	14.3	12.0	9.2	9.5	5.1
Glasgow													
1951/80 averages	8.6	3.1	3.3	5.1	7.5	10.5	13.3	14.5	14.3	12.3	9.6	5.6	4.1
1991	8.8	2.7	1.7	6.5	7.8	11.3	11.6	16.6	15.5	12.5	8.9	5.7	4.6
1992	8.8	3.9	5.5	6.7	7.7	12.1	14.9	14.6	13.6	11.8	5.9	5.7	3.7
1993	8.5	5.0	6.1	6.0	8.5	10.3	13.7	13.5	13.4	11.7	6.9	3.8	3.1
1994	8.9	3.9	2.5	5.7	7.1	9.9	12.4	15.5	14.0	11.4	9.1	9.3	5.3
Auchincruive													
1951/80 averages	8.7	3.6	3.5	5.3	7.4	10.2	13.0	14.1	14.1	12.4	9.9	6.1	4.6
1991	9.0	3.3	2.5	7.0	7.5	10.3	11.1	16.3	15.6	12.7	9.8	6.4	5.7
1992	9.1	4.5	5.9	6.7	7.7	12.5	14.7	14.3	13.5	11.8	6.3	6.8	4.5
1993	..	5.3	..	5.7	8.1	9.7	13.3	13.4	12.8	11.5	7.1	4.6	4.0
1994	9.0	4.4	2.7	5.9	7.0	9.7	12.3	15.3	13.8	11.5	9.5	9.7	6.0
Bowhill													
1951/80 averages	7.7	2.0	2.0	4.1	6.5	9.5	12.6	14.0	13.6	11.6	8.7	4.7	3.1
1991	7.9	1.1	1.3	6.1	6.6	10.3	10.9	15.7	15.3	11.8	8.4	4.8	3.3
1992	8.0	2.5	4.0	5.9	7.0	11.5	14.5	13.7	12.9	11.4	5.7	4.9	2.0
1993	7.5	3.7	5.1	5.2	7.1	9.1	13.1	13.5	12.7	10.4	6.3	2.3	2.3
1994	7.9	2.7	1.1	5.1	6.1	8.7	12.8	15.3	13.2	10.7	8.3	7.5	4.1
Braemar													
1951/80 averages	6.3	0.6	0.4	2.6	5.0	8.2	11.4	12.7	12.3	10.3	7.5	3.3	1.9
1991	6.9	0.6	0.1	4.3	5.3	9.3	9.5	14.9	14.1	10.7	6.9	4.0	2.7
1992	6.7	1.9	3.3	4.3	5.1	10.1	13.3	12.5	11.1	9.9	3.9	3.7	0.7
1993	6.2	2.1	4.6	3.6	6.1	8.1	11.9	11.6	11.2	8.7	4.5	1.3	0.3
1994	3.1	-0.9	-2.4	-0.1	1.6	2.0	7.0	9.1	7.9	5.4	2.8	3.8	0.4
Dumfries													
1951/80 averages	8.5	3.0	3.1	5.0	7.3	10.2	13.1	14.4	14.3	12.3	9.7	5.7	4.1
1991	8.7	2.7	2.1	6.9	7.3	10.4	11.0	16.3	15.6	12.8	9.3	6.0	4.3
1992	8.7	3.4	5.1	6.6	7.7	12.3	15.3	14.3	13.5	11.7	6.4	5.7	3.1
1993	8.3	4.8	5.5	5.5	8.3	9.9	13.5	13.5	13.1	11.3	7.3	3.9	3.5
1994	8.5	3.9	2.1	5.7	6.5	9.3	12.2	15.3	13.7	10.9	8.9	8.7	5.2
Inveress													
1951/80 averages	8.6	3.3	3.2	5.3	7.3	10.2	13.0	14.3	14.2	12.4	9.7	5.8	4.3
1991	9.2	3.5	2.4	6.8	8.0	11.0	11.9	15.9	16.1	12.9	9.3	6.7	5.8
1992	8.8	5.4	5.9	5.9	7.5	11.7	13.9	14.3	13.5	11.3	6.5	5.8	3.8
1993	..	4.7	6.8	6.7	8.3	9.1	13.0	13.8	13.6	11.6	..	4.2	2.1
1994	8.9	3.9	2.9	5.5	7.5	9.9	13.3	15.9	14.3	11.5	8.9	8.9	5.4
Lerwick													
1951/80 averages	6.9	3.0	2.8	3.8	5.2	7.5	10.0	11.4	11.7	10.3	8.3	5.3	3.9
1991	7.5	3.9	2.9	5.6	5.9	7.8	8.7	13.2	13.1	10.2	8.2	5.9	5.1
1992	7.5	5.2	4.8	4.3	5.7	9.1	11.9	11.8	11.7	10.4	6.5	5.3	4.1
1993	6.7	3.3	4.3	4.5	5.9	7.7	8.9	10.3	10.7	9.7	6.9	5.7	2.6
1994	6.9	2.7	2.5	3.1	5.3	6.9	9.2	12.5	12.0	9.7	7.2	7.1	4.3
Stornoway													
1951/80 averages	8.1	4.0	3.9	5.3	6.6	9.1	11.4	12.7	12.7	11.3	9.3	6.0	4.9
1991	8.5	4.3	3.7	6.6	6.9	9.3	9.7	14.8	14.3	11.5	8.7	6.5	6.7
1992	8.5	6.3	5.9	5.3	7.0	10.7	12.7	12.8	12.6	10.7	7.3	5.9	4.7
1993	8.1	4.3	6.5	5.9	7.5	8.4	11.2	11.9	12.0	11.2	7.9	6.4	3.7
1994	8.2	4.3	4.1	4.5	6.3	8.4	10.9	13.6	12.5	10.9	8.8	8.8	5.5
Wick													
1951/80 averages	7.6	3.2	3.1	4.5	6.1	8.4	11.0	12.4	12.5	11.2	9.2	5.5	4.1
1991	7.9	3.1	2.8	6.1	6.7	8.7	9.1	13.5	14.3	10.9	8.9	5.9	4.8
1992	7.9	4.7	4.9	4.8	6.7	9.3	11.9	12.8	12.3	10.9	6.8	5.4	3.3
1993	..	3.5	5.7	5.5	6.4	7.7	10.3	11.3	11.6	10.4	..	5.3	2.3
1994	..	3.1	2.8	3.9	5.9	7.5	11.2	13.4	12.6	10.5	8.1	8.0	..

Source: Meteorological Office (Edinburgh)

(1)   Temperatures given are over a 24 hour period commencing at 0900 GMT.

(2)   See introductory notes, paragraph 4.1 for site descriptions.

(3)   The altitude correction between this table and maps 4.1(a) and (b) is 0.6°C per 100m above mean sea level.

(4)   As of 1992 data recorded at the Royal Botanic Gardens is used.

..   Information not available.

Table 4.2   Days with air frost, 1991-1994[1][2]

days

	Year	Jan	Feb	Mar	Apr	May	June	July	Aug	Sept	Oct	Nov	Dec
Aberdeen													
1991	45	17	12	4	1	-	-	-	-	-	-	3	8
1992	55	16	10	4	-	-	-	-	-	-	2	6	17
1993	47	9	3	5	1	-	-	-	-	-	1	10	18
1994	54	13	13	8	7	1	-	-	-	-	1	2	9
Dundee													
1991	35	12	8	4	-	-	-	-	-	-	-	5	6
1992	34	13	3	2	-	-	-	-	-	-	4	4	8
1993	34	3	3	3	-	-	-	-	-	-	2	12	11
1994	24	10	6	2	1	-	-	-	-	-	-	-	5
Edinburgh[3]													
1991	53	14	17	3	1	-	-	-	-	-	-	6	6
1992	45	14	8	3	-	-	-	-	-	-	6	3	11
1993	51	5	4	4	2	-	-	-	-	1	7	17	11
1994	34	9	14	1	1	-	-	-	-	-	-	1	8
Glasgow													
1991	69	12	18	9	5	2	-	-	-	1	1	11	10
1992	63	15	8	5	2	1	-	-	-	-	12	7	13
1993	66	7	7	7	2	2	-	-	-	3	10	16	12
1994	41	8	11	3	6	3	-	-	-	-	1	1	8
Auchincruive													
1991	38	8	15	3	2	2	-	-	-	-	-	4	4
1992	35	12	4	2	-	-	-	-	-	-	8	1	8
1993	..	3	..	8	1	1	-	-	-	-	8	10	10
1994	31	5	14	-	4	2	-	-	-	-	1	0	5
Bowhill													
1991	83	19	21	10	8	2	1	-	-	1	-	10	11
1992	71	18	9	4	2	1	-	-	-	-	9	11	17
1993	80	10	6	8	7	2	-	-	-	2	6	20	19
1994	59	13	20	6	5	2	-	-	-	-	1	3	9
Braemar													
1991	110	22	22	16	9	1	2	-	-	3	4	12	19
1992	..	23	14	7	9	3	-	-	-	-	16	..	19
1993	110	18	8	14	3	3	-	-	-	7	15	18	24
1994	106	21	21	15	9	12	-	-	-	-	10	7	11
Dumfries													
1991	59	12	20	6	4	1	-	-	-	-	-	6	10
1992	54	14	8	1	-	-	-	-	-	-	8	7	16
1993	59	5	5	9	2	-	-	-	-	-	8	16	14
1994	56	8	15	7	11	2	-	-	-	-	1	1	11
Inverness													
1991	33	11	14	3	-	-	-	-	-	-	-	2	3
1992	30	5	2	4	-	-	-	-	-	-	2	6	11
1993	..	5	2	6	-	-	-	-	-	-	..	-	-
1994	27	9	13	1	-	-	-	-	-	-	-	-	4
Lerwick													
1991	23	6	9	-	4	-	-	-	-	-	-	1	3
1992	20	5	2	7	-	1	-	-	-	-	-	3	2
1993	36	8	7	8	1	-	-	-	-	-	2	1	9
1994	42	13	8	11	1	-	-	-	-	-	4	0	5
Stornoway													
1991	16	7	8	-	-	-	-	-	-	-	-	1	
1992	16	1	2	4	-	-	-	-	-	-	1	-	8
1993	23	5	2	5	-	-	-	-	-	-	1	3	7
1994	21	6	3	6	1	-	-	-	-	-	-	-	5
Wick													
1991	33	12	7	1	2	-	1	-	-	2	-	4	4
1992	41	7	6	5	1	2	-	-	-	-	3	6	11
1993	..	10	3	4	3	2	-	-	-	1	..	6	15
1994	..	11	6	7	7	2	-	-	-	-	1	2	..

Source: Meteorological Office (Edinburgh)

(1)   Days with minimum temperature of below 0.0 degrees C.
(2)   See introductory notes, paragraph 4.1 for site description.
(3)   As of 1992 data recorded at the Royal Botanic Gardens is used.
..   Information not available

Table 4.3 Mean daily sunshine, 1951-1994[1]

hours

	Year Average	Jan	Feb	Mar	Apr	May	June	July	Aug	Sept	Oct	Nov	Dec
Aberdeen													
1951/80 averages	3.7	1.7	2.6	3.4	5.0	5.7	6.0	5.2	4.7	3.9	3.0	2.1	1.5
1991	3.7	2.8	2.3	2.9	5.3	-	-	-	-	-	-	-	-
1992	..	..	..	..	..	..	..	..	..	..	..	..	..
1993	..	..	..	..	..	..	..	..	..	..	..	..	..
1994	..	..	..	..	..	..	..	..	..	..	..	..	..
Dundee													
1951/80 averages	3.7	1.8	2.6	3.3	5.0	5.6	5.8	5.2	4.7	3.9	3.0	2.2	1.5
1991	..	2.0	2.5	2.5	6.3	5.3	5.0	..	6.2	5.7	..	..	1.4
1992	..	2.1	2.9	3.4	3.9	8.0	6.7	5.8	5.6	..	..	..	..
1993	..	1.5	2.1	3.9	3.5	4.7	5.3	6.2	5.2	4.2	4.0	1.8	..
1994	..	..	2.0	4.8	5.3	7.4	7.6	5.7	5.5	3.9	3.2	2.0	2.3
Edinburgh(2)													
1951/80 averages	3.7	1.7	2.5	3.3	4.8	5.6	5.7	5.2	4.7	3.9	3.1	2.0	1.5
1991	3.7	1.9	2.6	2.6	5.7	4.9	5.1	4.4	5.3	5.0	2.2	2.1	1.4
1992	3.6	2.3	2.6	2.7	3.4	6.4	5.3	5.0	5.5	4.0	2.3	2.4	1.4
1993	3.4	1.4	1.8	3.8	3.5	4.0	4.6	5.7	5.1	4.1	3.6	1.9	1.5
1994	4.0	1.7	2.1	4.1	4.8	6.9	6.7	5.5	5.0	3.5	3.2	2.1	2.0
Glasgow													
1951/80 averages	3.6	1.3	2.2	3.1	5.1	6.0	6.2	5.3	4.7	3.7	2.6	1.7	1.0
1991	3.7	1.3	2.2	3.1	5.1	6.0	6.2	5.3	4.7	3.7	2.6	1.7	1.0
1992	3.3	1.1	1.9	2.7	2.8	6.6	6.3	4.5	4.9	3.1	3.4	1.6	0.8
1993	3.3	1.2	1.5	3.2	3.5	4.8	4.2	4.5	5.6	4.2	3.5	1.9	1.1
1994	3.4	1.2	1.9	2.9	4.7	6.5	4.9	5.2	5.3	4.0	2.4	1.5	1.0
Auchincruive													
1951/80 averages	3.8	1.6	2.7	3.4	5.3	6.3	6.3	5.3	4.9	3.8	2.8	1.9	1.3
1991	3.8	1.6	2.7	3.4	5.3	6.3	6.3	5.3	4.9	3.8	2.8	1.9	1.3
1992	3.2	1.9	1.9	2.6	2.4	7.5	6.1	3.8	4.7	3.3	2.7	1.1	0.9
1993	*	0.9	*	2.9	4.1	4.8	3.9	2.9	5.3	3.9	3.6	2.4	1.0
1994	3.3	1.2	2.3	2.2	4.2	6.2	3.9	5.4	4.9	3.7	2.5	1.5	1.0
Braemar													
1951/80 averages	3.1	0.8	1.9	2.9	4.5	5.2	5.5	4.9	4.2	3.4	2.1	1.1	0.6
1991	..	..	1.5	2.5	5.0	..	3.7	..	..	4.7	..	0.9	0.9
1992	..	1.6	1.8	2.3	3.2	8.6	7.3	4.1	4.2	3.2	2.6	..	1.0
1993	3.0	1.0	1.2	3.5	3.6	4.7	4.3	4.8	3.9	4.0	2.3	1.1	1.0
1994	*	1.0	1.0	3.5	4.1	6.5	5.8	5.1	4.6	3.3	*	1.0	1.1
Dumfries													
1951/80 averages	3.7	1.5	2.4	3.2	5.0	5.9	6.1	5.1	5.0	3.7	2.9	2.0	1.3
1991	3.4	1.5	2.0	2.3	5.2	5.1	4.1	5.1	4.6	5.8	2.3	2.4	0.7
1992	3.4	1.3	1.8	2.6	3.5	7.1	7.5	4.2	4.7	3.8	2.4	1.5	0.6
1993	2.8	1.3	1.2	3.0	3.6	3.9	4.3	3.7	4.4	2.8	3.0	2.0	1.0
1994	3.2	1.1	1.9	2.9	5.1	5.0	3.5	5.4	4.6	5.3	3.3	1.3	1.1
Inverness													
1951/80 averages	3.3	1.2	2.6	3.4	4.6	5.2	5.3	4.6	4.2	3.7	2.7	1.6	1.0
1991	3.2	1.2	2.6	3.4	4.6	5.2	5.3	4.6	4.2	3.7	2.7	1.6	1.0
1992	3.1	1.6	2.4	2.1	3.2	6.5	5.1	3.5	4.5	3.3	2.2	1.9	0.9
1993	2.7	1.0	1.6	3.7	3.5	3.7	3.4	3.4	3.7	3.8	1.9	2.2	1.0
1994	3.5	1.0	3.2	2.9	4.1	7.5	5.4	5.0	4.2	4.1	2.5	1.3	1.4
Lerwick													
1951/80 averages	2.9	0.8	1.9	2.7	4.5	4.9	5.3	4.0	3.8	3.2	2.1	1.1	0.5
1991	3.0	0.8	1.9	2.7	4.5	4.9	5.3	4.0	3.8	3.2	2.1	1.1	0.5
1992	3.1	0.5	1.7	2.4	3.5	7.5	7.9	4.5	4.0	1.7	2.8	0.9	0.4
1993	2.5	0.3	0.9	2.7	4.3	5.0	4.1	2.8	2.9	3.8	1.5	1.2	0.5
1994	3.4	0.5	1.9	3.3	5.0	8.1	4.6	4.7	4.7	4.1	2.5	1.0	0.4
Stornoway													
1951/80 averages	3.4	1.2	2.5	3.7	5.2	6.0	5.9	4.2	4.4	3.6	2.5	1.5	0.8
1991	3.1	1.3	2.4	3.8	3.8	4.2	5.5	5.5	4.1	3.8	1.6	1.2	0.5
1992	3.0	0.5	1.6	2.2	3.5	8.0	6.2	3.6	4.0	2.9	2.2	1.1	0.5
1993	2.8	0.6	0.8	3.3	4.7	7.0	3.4	2.3	2.8	3.8	1.7	2.1	1.0
1994	3.6	1.0	3.0	3.2	4.4	9.5	4.5	4.7	3.5	4.1	2.5	1.5	1.0
Wick													
1951/80 averages	3.4	1.3	2.6	3.4	5.0	5.2	5.4	4.4	4.3	3.7	2.8	1.6	1.0
1991	3.4	2.5	1.9	3.0	5.8	4.9	5.6	3.3	5.3	5.0	1.8	1.4	0.1
1992	3.2	1.3	2.1	2.1	3.5	7.6	5.1	3.7	4.3	3.0	2.4	1.7	1.5
1993	..	1.1	1.4	3.7	3.3	3.7	..	..	3.6	4.3	1.6	2.2	..
1994	..	..	..	..	..	..	..	..	..	..	..	..	..

Source: Meteorological Office (Edinburgh)

(1)   See introductory notes, paragraph 4.1 for site descritpions.
(2)   As of 1992 data recorded at the Royal Botanic Gardens is used.
*   An extreme occurred on more than one day in the month.
..   Information not available

Table 4.4   Total rainfall, 1951-1994[1]   millimetres

	Year	Jan	Feb	Mar	Apr	May	June	July	Aug	Sept	Oct	Nov	Dec
Aberdeen													
1951/80 averages	821	77	57	54	51	62	54	79	83	66	78	80	80
1991	749	29	106	73	47	35	128	48	24	27	113	100	19
1992	824	45	30	87	75	60	68	51	112	85	87	61	63
1993	..	64	27	45	98	94	59	99	68	65	121	76	..
1994	..	134	154	27	59	13	26	34	31	59	61	100	..
Dundee													
1951/80 averages	714	65	51	49	44	56	54	70	71	60	60	63	71
1991	649	63	64	59	26	19	135	62	19	60	61	43	38
1992	689	52	28	104	38	29	30	51	112	95	35	69	46
1993	833	145	5	26	117	88	36	74	49	43	117	58	75
1994	618	75	101	42	49	16	54	28	30	32	56	81	54
Edinburgh(2)													
1951/80 averages	646	49	39	41	39	52	45	69	79	58	56	61	58
1991	641	73	75	63	31	17	62	82	15	65	50	50	57
1992	676	55	47	72	45	19	21	44	117	109	42	73	32
1993	791	116	4	26	63	103	88	57	34	50	104	39	107
1994	646	61	66	81	52	13	36	39	34	33	60	77	94
Glasgow													
1951/80 averages	951	96	63	65	50	62	58	68	83	95	98	105	108
1991	1,113	135	59	90	102	7	90	109	39	93	92	171	126
1992	1,224	110	141	130	66	79	23	58	163	137	69	163	85
1993	1,081	231	18	91	110	88	42	56	57	64	59	82	183
1994	1,261	168	71	180	82	11	77	63	129	53	60	130	237
Auchincruive													
1951/80 averages	901	82	50	53	47	51	58	80	91	100	97	99	93
1991	987	85	59	73	91	14	77	76	37	92	93	174	116
1992	1,131	100	104	117	58	46	40	72	151	113	108	160	62
1993	..	124	..	50	82	80	74	67	67	54	55	77	187
1994	1,041	130	53	126	74	8	55	70	91	68	57	119	190
Bowhill													
1951/80 averages	844	84	63	58	53	64	51	68	84	74	76	84	85
1991	860	108	90	83	56	11	82	51	32	52	89	119	87
1992	943	55	62	129	91	43	26	42	137	105	46	127	80
1993	..	158	8	29	113	142	51	50	30	77	128	..	..
1994	980	132	99	119	58	17	40	33	76	50	69	119	168
Braemar													
1951/80 averages	859	93	59	59	51	65	55	58	76	73	87	87	96
1991	891	70	66	62	71	38	129	57	31	58	144	114	51
1992	870	62	57	116	53	43	42	43	126	93	73	86	76
1993	..	..	32	60	75	106	31	49	45	107	173	45	84
1994	903	124	113	149	73	12	46	32	42	72	83	69	88
Dumfries													
1951/80 averages	1,022	103	71	66	55	71	63	77	93	104	106	109	104
1991	1,087	123	87	119	102	8	80	56	64	53	162	140	93
1992	..	..	97	132	101	34	24	60	..	..	72	153	94
1993	..	184	16	..	..	100	51	60	43	53	47	68	223
1994	..	..	95	121	81	15	54	99	82	62	86	138	171
Inveress													
1951/80 averages	619	49	35	38	35	44	47	63	72	54	59	63	60
1991	660	57	33	60	21	29	141	73	23	56	52	70	45
1992	700	94	42	74	37	42	28	16	100	71	49	93	54
1993	718	145	18	31	24	99	53	39	27	26	140	16	100
Lerwick													
1951/80 averages	1,177	127	93	93	72	64	64	67	78	113	119	140	147
1991	1,198	136	56	121	46	33	56	104	57	121	158	190	120
1992	1,274	105	147	115	95	75	32	58	127	112	77	208	123
1993	1,121	227	115	124	76	46	47	51	53	38	100	64	180
1994	1,458	242	75	206	89	34	100	25	86	141	109	141	210
Stornoway													
1951/80 averages	1,096	115	77	80	66	62	67	72	74	103	126	129	125
1991	1,072	107	53	71	82	34	70	52	83	104	116	215	85
1992	1,447	73	146	158	94	50	33	128	191	149	131	171	123
1993	1,119	275	57	80	80	53	89	81	45	38	79	63	179
1994	1,288	154	57	165	104	36	112	49	105	131	64	121	190
Wick													
1951/80 averages	783	81	58	55	45	47	49	61	74	68	73	90	82
1991	722	45	45	89	24	50	74	64	35	45	72	128	51
1992	884	47	64	87	62	44	41	65	151	96	97	90	50
1993	718	94	31	66	34	66	45	86	64	31	85	41	75
1994	..	75	30	67	47	20	46	47	53	..	..	95	..

Source: Meteorological Office (Edinburgh)

(1)   See introductory notes, paragraph 4.1 for site descritpions.
(2)   As of 1992 data recorded at the Royal Botanic Gardens is used.
..   Information not available.

Table 4.5   Days with rain, 1991-1994[1][2]

days

	Year	Jan	Feb	Mar	Apr	May	June	July	Aug	Sept	Oct	Nov	Dec
Aberdeen													
1991	183	13	15	20	11	14	21	17	8	12	22	21	9
1992	195	8	13	20	24	12	14	14	21	22	18	18	11
1993	..	21	15	15	17	18	15	19	18	17	21	15	..
1994	..	25	17	17	14	6	10	13	12	15	13	12	8
Dundee													
1991	157	14	15	12	10	10	23	14	9	10	16	14	10
1992	171	8	13	17	17	9	7	16	21	22	11	19	11
1993	170	23	4	16	19	14	14	14	14	14	12	10	16
1994	162	20	15	17	11	9	12	9	8	12	15	16	18
Edinburgh[3]													
1991	..	18	12	17	13	5	22	15	7	-	18	21	12
1992	194	10	15	16	22	16	7	15	20	23	14	21	15
1993	171	22	4	15	13	16	14	12	14	15	11	14	21
1994	191	22	12	26	17	7	14	14	12	13	16	16	22
Glasgow													
1991	189	18	15	19	17	9	17	13	11	16	14	25	15
1992	231	11	23	26	21	16	8	17	25	24	14	27	19
1993	191	27	7	17	20	12	11	18	18	12	10	12	27
1994	223	27	14	28	22	4	21	14	16	16	16	21	24
Auchincruive													
1991	200	19	14	18	15	9	19	14	19	16	16	25	16
1992	232	15	22	25	21	13	9	17	27	22	16	27	18
1993	..	29	..	15	18	14	15	20	15	13	10	12	28
1994	225	25	14	28	22	5	20	12	18	16	18	21	26
Bowhill													
1991	204	19	18	20	19	10	20	18	11	15	18	23	13
1992	224	11	19	24	22	12	7	18	23	25	20	26	17
1993	..	25	10	15	21	16	10	18	15	17	16	..	..
1994	219	26	14	30	19	10	15	14	18	18	15	18	22
Braemar													
1991	215	14	16	20	19	14	26	18	9	17	24	28	10
1992	219	12	22	27	23	12	10	15	24	23	15	22	14
1993	..	15	16	24	15	13	19	21	17	21	13	23	..
1994	239	28	20	29	21	9	15	14	16	18	19	23	27
Dumfries													
1991	..	16	12	16	12	4	..	12	14	11	14	20	13
1992	..	-	19	23	20	10	7	15	..	..	14	26	13
1993	..	24	8	..	..	14	11	19	15	15	9	10	24
1994	..	..	13	25	19	6	15	18	14	12	16	24	26
Inveress													
1991	172	9	14	17	13	8	25	13	12	16	16	18	11
1992	179	10	12	23	18	9	10	11	23	16	14	19	14
1993	197	26	11	15	16	19	18	15	18	12	18	5	24
1994	221	26	8	29	21	13	19	15	18	16	16	15	25
Lerwick													
1991	253	23	20	24	17	18	17	16	17	25	24	29	23
1992	272	21	27	22	25	13	14	22	24	24	27	29	24
1993	253	30	24	22	19	15	13	20	24	14	25	19	28
1994	250	29	15	30	23	9	24	12	13	23	22	22	28
Stornoway													
1991	239	17	15	23	17	15	23	16	20	21	22	28	22
1992	271	17	26	28	25	15	13	23	23	26	25	27	23
1993	258	30	25	23	19	14	21	27	19	13	21	19	27
1994	270	29	14	29	25	13	24	19	20	23	23	25	26
Wick													
1991	230	17	16	20	17	19	19	15	19	24	22	24	18
1992	238	14	18	23	25	13	13	18	25	22	22	25	20
1993	233	25	14	16	17	17	17	27	23	15	23	16	23
1994	..	29	18	27	20	11	23	20	21	..	..	23	..

Source: Meteorological Office (Edinburgh)

(1)   0.2mm or more
(2)   See introductory notes, paragraph 4.1 for site description.
(3)   As of 1992 data recorded at the Royal Botanic Gardens is used.
..   Information not available

Table 4.6   Days with snow lying, 1991-1994[1][2]
days

	Year	Jan	Feb	Mar	Apr	May	June	July	Aug	Sept	Oct	Nov	Dec
Aberdeen													
1991	29	11	17	-	-	-	-	-	-	-	-	-	1
1992	13	2	5	4	-	-	-	-	-	-	-	-	2
1993	32	5	2	4	-	-	-	-	-	-	1	7	13
1994	21	5	11	2	1	-	-	-	-	-	-	-	2
Dundee													
1991	21	9	9	-	-	-	-	-	-	-	-	-	3
1992	4	-	2	-	-	-	-	-	-	-	-	-	2
1993	19	5	1	2	-	-	-	-	-	-	-	8	3
1994	13	1	12	-	-	-	-	-	-	-	-	-	-
Edinburgh[3]													
1991	16	4	12	-	-	-	-	-	-	-	-	-	-
1992	5	-	2	-	-	-	-	-	-	-	-	-	3
1993	9	3	-	-	-	-	-	-	-	-	-	2	4
1994	3	-	3	-	-	-	-	-	-	-	-	-	-
Glasgow													
1991	16	4	11	-	-	-	-	-	-	-	-	-	1
1992	3	-	-	2	-	-	-	-	-	-	-	-	1
1993	4	3	-	-	-	-	-	-	-	-	-	-	1
1994	7	2	5	-	-	-	-	-	-	-	-	-	-
Auchincruive													
1991	5	2	3	-	-	-	-	-	-	-	-	-	-
1992	1	-	-	1	-	-	-	-	-	-	-	-	-
1993	-	-	..	-	-	-	-	-	-	-	-	-	-
1994	4	1	3	-	-	-	-	-	-	-	-	-	-
Bowhill													
1991	35	16	17	-	-	-	-	-	-	-	-	-	2
1992	9	-	3	2	-	-	-	-	-	-	1	2	1
1993	26	8	0	2	-	1	-	-	-	-	-	7	8
1994	24	11	9	4	-	-	-	-	-	-	-	-	-
Braemar													
1991	..	..	16	2	1	-	-	-	-	-	-	2	4
1992	43	5	9	7	3	-	-	-	-	-	2	7	10
1993	71	18	4	8	1	1	-	-	-	-	4	10	25
1994	69	16	18	20	5	-	-	-	-	-	1	0	9
Dumfries													
1991	7	3	3	-	-	-	-	-	-	-	-	-	1
1992	3	-	1	2	-	-	-	-	-	-	-	-	-
1993	1	-	-	-	-	-	-	-	-	-	-	-	1
1994	7	2	4	1	-	-	-	-	-	-	-	-	-
Inverness													
1991	13	2	10	-	-	-	-	-	-	-	--	-	1
1992	8	-	1	2	-	-	-	-	-	-	-	1	4
1993	12	4	1	1	-	-	-	-	-	-	-	-	6
1994	5	2	2	1	-	-	-	-	-	-	-	-	-
Lerwick													
1991	4	1	1	-	-	-	-	-	-	-	-	1	1
1992	12	2	3	5	-	1	-	-	-	-	-	-	1
1993	26	6	5	3	-	-	-	-	-	-	1	2	9
1994	25	8	5	8	1	-	-	-	-	-	1	-	2
Stornoway													
1991	1	1	-	-	-	-	-	-	-	-	-	-	-
1992	6	1	-	3	-	-	-	-	-	-	-	-	2
1993	11	2	1	1	-	-	-	-	-	-	-	-	7
1994	8	2	0	4	1	0	0	0	0	0	0	0	1
Wick													
1991	11	5	5	-	-	-	-	-	-	-	-	-	1
1992	8	2	1	5	-	-	-	-	-	-	-	-	-
1993	..	8	3	4	-	..	..	..	..	..	..	..	..
1994	..	..	..	..	..	..	..	..	..	..	..	..	..

Source: Meteorological Office (Edinburgh)

(1) A day when over half of the ground representative of the site is covered with snow at 0900 GHT.

(2) See introductory notes, paragraph 4.1 for site description.

(3) As of 1992 data recorded at the Royal Botanic Gardens is used.

.. Information not available.

Table 4.7   Days with Gales, 1991-1994[1][2]

days

	Year	Jan	Feb	Mar	Apr	May	June	July	Aug	Sept	Oct	Nov	Dec
Aberdeen													
1991	3	-	-	-	-	-	-	-	-	1	2	-	-
1992	1	-	-	-	-	-	-	-	-	.-	-	1	-
1993	3	2	-	1	-	-	-	-	-	-	-	-	-
1994	-	-	-	-	-	-	-	-	-	-	-	-	-
Dundee													
1991	..	-	-	-	-	-	-	-	..	-	-	-	-
1992	-	-	-	-	-	-	-	-	-	-	-	-	-
1993	1	1	-	-	-	-	-	-	-	-	-	-	-
1994	..	-	-	-	-	-	-	-	..	-	-	-	-
Edinburgh(3)													
1991	1	-	-	-	1	-	-	-	-	-	-	-	1
1992	1	1	-	-	-	-	-	-	-	-	-	-	-
1993	7	6	-	1	-	-	-	-	-	-	-	-	-
1994	1	-	-	1	-	-	-	-	-	-	-	-	-
Glasgow													
1991	3	1	-	-	-	-	-	-	-	-	1	-	1
1992	6	4	2	-	-	-	-	-	-	-	-	-	-
1993	15	12	-	1	-	-	-	-	-	-	-	-	2
1994	5	2	-	2	-	-	-	-	-	-	-	-	1
Auchincruive													
1991	-	-	-	-	-	-	-	-	-	-	-	-	-
1992	-	-	-	-	-	-	-	-	-	-	-	-	-
1993	..	-	..	-	-	-	-	-	-	-	-	-	-
1994	-	-	-	-	-	-	-	-	-	-	-	-	-
Bowhill													
1991	3	1	-	-	-	-	-	-	-	-	2	-	-
1992	2	2	-	-	-	-	-	-	-	-	-	-	-
1993	6	5	-	1	-	-	-	-	-	-	-	-	8
1994	-	-	-	-	-	-	-	-	-	-	-	-	-
Braemar													
1991	..	4	-	1	..	1	..	..	..	1	5	2	2
1992	..	..	2	-	-	..	..	..	..	..	..	1	1
1993	..	..	4	..	..	..	..	..	..	..	..	..	..
1994	..	3	3	8	1	..	..	..	..	..	..	-	1
Dumfries													
1991	..	-	-	-	-	-	-	-	-	..	-	-	-
1992	1	-	-	-	-	-	-	-	-	-	-	-	1
1993	..	-	-	-	-	-	-	..	-	..	-	..	..
1994	..	3	3	8	..	-	-	-	..	..	..	-	-
Inverness													
1991	-	-	-	-	-	-	-	-	-	-	-	-	-
1992	-	-	-	-	-	-	-	-	-	-	-	-	-
1993	-	-	-	-	-	-	-	-	-	-	-	-	-
1994	1	1	-	-	-	-	-	-	-	-	-	-	-
Lerwick													
1991	31	6	4	1	1	1	-	-	-	1	3	6	8
1992	47	8	8	5	2	2	2	-	1	3	5	5	6
1993	62	25	6	8	3	-	1	-	-	-	4	7	8
1994	59	13	4	16	3	1	1	-	-	1	4	6	10
Stornoway													
1991	21	5	-	-	1	-	-	-	-	1	4	6	4
1992	21	3	5	2	-	1	-	-	-	2	-	4	4
1993	26	14	3	1	-	1	-	-	-	-	1	4	2
1994	17	3	1	4	-	0	-	-	-	-	1	0	8
Wick													
1991	13	-	-	1	-	1	-	-	-	1	3	1	6
1992	11	1	2	4	1	2	-	-	-	-	-	1	-
1993	..	7	3	3	1	..	..	..	..	-	..	..	..
1994	..	..	..	..	..	..	..	..	..	..	..	..	..

Source: Meteorological Office (Edinburgh)

(1)   Days on which mean wind speed over any 10 consecutive minutes reached 34 knots (Force 8) or more (00h-24h GMT).

(2)   See introductory notes, paragraph 4.1 for site description.

(3)   As of 1992 data recorded at the Royal Botanic Gardens is used.

..   Information not available.

Table 4.8   Days with Fog, 1991-1994[1][2]

days

	Year	Jan	Feb	Mar	Apr	May	June	July	Aug	Sept	Oct	Nov	Dec
Aberdeen													
1991	-	-	5	4	-	-	-	-	3	1	9	4	-
1992	19	-	-	2	2	2	2	-	2	6	1	1	1
1993	8	-	2	-	1	-	-	1	-	2	2	-	-
1994	9	-	2	-	-	-	-	1	-	-	3	2	1
Dundee													
1991	15	1	1	3	-	-	-	-	..	2	4	1	3
1992	9	2	-	-	1	-	-	-	-	4	-	-	2
1993	11	2	2	2	2	-	-	1	-	-	-	2	-
1994	9	-	2	1	-	-	-	-	-	-	5	1	-
Edinburgh[3]													
1991	16	-	-	4	-	-	-	4	-	-	-	-	-
1992	7	2	1	-	-	2	2	-	-	-	-	-	-
1993	4	-	-	-	-	-	-	-	-	2	-	2	-
1994	..	-	-	-	-	-	1	-	..	1	-	1	-
Glasgow													
1991	10	-	1	1	-	-	-	-	-	2	2	1	3
1992	10	5	-	-	-	-	-	-	-	1	-	-	4
1993	3	-	-	-	-	-	-	-	-	-	1	2	-
1994	7	1	-	-	-	-	-	-	-	-	4	-	2
Auchincruive													
1991	1	-	-	1	-	-	-	-	-	-	-	-	-
1992	1	1	-	-	-	-	-	-	-	-	-	-	-
1993	..	-	..	-	-	-	-	-	-	-	-	-	-
1994	1	1	-	-	-	-	-	-	-	-	-	-	-
Bowhill													
1991	10	2	1	5	-	-	-	-	-	1	1	-	-
1992	..	-	-	-	..	-	-	-	-	3	-	-	-
1993	5	-	-	-	-	-	-	-	-	-	3	2	-
1994	6	-	1	-	..	-	-	-	-	-	1	4	-
Braemar													
1991	..	..	..	2	-	-	-	-	-	1	-	-	-
1992	..	1	-	-	..	-	-	-	-	2	1	..	1
1993	..	..	1	-	-	..	-	-	-	-	-	-	..
1994	..	-	-	-	..	-	..	-	..	-	6	-	-
Dumfries													
1991	8	2	-	-	-	-	-	-	-	-	-	3	3
1992	7	4	2	-	-	-	-	-	-	1	-	-	-
1993	..	-	-	-	-	-	-	..	..	1	1	3	..
1994	..	..	2	-	-	-	1	-	3	..	..	..	5
Inveress													
1991	7	-	-	-	-	-	-	1	-	1	4	1	-
1992	9	-	2	-	-	-	-	-	-	4	1	-	2
1993	6	-	2	-	-	2	-	-	-	-	1	-	1
1994	6	-	-	-	-	-	-	1	-	2	2	1	-
Lerwick													
1991	20	1	-	3	-	1	-	7	4	1	3	-	-
1992	11	1	-	-	-	1	1	3	-	4	1	-	-
1993	11	-	2	-	2	4	1	-	1	1	-	-	-
1994	12	1	-	-	-	2	2	3	1	1	-	2	-
Stornoway													
1991	2	-	-	-	-	2	-	-	-	-	-	-	-
1992	2	2	-	-	-	-	-	-	-	-	-	-	-
1993	2	-	-	-	-	1	-	-	-	1	-	-	-
1994	-	-	-	-	-	-	-	-	-	-	-	-	-
Wick													
1991	9	1	-	1	-	-	-	4	1	-	2	-	-
1992	6	2	-	-	-	1	1	-	1	1	-	-	-
1993	..	-	-	-	..	..	..	..	..	..	..	..	..
1994	..	..	..	..	..	..	..	..	..	..	..	..	..

Source: Meteorological Office (Edinburgh)

(1)   Day with fog at 0900 GMT.
(2)   See introductory notes, paragraph 4.1 for site description.
(3)   As of 1992 data recorded at the Royal Botanic Gardens is used.
..   Information not available.

Map 4.3 Electricity generating stations, 1994 (see notes, paragraph 4.3)

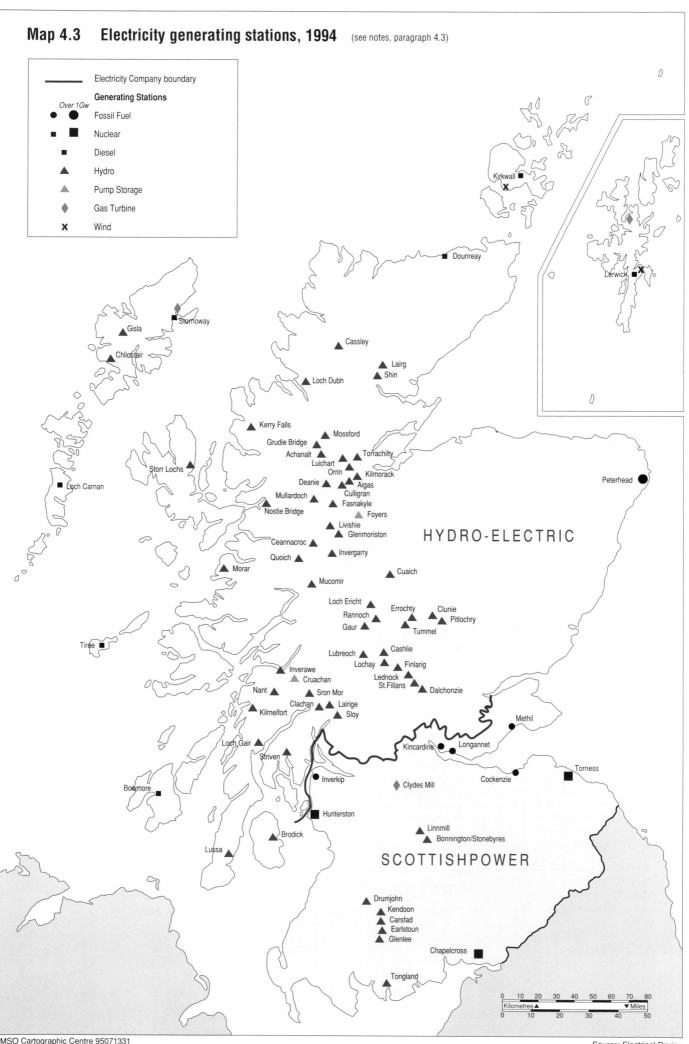

Legend:

—— Electricity Company boundary

Generating Stations

Over 1Gw

● ● Fossil Fuel

■ ■ Nuclear

■ Diesel

▲ Hydro

▲ Pump Storage

◆ Gas Turbine

X Wind

Labels on map:

Kirkwall ■ X

◆ Lerwick ■ X

■ Dounreay

◆ ■ Stornoway

▲ Gisla

▲ Chliostair

▲ Cassley

▲ Lairg
▲ Shin

▲ Loch Dubh

▲ Kerry Falls

▲ Mossford
Grudie Bridge ▲
Achanalt ▲ ▲ Torrachilty
Luichart ▲
Orrin ▲ ▲ Kilmorack
Deanie ▲ ▲ Aigas
Culligran
Mullardoch ▲ ▲ Fasnakyle
Nostie Bridge ▲ Foyers
▲ Livishie
▲ Glenmoriston
Ceannacroc ▲
Quoich ▲ ▲ Invergarry
▲ Morar
▲ Mucomir
▲ Cuaich

Storr Lochs ▲
■ Loch Carnan
Peterhead ●

HYDRO-ELECTRIC

Loch Ericht ▲
Rannoch ▲ Errochty ▲ ▲ Clunie
Gaur ▲ ▲ Pitlochry
▲ Tummel

Tiree ■

Lubreoch ▲ ▲ Cashlie
Lochay ▲ ▲ Finlarig
Inverawe ▲
▲ Cruachan
Nant ▲ ▲ Sron Mor
Clachan ▲ ▲ Lairige
Kilmelfort ▲ ▲ Sloy
Lednock ▲
St.Fillans ▲ ▲ Dalchonzie
Loch Gair ▲
Striven ▲

● Methil

Kincardine ● ● Longannet

Torness ■

Cockenzie ●

● Inverkip

◆ Clydes Mill

Bowmore ■

■ Hunterston

▲ Brodick

Lussa ▲

SCOTTISHPOWER

▲ Linnmill
▲ Bonnington/Stonebyres

▲ Drumjohn
▲ Kendoon
▲ Carsfad
▲ Earlstoun
▲ Glenlee

Chapelcross ■

▲ Tongland

Scale: 0 10 20 30 40 50 60 70 80 Kilometres / 0 10 20 30 40 50 Miles

Source: Electrical Review

Map 4.4   UK Air Quality Network, Operational Sites
(see notes, paragraph 4.4)

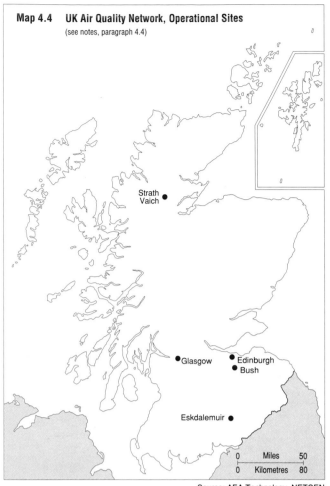

Strath
Vaich ●

● Glasgow   ● Edinburgh
              Bush ●

Eskdalemuir ●

| 0 | Miles | 50 |
| 0 | Kilometres | 80 |

Source: AEA Technology, NETCEN

**Map 4.5   Annual mean SO₂ concentrations in urban/suburban areas
of Scotland, April 1993 - March 1994** (see notes, paragraph 4.8)

Annual mean SO₂ concentration ppb
■ > 12
▦ 8 - 12   The squares represent
▨ 4 - 8   a 20 x 20 km grid
░ < 4

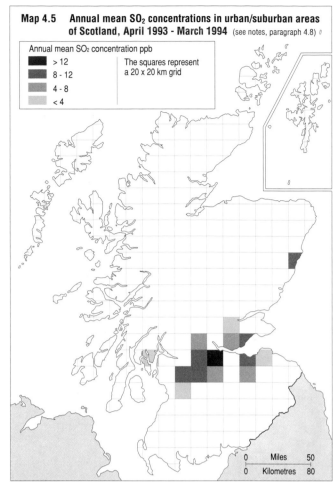

| 0 | Miles | 50 |
| 0 | Kilometres | 80 |

Source: AEA Technology, NETCEN

Map 4.6   Sulphur dioxide emissions, 1993

Tonnes
■ Above 1000   ▦ 2 > 8
▨ 200 > 1000   ░ < 2
▨ 30 > 200   The squares represent
░ 8 > 30   a 10 x 10 km grid

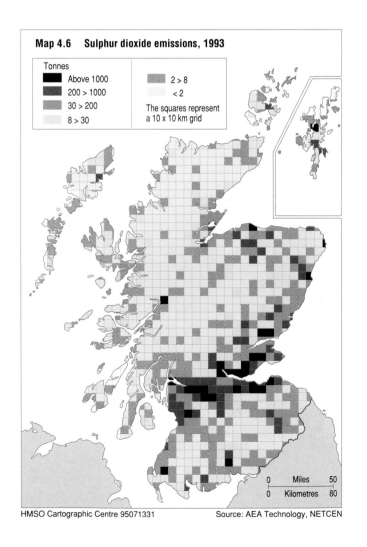

| 0 | Miles | 50 |
| 0 | Kilometres | 80 |

HMSO Cartographic Centre 95071331   Source: AEA Technology, NETCEN

**Map 4.7   Rural sulphur dioxide and precipitation composition
monitoring sites**

● SO₂ only
● Rain only
● Both

| 0 | Miles | 50 |
| 0 | Kilometres | 80 |

Source: AEA Technology, NETCEN

Table 4.9   **Trace element trends in annual average urban concentrations of lead, iron and zinc in air, 1981/82-1992/93[1]**

Nanogram/m³[2]

	1981/82	1982/83	1983/84	1984/85	1985/86	1986/87	1987/88	1988/89	1989/90	1990/91	1991/92	1992/93
Lead												
Glasgow	340	210	240	210	210	140	160	110	130	111	95	82
Motherwell	260	280	260	160	250	180	120	-	249	181	114	52
Iron												
Glasgow	660	500	640	540	530	420	510	480	426	539	483	375
Motherwell	2,000	2,130	2,180	1,410	2,060	1,600	1,500	2,400	1,789	1,780	1,520	964
Zinc												
Glasgow	450	120	120	120	110	130	160	140	96	95	79	65
Motherwell	200	190	130	120	240	220	220	400	221	212	122	69

Source: AEA Technology NETCEN

1) "Population" year period (eg Apr 1980 - March 1981)
2) A nonogram is a thousand millionth (10⁻⁹) of a gram. The following conversion formula may be used to convert from nanograms/kg of air to nanograms/m³ of air - the more common measurement of pollutant concentrations in the atmosphere. 1m³ air at 15°C, 760mm Mercury (Standard Cubic Metre) = 1.226kg.

Table 4.10   **Ozone measurements, 1988-1993[1]**

	1988	1989	1990	1991	1992	1993
Strath Vaich						
Annual mean (ppb)[2]	34	32	33	33	35	34
98% percentile of hourly values (ppb)	52	48	53	56	59	50
Number of hours ≥ 76ppb[3]	-	5	6	-	2	-
Number of poor ≥ 90ppb[4]	-	-	-	-	-	-
Number of very poor ≥ 180ppb[4]	-	-	-	-	-	-
Number running 8 hour/means[5] ≥ 50ppb[6]	215	72	211	330	360	109
Data capture, %	96.4	78.9	88.3	89.3	94.9	81
Bush						
Annual mean (ppb)[2]	27	27	28	24	27	26
98% percentile of hourly values (ppb)	48	50	52	42	50	44
Number of hours≥76ppb[3]	1	21	17	3	2	-
Number of poor ≥ 90ppb[4]	-	8	8	-	-	-
Number of very poor ≥ 180ppb[4]	-	-	-	-	-	-
Number running 8 hour/means[5] ≥ 50ppb[6]	116	143	160	17	145	0
Data capture, %	97.3	97.6	94.7	97.4	98.8	96
Eskdalemuir						
Annual mean (ppb)[2]	26	28	28	26	27	25
98% percentile of hourly values (ppb)	46	53	55	54	54	46
Number of hours ≥ 76ppb[3]	-	43	46	3	10	15
Number of poor ≥ 90ppb[4]	-	1	9	-	-	6
Number of very poor ≥ 180ppb[4]	-	-	-	-	-	-
Number running 8 hour/means[5] ≥ 50ppb[6]	87	188	216	165	258	79
Data capture, %	95.3	92.1	96.9	97.4	98.1	97
Edinburgh						
Annual mean (ppb)[2]	..	..	..	..	9*	13
98% percentile of hourly values (ppb)	..	..	..	..	27	32
Number of hours ≥ 76ppb[3]	..	..	..	..	-	-
Number of poor ≥ 90ppb[4]	..	..	..	..	-	-
Number of very poor ≥ 180ppb[4]	..	..	..	..	-	-
Number running 8 hour/means[5] ≥ 50ppb[6]	-	-	-	-	0	0
Data capture, %	..	..	..	..	24	95.1

Source: AEA Technology NETCEN

1) Figures are for calendar year
2) Parts per billion.
3) Lower limit of WHO hourly guideline.
4) DoE air quality bands and EC Directive Population Information (90 ppb) and Population Warming Thresholds (180 ppb)
5) Calculated for each hour "h" by averaging concentrations between hours "h" and "h-7".
6) EPAQS standard
Oct-Dec only.

Table 4.11   **Nitrogen Dioxide concentrations in Glasgow, Edinburgh and Strath Vaich 1988-1993[1]**

	1988	1989	1990	1991	1992	1993
Glasgow						
Annual mean (ppb)[2]	30	27	26	26	25	27
98% percentile of hourly values (ppb)	57	61	53	52	50	56
Number of hours $\geq$ 210 ppb[3]	-	2	-	1	-	-
Number of poor $\geq$ 100 ppb[4]	7	37	4	21	-	2
Number of very poor $\geq$ 300 ppb[4]	-	-	-	-	-	-
Data capture %	85	99	89	99	99	89
Edinburgh						
Annual mean (ppb)[2]	..	..	..	..	28*	27
98% percentile of hourly values (ppb)	..	..	..	..	48	54
Number of hours$\geq$210 ppb[3]	..	..	..	..	-	-
Number of poor $\geq$ 100 ppb[4]	..	..	..	..	-	1
Number of very poor$\geq$300 ppb[4]	..	..	..	..	-	-
Data capture %	..	..	..	..	24	95
Strath Vaich						
Annual mean (ppb)[2]	..	..	1	2	1	1
98% percentile of hourly values (ppb)	..	..	7	13	5	7
Number of hours$\geq$210 ppb[3]	..	..	-	-	-	-
Number of poor $\geq$ 100 ppb[4]	..	..	-	-	-	-
Number of very poor $\geq$ 300 ppb[4]	..	..	-	-	-	-
Data capture %	..	..	17	44	85	42

Source: AEA Technology NETCEN

(1) Figures are for calendar year
(2) Parts per billion.
(3) WHO hourly guidelines.
(4) DoE air quality bands.
*   Oct-Dec only

Table 4.12   **Sulphur Dioxide concentrations in Strath Vaich and Edinburgh, 1991-1993[1]**

	Strath Vaich			Edinburgh		
	1991	1992	1993	1991	1992	1993
Annual average, ppb[2]	0.7	0.3	0.4	..	10*	8
98th percentile of hourly averages, ppb	8.3	2.3	3	..	37	38
Number of hours $\geq$ 122 ppb[3]	-	-	-	..	-	4
Number of poor $\geq$ 125 ppb[4]	-	-	-	..	-	4
Number of very poor $\geq$ 400 ppb[4]	-	-	-	..	-	-
Data Capture %	56.1	69.7	77	..	24.2	96

Source: AEA Technology NETCEN

(1) Figures are for calendar year
(2) Parts per billion.
(3) WHO hourly guidelines.
(4) DoE air quality bands.
*   Oct-Dec only

Table 4.13   **Carbon Monoxide concentrations in Glasgow and Edinburgh, 1991-1993[1]**

	Glasgow			Edinburgh		
	1991	1992	1993	1991	1992	1993
Annual average, ppb[2]	1.4	1.2	0.9	..	0.9*	0.6
98th percentile of hourly averages, ppb	5.0	4.5	3.6	..	2.9	1.9
Number of hours $\geq$ 25 ppb[3]	-	-	-	..	-	-
Number of running 8 hours [4] $\geq$ 10 ppb[5]	2	-	-	..	-	-
Data Capture %	96.7	92.3	89	..	21.5	95

Source: AEA Technology NETCEN

(1) Figures are for calendar year
(2) Parts per billion.
(3) WHO hourly guidelines.
(4) Calculated for each hour "h" by averaging concentrations between hours "h" and "h-7".
(5) WHO 8 hourly guideline and EPAQS standard.
*   Oct-Dec only

Table 4.14 Thoracic Particles, PM$_{10}$ Edinburgh 1992 and 1993

	Edinburgh	
	1992[1]	1993
Annual average, μgm^{-3}[2]	23	23
98th percentile of hourly averages, μgm^{-3}[2]	78	57
Number of daily averages ^{3} 70 μgm^{-3}[3]	1	-
Data Capture %	17.3	82

Source: AEA Technology, NETCEN

(1) Figures are per calendar year
(2) μg = 10^{-6} gram
(3) WHO daily guideline

Table 4.15 Smoke control orders and clean air grants, 1993/94

	Smoke control orders		Clean air grants[1] (£ thousands)
	Total number of orders	Number of hectares affected	
Scotland	**5**	**17,098**	**537**
Central	1	593	7
Fife	1	213	192
Lothian	1	13,070	41
Strathclyde	2	3,222	297

Source: EAG, SOAEFD

(1) Includes Payments for smoke control orders made prior to 1992/93.

Table 4.16 Summary recorded contraventions of air pollution acts, 1983-1992[1]

	1983	1984	1985	1986	1987	1988	1989	1990	1991	1992
Clean Air Acts 1956/68										
Contraventions	931	712	496	494	508	876	500	627	574	391
Prosecutions	17	16	7	3	3	124	28	45	32	23
Convictions	59	13	7	-	-	4	-	13	2	6
Control of Pollution Act 1974 (Section 78)										
Contraventions	..	..	33	81	81	40	50	26	62	23
Prosecutions	..	..	1	3	3	-	3	4	2	6
Convictions	..	..	1	-	-	-	2	2	-	2

Source: Royal Environmental Health Institute of Scotland

1) "Population" year period (eg Apr 1980-March 1981)

Table 4.17 Recorded contraventions of air pollution acts, 1992[1]

	Clean Air Acts 1956/68			Control of Pollution Act 1974 Section 78
	Dark Smoke emissions	Grit or dust emissions	Sale of unauthorised fuel	
Contraventions	170	155	66	23
Prosecutions[2]	3	7	13	6
Convictions[2]	4	-	2	2

Source: Royal Environmental Health Institute of Scotland

1) "Population" year period (eg Apr 1980-March 1981)

Table 4.18 Noise complaints received by Environmental Health Offices, 1992[1]

	Industrial and commercial	Domestic premises	Vibration	Construction sites	Entertainment (include licences premises)	Total
Complaints received	1,462	1,950	129	403	766	4,710
Investigations	610	513	38	159	384	1,704
Nuisances confirmed	405	275	12	161	376	1,229
Nuisances remedied informally	621	383	29	191	362	1,586
Notices served	53	7	1	25	45	131
Continuing investigation	159	79	3	58	149	448
Appeals pending	-	-	-	-	-	
Prosecutions[2]	2	-	-	1	-	3
Convictions[2]	-	-	-	-	-	-

1) "Population" year period (eg Apr 1980-March 1981)

	Aircraft noise	Traffic noise	Others	Total
Complaints	66	159	776	1,001
Surveys	11	43	483	537

Source: Royal Environmental Health Institute of Scotland

1) Not all Environmental Health Offices covered, see introductory note, paragraph 4.17 for details.
2) Prosecutions and convictions may relate to complaints received in preceding years.

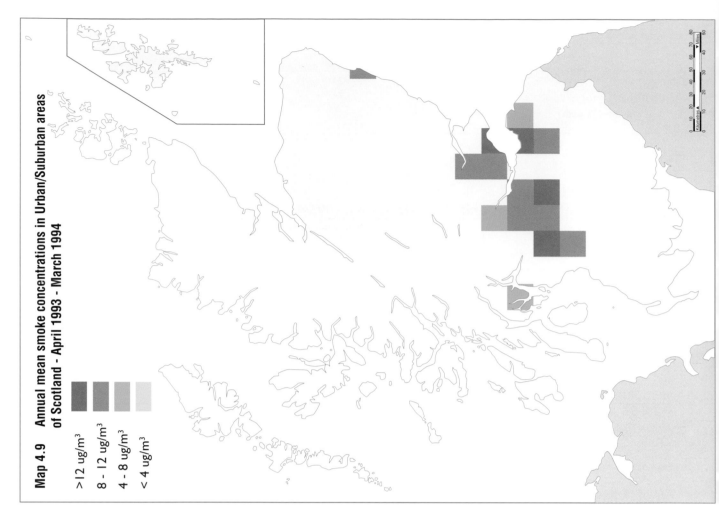

Map 4.9 Annual mean smoke concentrations in Urban/Suburban areas of Scotland - April 1993 - March 1994

>12 ug/m³

8 - 12 ug/m³

4 - 8 ug/m³

< 4 ug/m³

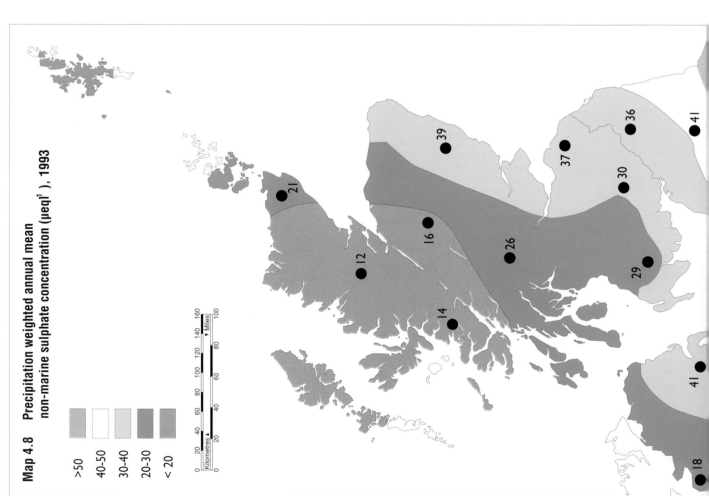

Map 4.8 Precipitation weighted annual mean non-marine sulphate concentration (μeql¹), 1993

>50

40-50

30-40

20-30

< 20

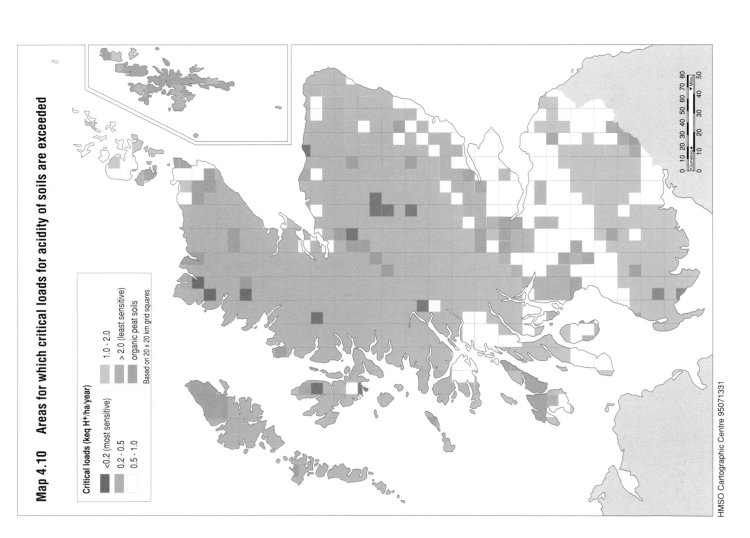

Map 4.11   Areas for which critical loads for sulphur of soils are exceeded

(see notes, paragraph 4.16)

Exceedance of sulphur   (keq H$^+$ ha^{-1} year^{-1})

- Not exceeded
- 0.0 - 0.2
- 0.2 - 0.5
- 0.5 - 1.0
- > 1.0

Based on 20 x 20 km grid squares

0 10 20 30 40 50 60 70 80 Kilometres
0 10 20 30 40 50 Miles

Source: MLURI

Map 4.10   Areas for which critical loads for acidity of soils are exceeded

Critical loads (keq H$^+$/ha/year)

- <0.2 (most sensitive)
- 0.2 - 0.5
- 0.5 - 1.0
- 1.0 - 2.0
- > 2.0 (least sensitive)
- organic peat soils

Based on 20 x 20 km grid squares

0 10 20 30 40 50 60 70 80 Kilometres
0 10 20 30 40 50 Miles

HMSO Cartographic Centre 95071331

Map 4.12   Annual Average Kerbside NO$_2$ Concentrations 1993

NO$_2$ (ppb)

>40

30 - 40

20 - 30

10 - 20

<10

Source: AEA Technology

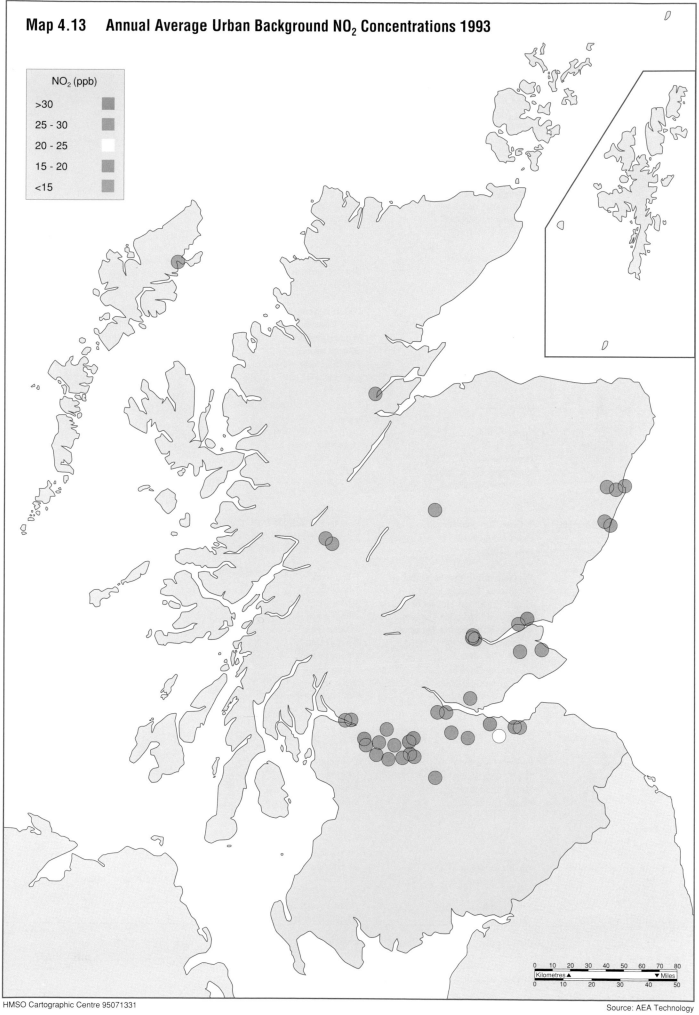

Map 4.13   Annual Average Urban Background NO$_2$ Concentrations 1993

NO$_2$ (ppb)

>30

25 - 30

20 - 25

15 - 20

<15

Kilometres
0 10 20 30 40 50 60 70 80

Miles
0 10 20 30 40 50

HMSO Cartographic Centre 95071331

Source: AEA Technology

Table 4.19 DoE Air Quality Bands, EC Directive and WHO Guidelines for NO_2 SO_2 O_3 CO and Thoracic particles

Guideline Set By	Description	Criteria Based On	Value/ppb	(μgm^{-3})
Nitrogen Dioxide				
Department of the Environment	V Good Air Quality	Peak hourly average	<50	(95)
	Good Air Quality	concentration in a 24-hour	50-99	(95-190)
	Poor Air Quality	period	100-299	(190-570)
	V Poor Air Quality	Calendar year of data	≥300	(570)
European Council	Limit Value	98%ile of hourly means	104.6	(200)
	Guide Value	98%ile of hourly means	70.6	(135)
	Guide Value	50%ile of hourly means	26.2	(50)
World Health Organisation	Health Guideline	1-hour mean	210	(400)
	Health Guideline	Daily mean	80	(150)
	Vegetation Guideline	4-hour mean	50	(95)
	Vegetation Guideline	Annual mean	16	(30)
Sulphur Dioxide				
Department of the Environment	V Good Air Quality	Peak hourly average	<60	(160)
	Good Air Quality	concentration in a 24-hour	60-124	(160-330)
	Poor Air Quality	period	125-399	(330-1,050)
	V Poor Air Quality		≥400	(1,050)
European Council	Limit Value	Pollution Year (median of daily values	30(80) if smoke[1] 45(120) if smoke	>34 ≤34
	Limit Value	Winter (median of daily values October-March)	49(130) if smoke 68(180) if smoke	>51 ≤51
	Limit Value[2]	Pollution Year (98%ile of daily values).	94(250) if smoke[2] 131(350) if smoke[2]	>128 ≤128
	Guide Value	Pollution Year (mean of daily values)	15-23	(40-60)
	Guide Value	24 hours (daily mean value)	38-56	(100-150)
World Health Organisation	Health Guideline	10-minute mean	175	(500)
	Health Guideline	1-hour mean	122	(350)
	Vegetation Guideline	Daily mean	48	(125)
	Vegetation Guideline	Annual mean	10.4	(30)
Ozone				
Department of the Environment	V Good Air Quality	Peak hourly average	<50	(100)
	Good Air Quality	concentration in a 24-hour	50-89	(100-179)
	Poor Air Quality	period	90-179	(180-350)
	V Poor Air Quality		≥180	(360)
European Council	Population Information Threshold	1-hour mean	90	(180)
	Population Warning Value	1-hour mean	180	(360)
	Health Protection Threshold	8-hour mean	55	(110)
	Vegetation Protection Threshold	1-hour mean	100	(200)
	Vegetation Protection Threshold	24-hour mean	32	(65)
World Health Organisation	Health Guideline	1-hour mean	76-100	(150-200)
	Health Guideline	8-hour mean	50-60	(100-120)
	Vegetation Guideline	1-hour mean	100	(200)
	Vegetation Guideline	Daily mean	33	(65)
	Vegetation Guideline	Growing Season mean[3]	30	(60)
Carbon Monoxide				
Department of the Environment	-	-	-	-
European Council	-	-	-	
World Health Organisation	Health Guideline	15-minute mean	87	(100)
	Health Guideline	30-minute mean	50	(60)
	Health Guideline	1-hour mean	25	(30)
	Health Guideline	8-hour mean	10	(10)
Thoracic Particles				
Department of Environment	-	-	-	-
European Council	-	-	-	-
World Health Organisation	Health Guideline	24-hour mean	-	70
			If SO_2 ≥ 125 μgm^{-3} (48ppb)	
Lead				
EC Directive	Limit Value	Annual Average		2
World Health Organisation	Guideline	Annual Average		0.5-1

Source: AEA Technology

(1)   Limits for black smoke are given in μgm^{-3} for the BSI method as used in the UK.
      The limits stated in the EC Directive relate to the OECD method, where OECD = BSI/0.85.
(2)   Member states must take all appropriate steps to ensure that 3 consecutive days do not exceed this limit value.
(3)   Growing season is defined as April-September for WHO guidelines.

Air quality standards and guidelines:

Table 4.20(a)   **Nitrogen Dioxide**

Guideline Set By	Description	Criteria Based On	Value/ppb (μgm^{-3})	
Department of the Environment	V Good Air Quality Good Air Quality Poor Air Quality V Poor Air Quality	Peak hourly average concentration in a 24 hour period.	< 50 50 - 99 100 - 299 > = 300	(96) (96 - 190) (191 - 572) (573)
Expert Panel on Air Quality Standards	-	-	-	
European Council	 Limit Value Guide Value Guide Value	Calendar year of data; 98%ile of hourly means. 98%ile of hourly means. 50%ile of hourly means.	- 104.6 70.6 26.2	 (200) (135) (50)
World Health Organisation	Health Guideline Health Guideline Vegetation Guideline Vegetation Guideline	1 hour mean Daily mean Running 4 hour mean Annual mean	210 80 50 16	(400) (150) (95) (30)
United Nations Economic Commission for Europe	Vegetation Guideline	Annual mean	15	(29)

Table 4.20(b)   **Sulphur Dioxide**

Guideline Set By	Description	Criteria Based On	Value/ppb (μgm^{-3})	
Department of the Environment	V Good Air Quality Good Air Quality Poor Air Quality V Poor Air Quality	Peak hourly average concentration in a 24 hour period.	< 60 60 - 124 125 - 399 > = 400	(160) (160-332) (333-1,063) (1,064)
Expert Panel on Air Quality Standards	-	-	-	
European Council	Limit Value Limit Value Limit Value[2] Guide Value Guide Value	Pollution Year (median of daily values) Winter (median of daily values October-March) Pollution Year (98%ile of daily values) Pollution Year (mean of daily values) 24 Hours (daily mean value)	30 (80) if smoke[1] > 34 45 (120) if sm. <=34 49 (130) if sm. >51 68 (180) if sm. <=51 94 (250) if sm. < 128 131 (350) if sm. <=128 15-23 (40-60) 38-56 (100-150)	
World Health Organisation	Health Guideline Health Guideline Vegetation Guideline Vegetation Guideline	10 minute mean 1 hour mean Daily mean Annual mean	175 122 38 10.4	(500) (350) (100) (30)
United Nations Economic Commission for Europe	Vegetation Guideline Vegetation Guideline	Daily mean Annual mean	26 7.5	(70) (20)

(1)   Limits for black smoke are given μgm^{-3} for the BSI method as used in the UK. The limits stated in the EC Directive relate to the OECD method, where OECD = BSI/0.85.
(2)   Member states must take all appropriate steps to ensure that three consecutive days do not exceed this limit value.

Table 4.20(c) **Benzene**

Guideline Set By	Description	Criteria Based On	Value/ppb
Department of the Environment	Low Medium High Very High	Running 24 hour mean	< 4.5 4.5 - 9.99 10 - 29.99 > = 30
Expert Panel on Air Quality Standards	Health Guideline Target Value	Running annual mean Running annual mean	5 1
European Council	-	-	-
World Health Organisation	-	-	-
United Nations Economic Commission for Europe	-	-	-

Table 4.20(d) **1, 3 - Butadiene**

Guideline Set By	Description	Criteria Based On	Value/ppb
Department of the Environment	Low Medium High Very High	Running 24 hour mean	<0.9 0.9-1.99 2-5.99 > = 6
Expert Panel on Air Quality Standards	Health Guideline	Running annual mean	1
European Council	-	-	-
World Health Organisation	-	-	-
United Nations Economic Commission for Europe	-	-	-

Table 4.20(e) **Thoracic Particulates**

Guideline Set By	Description	Criteria Based On	Value/(μgm^{-3})
Department of the Environment	-	-	-
Expert Panel on Air Quality Standards	-	-	-
European Council	-	-	-
World Health Organisation	Health Guideline	24 hour mean	70 (If SO_2 > = 125 (48ppb))
United Nations Economic Commission for Europe	-	-	-

Table 4.20(f) **Lead**

Guideline Set By	Description	Criteria Based On	Value/(μgm^{-3})
Department of the Environment	-	-	-
Expert Panel on Air Quality Standards	-	-	-
European Council	Limit Value	Annual Average	2
World Health Organisation	Health Guideline	Annual Average	0.5 - 1
United Nations Economic Commission for Europe	-	-	-

Table 4.20(g)　Ozone

Guideline Set By	Description	Criteria Based On	Value/ppb (μgm^{-3})	
Department of the Environment	V Good Air Quality Good Air Quality Poor Air Quality V Poor Air Quality	Peak hourly average concentration in a 24 hour period.	< 50 50 - 89 90 - 179 > = 180	(100) (100 - 179) (180 - 359) (360)
Expert Panel on Air Quality Standards	Health Guideline	Running 8 hour Mean	50	(100)
European Council	Population Information Threshold Population Warning Value Health Protection Threshold Vegetation Protection Threshold Vegetation Protection Threshold	1 hour mean 1 hour mean Fixed 8 hour means (hours 1-8, 9-16, 17-0, 13-20) 1 hour mean 24 hour mean	90 180 55 100 32	(180) (360) (110) (200) (65)
World Health Organisation	Health Guideline Health Guideline Vegetation Guideline Vegetation Guideline Vegetation Guideline	1 hour mean Running 8 hour mean 1 hour mean Daily mean Growing Season[3] mean	76 - 100 50 - 60 100 33 30	(150 - 200) (100 - 120) (200) (65) (60)
United Nations Economic Commission for Europe	Vegetation Guideline Vegetation Guideline Vegetation Guideline	Growing Season[3] mean 1 hour mean Running 8 hour mean	25 75 30	(50) (150) (60)

(3)　Growing season is defined as April to September for WHO guidelines, but is DAYTIME (0900-1500) April to September for UNECE guidelines.

Table 4.20(h)　Carbon Monoxide

Guideline Set By	Description	Criteria Based On	Value/ppb (μgm^{-3})	
Department of the Environment	-	-	-	
Expert Panel on Air Quality Standards	Health Guideline	Running 8 hour mean	10	(11.6)
European Council	-	-	-	
World Health Organisation	Health Guideline Health Guideline Health Guideline Health Guideline	15 minute mean 1 hour mean 1 hour mean 8 hour mean	87 50 25 10	(100) (60) (30) (10)
United Nations Economic Commission for Europe	-	-	-	

Source: AEA Technology

Table 4.21　Annual mean concentrations of ions in precipitation at rural sites in Scotland, 1993

Site	Rainfall	Sulphate	Non-Marine Sulphate[1]	Nitrate	Chloride	Acidity	Ammonium	Sodium	Calcium	Magnesium
	mm	μeql^{-1}								
Loch Dee	1,950	38	28	19	89	22	21	79	9	22
Eskdalemuir	1,330	37	29	19	71	26	18	63	9	17
Whiteadder	722	49	37	29	117	34	22	103	12	26
Balquhidder	1,575	43	26	18	166	24	15	145	11	37
Polloch	1,790	39	14	9	226	15	5	204	13	52
Glen Dye	969	48	38	33	102	35	28	86	10	22
River Mhareaidh	826	32	16	7	158	17	4	143	11	35
Strathvaich Dam	1,147	35	11	8	227	13	4	212	13	51
Achanarras	567	47	20	18	255	22	8	224	18	56

Source: AEA Technology NETCEN

(1)　Rainwater contains ions derived from sea spray. By assuming the ratio of sodium to sulphate in sea spray is the same as that in sea water and that all sodium in rain water is of marine origin, the measured rain water sulphate can be corrected for sulphate of marine origin.

water

5 water

5.1   Tables 5.1 and 5.2 show developed water resources. The Central Scotland Water Development Board was established by enactment in 1967, and has been operational since 16 May 1968. The Board's statutory function is to develop and operate sources of supply to provide water in bulk to 2 or more of its constituency regional water authorities - Fife, Tayside, Lothian, Central and Strathclyde. It does not supply consumers directly (table 5.1). Maps 5.1 and 5.2 show the main reservoirs and lochs, and rivers and streams respectively, used as developed water resources in Scotland, and map 5.3 shows underground sources. Table 5.4 and chart 5.1 show the non-domestic metered demand for large consumers using on average, in excess of 1,000 cubic metres per quarter.

SEWAGE WORKS AND DISCHARGES

5.2   From 1975, Regional Councils (RCs) have operated the public sewage disposal facilities on the mainland, whilst water pollution control and monitoring are the duty of the seven River Purification boards (RPBs). On the islands, the Island Councils (ICs) are both the river purification authority and the operators of sewage disposal facilities.

5.3   Data in the tables are, in the main, obtained from the 9 RCs, 3ICs and 7 RPBs. Table 5.6 relates to industrial charges direct to waters. In tables 5.8 and 5.9 the term "sludge disposal" refers to the disposal of waste after treatment at a sewage treatment works.

DISPOSAL OF WASTE AT SEA BY METHODS OTHER THAN PIPELINE

5.4   The deposit of substances or articles at sea, other than discharges from a pipeline, is regulated by licences issued under part II of the Food and Environment Protection Act 1985. Certain operations are exempt from licensing under the Deposits in the Sea (Exemptions) Order 1985. In Scotland, the licensing function is administered by SOAEFD on behalf of the Secretary of State for Scotland. The disposal of sewage sludge in Scottish waters (table 5.9) must cease by 31 December 1998. Tables 5.9 and 5.10 prepared by SOAEFD are used by the Oslo Commission (the inter-governmental organisation which controls the disposal of waste at sea by regulating dumping and incineration activities in the North East Atlantic) and are included in the Aquatic Environment Monitoring Report published by the Ministry of Agriculture Fisheries and Food (MAFF).

LOCAL AUTHORITY CAPITAL EXPENDITURE ON SEWERAGE AND SEWAGE TREATMENT

5.5   The information in table 5.11 is derived from local authority returns to the Scottish Office.

WATER POLLUTION EVENTS ARISING FROM AGRICULTURAL PRACTICE

5.6   Data for table 5.12 is provided by the Scottish Farm Waste Liaison Group. The group, which comprises representatives from RPBs, SOAEFD and the Scottish Agricultural College, compiles and collates the data from recorded cases reported by the RPBs.

WATER TREATMENT WORKS

5.7   Map 5.5 shows the locations and capacities of water treatment works in Scotland.

5.8   Maps 5.6 to 5.8 and table 5.13 were taken from the Water Quality Survey of 1990 which was published by SODD.

5.9   Using their knowledge of their areas and assessing the information available to them, the RPBs assign to each strategy of river, loch and canal, one of 4 classifications;

> Class 1 - unpolluted
> Class 2 - fairly good
> Class 3 - poor
> Class 4 - grossly polluted

Similarly, taking account of biological, aesthetic, and chemical quality, points are awarded to each area of the major estuaries and classified according to the following scale:

Class	Points	Description
A	30-24	good
B	23-16	fair
C	15-9	poor
D	8-0	bad

5.10   Parallel to the changes in national legislation concerned with water quality, which have taken place over the last few years (for more details see "Water Quality Survey of Scotland 1990"), there has been the development of EC Directives related to the Environmental Action Programme and Water Pollution Control.

5.11   List I substances include cadmium, mercury from non-chloralkali sources, hexachlorocyclohexane (HCH) - lindane, DDT, pentachchlorophenol (PCP) and carbon tetrachchloride (CTC). Action on list II substances has begun in respect of nickel, lead, chromium, arsenic, copper and zinc, and a further set of substances has been selected. The "change of class" data in this table refers to the classification system in paragraph 5.10. In practice there will be a reduction in class due to the polluting influence of the discharge in question.

5.12   The Fresh Water Fish Directive (78/659/EEC) requires member states to designate fresh waters needing protection or improvement in order to support fish life. The categories of fish life referred to are salmonoid, (salmon, trout) and cyprinid (coarse fish). The Directive contains minimum physical and chemical standards which must be met and monitoring is carried out by RPBs.

5.13   Tables 5.16(a) to (d) show the results of monitoring the 23 waters of Scotland identified as bathing waters in terms of EC Directive 76/160/EEC. The monitoring is the responsibility of the River Purification Boards. Further details are available from the SOAEFD reports "Bathing Waters in Scotland - Results of Monitoring".

5.14   In 1972, a comprehensive monitoring scheme was initiated by the Government departments responsible for the national management of freshwater in order to enable:

a.   an estimate to be made, in connection with the UK's international obligations, of materials carried down rivers into estuaries; and

b.   long-term trends in river quality to be identified.

To meet the objectives of the monitoring scheme, 57 sampling points were selected in Scotland (map 5.4) and regular sampling and analysis of a variety of determinands was started in 1975. Table 5.17 shows some results from this monitoring in 1993.

5.15   Under the requirements of the EC Exchange of Information Decision, harmonised monitoring results at 3 Scottish sites, Fochabers on the Spey, Craighall on the Almond, and Renton Footbridge on the Leven, are passed to the EC Commission. The Harmonised Monitoring Scheme (HMS) is also used to provide data for a number of other international commitments such as the World Health Organisations - Global Environmental Monitoring System (GEMS) data for OECE, and estimation of contaminant loads into the North Sea (Paris Commission). In addition, HMS data are presented in a number of other Government publications.

OIL PRODUCTION

5.16   Detail of oil production and related employment are given in tables 5.18 and 5.19, and map 5.10. Further information is available in the Scottish Office Industry and Education Department (SOEID) publications:

> "Scottish Economics Bulletin"
> "Scotland - An Economic Profile"

OIL POLLUTION

5.17   Map 5.11, charts 5.5 and 5.6, table 5.20 to 5.23 are provided by the Advisory Committee on the Protection of the Sea (ACOPS). Each year, questionnaires are issued to, inter alia, local authorities and RPBs. Information is also obtained from the Department of Trade and Industry, for offshore North Sea spills, and the Department of Transport's Marine Pollution Control Unit. Each completed questionnaire, concerning details of observed spills, is returned to ACOPS for analysis. Further details can be obtained from the ACOPS reports "Survey of Oil Pollution Around the Coast of the UK".

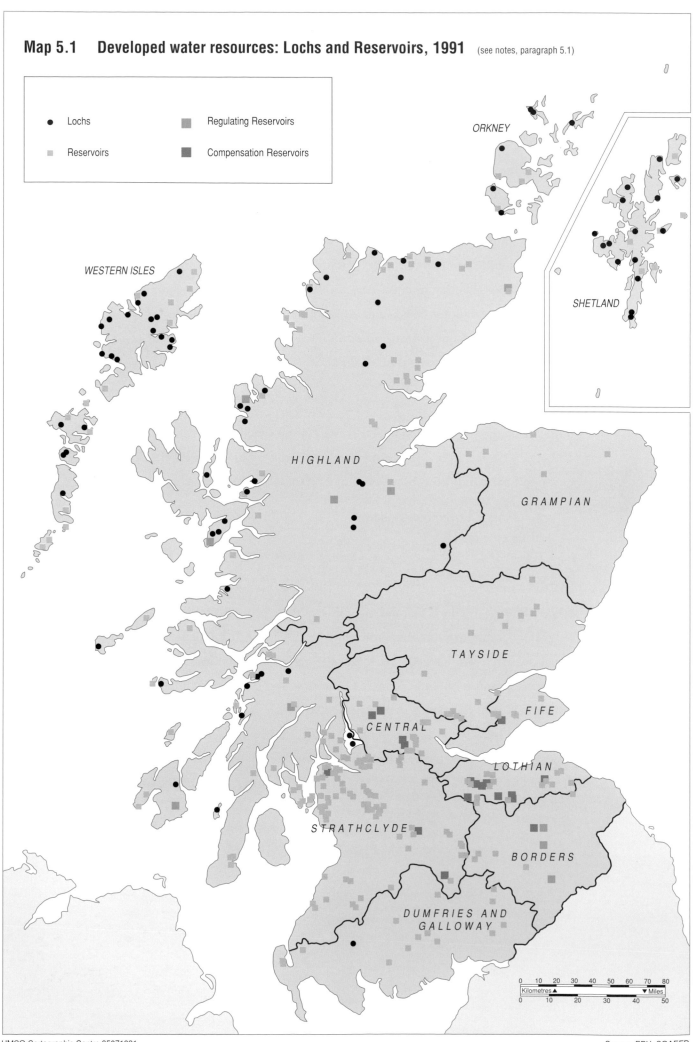

Map 5.1   Developed water resources: Lochs and Reservoirs, 1991   (see notes, paragraph 5.1)

Lochs
Reservoirs
Regulating Reservoirs
Compensation Reservoirs

ORKNEY

SHETLAND

WESTERN ISLES

HIGHLAND

GRAMPIAN

TAYSIDE

FIFE

CENTRAL

LOTHIAN

STRATHCLYDE

BORDERS

DUMFRIES AND
GALLOWAY

Kilometres
0 10 20 30 40 50 60 70 80
Miles
0   10   20   30   40   50

Source: EPU, SOAEFD

Map 5.2   Developed water resources: Rivers and Streams, 1991 <small>(see notes, paragraphs 5.1)</small>

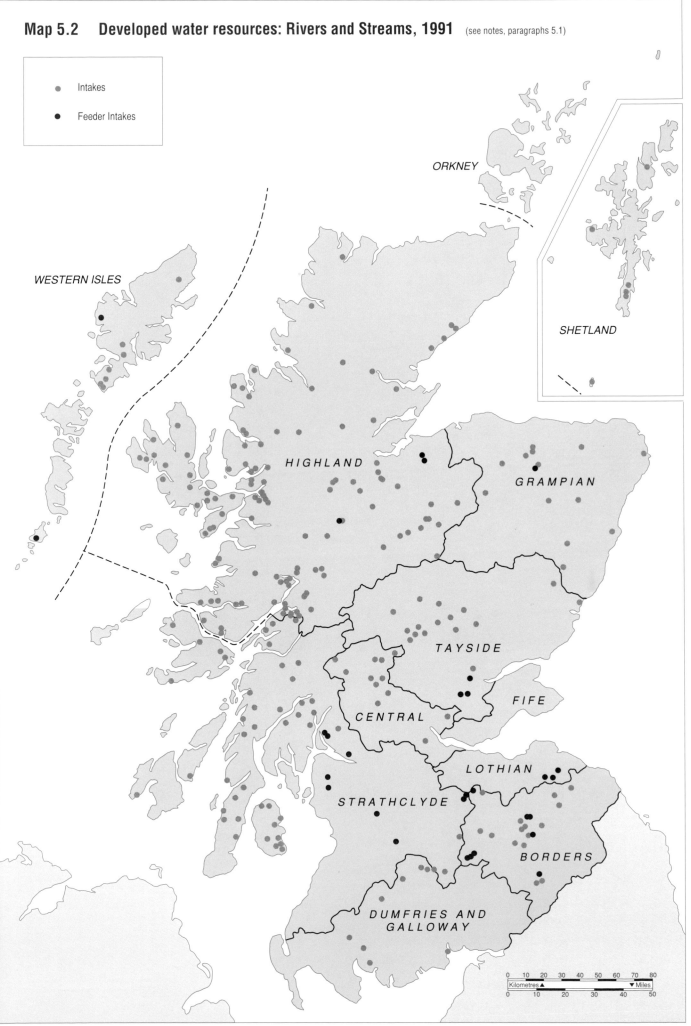

- Intakes
- Feeder Intakes

ORKNEY

WESTERN ISLES

SHETLAND

HIGHLAND

GRAMPIAN

TAYSIDE

FIFE

CENTRAL

LOTHIAN

STRATHCLYDE

BORDERS

DUMFRIES AND
GALLOWAY

Kilometres ▲
0 10 20 30 40 50 60 70 80
▼ Miles
0   10   20   30   40   50

Source: EPU, SOAEFD

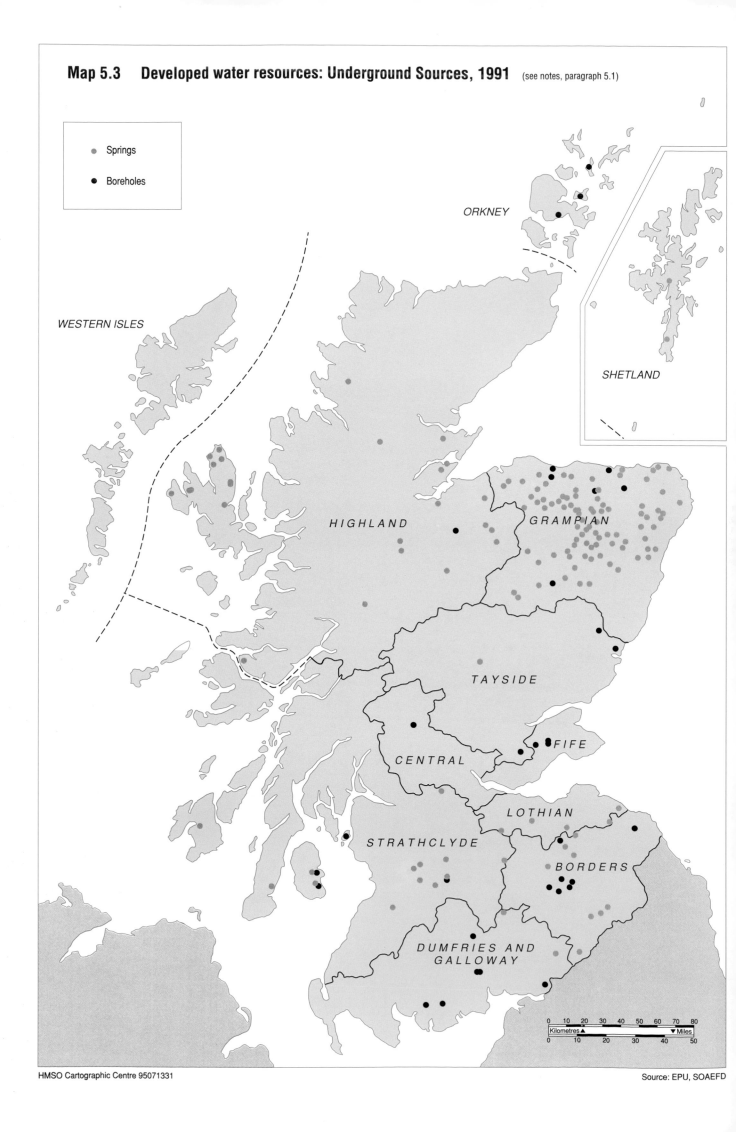

Map 5.3 Developed water resources: Underground Sources, 1991 (see notes, paragraph 5.1)

Springs

Boreholes

ORKNEY

SHETLAND

WESTERN ISLES

HIGHLAND

GRAMPIAN

TAYSIDE

FIFE

CENTRAL

LOTHIAN

STRATHCLYDE

BORDERS

DUMFRIES AND
GALLOWAY

0 10 20 30 40 50 60 70 80
Kilometres ▲   ▼ Miles
0 10 20 30 40 50

HMSO Cartographic Centre 95071331

Source: EPU, SOAEFD

Table 5.1   Developed water resources, 1982-1993   MI/d[1]

| | Reservoirs and lochs[3] | | Feeder intakes | River intakes | | Underground sources | | | | Total | |
| | | | | | | Boreholes | | Springs | | | |
	Yield	No.	No.	Yield	No.	Yield	No.	Yield	No.	Yield	No.[4]
1982	2,992	356	28	264	225	19	28	63	157	3,338	794
1983	2,993	368	28	262	222	37	28	67	154	3,359	800
1984	3,031	358	29	258	236	36	28	68	162	3,393	813
1985	2,973	360	29	409	248	36	29	44	156	3,462	822
1986	2,954	345	30	401	238	47	30	41	148	3,443	791
1987	2,932	345	31	386	237	56	39	37	161	3,411	831
1988	2,988	345	27	415	252	51	40	61	169	3,516	852
1989	2,993	355	30	405	247	55	49	62	165	3,515	864
1990	2,971	357	30	403	246	55	51	57	160	3,486	862
1991	2,982	353	30	402	242	55	52	56	153	3,495	850
1992	3,028	330	29	427	237	51	35	54	131	3,560	780
1993	3,015	316	27	428	243	50	35	56	129	3,547	768
1993 by authority[5]											
Borders	24	5	4	16	12	8	8	2	10	50	40
Central	184	12	0	4	11	0	1	1	1	189	27
Dumfries and Galloway	95	14	0	5	9	11	4	2	2	113	29
Fife	166	15	3	0	0	14	6	0	0	180	25
Grampian	18	5	1	212	12	12	6	13	61	256	85
Highland	176	61	2	143	123	1	2	9	34	328	222
Lothian	349	18	9	0	0	0	0	25	2	374	37
Strathclyde	1,256	109	6	13	50	1	4	4	14	1,274	189
Tayside	136	7	0	33	15	2	1	0	0	171	23
Orkney	20	10	0	0	0	1	3	0	2	20	15
Shetland	27	21	0	1	6	0	0	0	3	29	30
Western Isles	24	37	2	1	5	0	0	0	0	24	44
CSWDB[6]	540	2	0	0	0	0	0	0	0	540	2

Number and yield of sources in each category[2]

Source: EPU, SOAEFD

1)   MI/d = Megalitres per day = 1,000 m3/d.
2)   The division of yields into separate categories is approximate.
3)   Yield from feeder intakes is included with that of reservoir fed.
4)   From 1987 on end column total includes compensation reservoirs, other columns do not.
5)   These figures show the position at the end of the 12 month period starting 1 April 1992.
6)   Central Scotland Water Development Board (CSWDB) provides bulk supplies to Regions; it does not supply consumers directly.

Table 5.2   Public water supplies, average daily potable and non-potable consumption   Ml/d[1]

| Year | Total demand | Potable[2][3] | | | Non-potable[3] |
		Total	Unmetered[4]	Metered[4]	
1984	2,199	2,172	1,537	635	27
1985	2,198	2,169	1,540	629	29
1986	2,243	2,214	1,602	612	30
1987	2,194	2,172	1,553	619	22
1988	2,205	2,189	1,576	613	16
1989	2,248	2,225	1,571	654	23
1990	2,301	2,281	1,645	636	19
1991	2,239	2,222	1,596	626	17
1992	2,206	2,188	1,603	585	18
1993	2,272	2,258	1,662	596	14
1993 by authority					
Borders	32	32	24	9	-
Central[5]	218	217	125	92	1
Dumfries and Galloway	76	76	50	26	-
Fife[5]	146	146	108	39	-
Grampian	166	166	117	49	-
Highland	95	89	72	17	6
Lothian	284	284	215	69	0
Strathclyde[5]	1,098	1,090	838	252	7
Tayside[5]	123	123	88	36	-
Orkney	11	11	7	4	-
Shetland	11	11	8	3	-
Western Isles	12	12	11	2	-

Source: EPU, SOAEFD

(1) See note (1) table 5.1.
(2) Figures are taken over the 12 month period commencing 1 April in the year stated.
(3) Almost all water supplied by Public Authorities is "potable" ie fit for drinking; limited amounts of water, referred to as "non-potable", are supplied separately to some consumers for industrial purposes and are not intended for drinking.
(4) Metered supplies in general relate to commercial and industrial use and unmetered to domestic use, smaller trade supplies, temporary supplies and leakage.
(5) Central and Fife Region supply areas in Strathclyde and Tayside Regions respectively. The figures show the actual quantities supplied by each Authority.

Table 5.3   Per capita average daily water consumption, 1984-1993

| Year | Population (thousands) | | | Unit consumption L/hd/d[1] | | | Consumption(%) | |
				Total	Unmetered	Metered[2] and non-Metered[3]	Unmetered	Metered[2] and non-potable[3]
1984	5,146			**427**	300	127	70	30
1985	5,137			**428**	301	127	70	30
1986	5,121			**438**	313	125	71	29
1987	5,112			**429**	304	125	71	29
1988	5,094			**433**	309	124	71	29
1989	5,090			**442**	309	133	70	30
1990	5,102			**451**	322	129	71	29
1991	5,100			**439**	313	126	71	29
1992	5,107			**446**	326	119	73	27
1993	5,120			**444**	325	119	73	27
1993 by authority[4]	Regional population	Adjustment for "added areas"(5)	Population within area served					
Borders	105	-	105	**303**	223	80	73	27
Central	273	113	386	**566**	324	242	57	43
Dumfries and Galloway	148	-	148	**510**	337	174	66	34
Fife	351	9	360	**407**	300	107	74	26
Grampian	528	-	528	**314**	222	92	71	29
Highland	207	-	207	**460**	349	111	76	24
Lothian	754	-	754	**377**	285	91	76	24
Strathclyde	2,287	-113	2,174	**505**	385	120	76	24
Tayside	395	-9	387	**319**	227	92	71	29
Orkney	20	-	20	**542**	336	206	62	38
Shetland	23	-	23	**487**	367	120	75	25
Western Isles	29	-	29	**416**	367	49	88	12

Source: EPU, SOAEFD

(1) L/hd/d = litres per head per day.
(2) See note (4) table 5.3.
(3) See notes (2) and (3) table 5.3.
(4) Figures may not sum to 1993 total due to rounding.
(5) Central and Fife Regions supply areas in Strathclyde and Tayside Regions respectively. To take account of this the populations have been adjusted and the Unit Consumptions are the total consumptions divided by the populations within the area served.

Table 5.4　**Non-domestic water consumption, by large industrial users, 1993**　Ml/d

| | Agriculture, Forestry and Fishing | Energy and Water Supply | Manufacturing | | | Construction | Services | Total[1] |
			Chemicals and Man-made fibres	Food Industries	Other Manufacturing			
Scotland	**13.79**	**55.6**	**51.1**	**35.71**	**153.18**	**1.9**	**150.31**	**471.54**
Borders	-	-	0.02	0.47	1.48	-	0.8	2.77
Central	0.31	30.49	38.06	0.37	4.12	0.15	4.96	78.44
Dumfries and Galloway	2.40	-	5.50	4.30	1.20	-	0.60	14.00
Fife	1.00	4.90	-	0.40	24.30	0.40	4.30	35.30
Grampian	2.68	3.78	0.04	10.13	2.79	0.32	16.75	36.47
Highland	0.47	0.20	0.25	0.65	1.92	0.30	4.85	8.64
Lothian	0.87	5.85	1.28	4.92	3.82	0.20	26.11	53.05
Strathclyde	2.49	6.16	4.86	12.79	106.69	0.50	81.18	214.67
Tayside	1.64	0.18	1.09	1.52	6.73	-	9.76	20.92
Orkney	1.66	2.01	-	-	-	-	-	3.67
Shetland	0.25	2.00	-	-	-	-	0.50	2.75
Western Isles	0.02	0.03	-	0.16	0.13	0.03	0.50	0.86

Source: EPU, SOAEFD

(1)　Figures may not sum to total due to rounding.

Chart 5.1　Non domestic water use: large industrial users by sector, 1993[1]

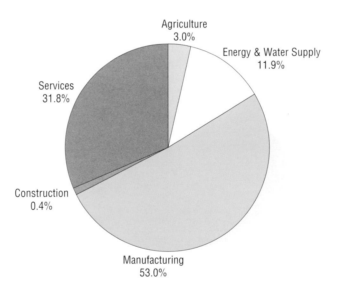

Agriculture
3.0%

Energy & Water Supply
11.9%

Services
31.8%

Construction
0.4%

Manufacturing
53.0%

(1) Figures may not sum due to rounding

Source: EWWD, SOAEFD

Map 5.4 River Purification Boards and harmonised monitoring sites, 1989

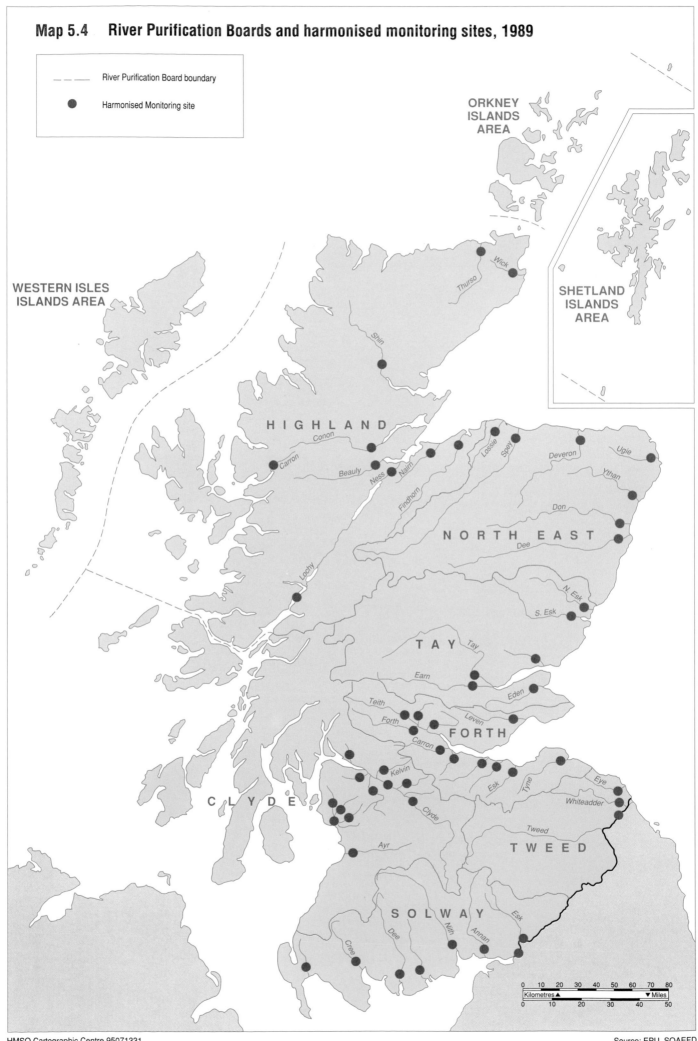

—— —— River Purification Board boundary

● Harmonised Monitoring site

ORKNEY
ISLANDS
AREA

SHETLAND
ISLANDS
AREA

WESTERN ISLES
ISLANDS AREA

Wick

Thurso

Shin

HIGHLAND

Conon

Carron

Beauly

Ness

Nairn

Findhorn

Lossie

Spey

Deveron

Ugie

Ythan

Don

NORTH EAST

Dee

Lochy

N. Esk

S. Esk

TAY

Tay

Earn

Eden

Teith

Leven

Forth

FORTH

Carron

CLYDE

Kelvin

Clyde

Esk

Tyne

Eye

Whiteadder

Ayr

Tweed

TWEED

SOLWAY

Esk

Cree

Dee

Nith

Annan

0 10 20 30 40 50 60 70 80
Kilometres ▲ ▼ Miles
0 10 20 30 40 50

Table 5.5   **Area and population served by River Purification Authorities 1994**

Authority	Area[1]		Population served[2]	
	Km2	% of Scotland	thousands	% of Scotland
Scotland	**77,170**	**100.0**	**5,132**	**100.0**
Clyde	13,555	17.6	2,280	44.4
Forth	4,520	5.9	1,320	25.7
Highland	23,110	29.9	207	4.0
North East	10,420	13.5	532	10.4
Solway	6,970	9.0	148	2.9
Tay	8,710	11.3	468	9.1
Tweed	4,580	5.9	106	2.1
Orkney	975	1.3	19	0.4
Shetland	1,430	1.8	23	0.4
Western Isles	2,900	3.8	29	0.6

Source: EPU, SOAEFD

(1) Established in 1975.
(2) Represents population served by area. Population figures are for 1994, from GRO (Scotland).

Table 5.6   **Number of direct industrial discharges, by classification, 1991**

RPB/Islands Council	Coastal	Estuarine	Inland	Satisfactory	Unsatisfactory	Borderline	Not classified
Scotland	**179**	**96**	**838**	**974**	**113**	**26**	-
Clyde	47	19	228	254	30	10	-
Forth	14	25	150	159	27	3	-
Highland	93	41	126	260	-	-	-
North East	18	2	124	105	30	9	-
Solway	2	5	39	38	7	1	-
Tay	-	3	54	45	10	2	-
Tweed	-	-	61	52	9	-	-
Western Isles	5	1	56	61	-	1	-

Source: EPU, SOAEFD

107

EC Urban Waste Water Treatment Directive Compliance Position in Scotland as at 31 December 1992

Table 5.7(a) Discharges to Freshwater and Estuary

Size of Agglomeration	Sensitive areas (Article 4)						Normal areas					
	Total No.	No. complying	% complying	Total pe	pe complying	% complying	Total No.	No. complying	% complying	Total pe	pe complying	% complying
from 2 to 10,000 pe	1	1	100.00	6,568	6,568	100.00	101	88	87.13	454,260	406,321	89.45
from 10 to 15,000 pe	3	2	66.67	36,495	23,080	63.24	19	15	78.95	232,441	183,648	79.01
from 15 to 150,000 pe	4	3	75.00	201,920	179,920	89.10	37	28	75.68	1,276,039	949,888	74.44
> 150,000 pe	0	0	-	0	0	-	5	4	80.00	2,106,597	1,726,597	81.96
Total	8	6	75.00	244,983	209,568	85.54	162	135	83.33	4,069,337	3,266,454	80.27

Discharges to Freshwater and Estuary (cont)

Size of Agglomeration	Less sensitive areas (Article 6) HNDA						Total for all areas [3]					
	Total No.	No. complying	% complying	Total pe	pe complying	% complying	Total No.	No. complying	% complying	Total pe	pe complying	% complying
from 2 to 10.000 pe	11	3	27.27	57,280	11,070	19.33	113	92	81.42	518,108	423,959	81.83
from 10 to 15,000 pe	0	0	..	0	0	..	22	17	77.27	268,936	206,728	76.87
from 15 to 150,000 pe	4	1	25.00	218,864	76,538	34.97	45	32	71.11	1,696,823	1,206,346	71.09
> 150,000 pe	1	0	0.00	358,700	0	0.00	6	4	66.67	2,465,297	1,726,597	70.04
Total	16	4	25.00	634,844	87,608	13.80	186	145	77.96	4,949,164	3,563,630	72.00

Table 5.7(b) Discharges to Coastal Waters

Size of Agglomeration	Sensitive areas (Article 4)						Normal areas					
	Total No.	No. complying	% complying	Total pe	pe complying	% complying	Total No.	No. complying	% complying	Total pe	pe complying	% complying
from 2 to 10,000 pe	0	-	..	0	-	..	-	-	..	-	-	..
from 10 to 15,000 pe	0	0	..	0	0	..	1	0	0.00	10,500	0	0.00
from 15 to 150,000 pe	0	0	..	0	0	..	5	0	0.00	128,470	0	0.00
> 150,000 pe	0	0	..	0	0	..	0	0	..	0	0	..
Total	0	0	..	0	0	..	6	0	0.00	138,970	0	0.00

Discharges to Coastal Waters (cont)

Size of Agglomeration	Less sensitive areas (Article 6) HNDA						Total for all areas [3]					
	Total No.	No. complying	% complying	Total pe	pe complying	% complying	Total No.	No. complying	% complying	Total pe	pe complying	% complying
from 2 to 10,000 pe	-	-	..	-	-	..	-	-	..	-	-	..
from 10 to 15,000 pe	10	1	10.00	114,156	12,750	11.71	11	1	9.09	124,656	12,750	10.23
from 15 to 150,000 pe	17	1	5.88	889,624	67,750	7.62	22	1	4.55	1,018,094	67,750	6.65
> 150,000 pe	5	0	0.00	3,117,831	0	0.00	5	0	0.00	3,117,831	0	0.00
Total	32	2	6.25	4,121,611	80,500	1.95	38	2	5.26	4,260,581	80,500	1.89

Table 5.7(c) Discharges to All Waters

Size of Agglomeration	Sensitive areas (Article 4)						Normal areas					
	Total No.	No. complying	% complying	Total pe	pe complying	% complying	Total No.	No. complying	% complying	Total pe	pe complying	% complying
from 2 to 10,000 pe	1	1	100.00	6,568	6,568	100.00	101	88	87.13	454,260	406,321	89,45
from 10 to 15,000 pe	3	2	66.67	36,495	23,080	63.24	20	15	75.00	242,941	183,648	75.59
from 15 to 150,000 pe	4	3	75.00	201,920	179,920	89.10	42	28	66.67	1,404,509	949,888	67.63
> 150,000 pe	0	0	..	0	0	..	5	4	80.00	2,106,597	1,726,597	81.96
Total	8	6	75.00	244,983	209,568	85.54	168	135	80.36	4,208,307	3,266,454	77.62

Discharges to All Waters (cont)

Size of Agglomeration	Less sensitive areas (Article 6) HNDA						Total for all areas [3]					
	Total No.	No. complying	% complying	Total pe	pe complying	% complying	Total No.	No. complying	% complying	Total pe	pe complying	% complying
from 2 to 10,000 pe	11	3	27.27	57,280	11,070	19.33	113	92	81.42	518,108	423,959	81.83
from 10 to 15,000 pe	10	1	10.00	114,156	12,750	11.17	33	18	54.55	393,592	219,478	55.76
from 15 to 150,000 pe	21	2	9.52	1,108,488	144,288	13.02	67	33	49.25	2,714,917	1,274,096	46.93
> 150,000 pe	6	0	0.00	3,476,531	0	0.00	11	4	36.36	5,583,128	1,726,597	30.93
Total	48	6	12.50	4,756,455	168,108	3.53	224	147	65.63	9,209,745	3,644,130	39,57

Source: EPU, SOAEFD

.. compliance not relevant as no discharges in this category.
- appropriate treatment only required in this category.
(3) Compliance assessed against Articles 4 and 6 only.
pe Population equivalent

Chart 5.2a   UWWT - Coastal Discharges 1992
(discharges > 10,000 p.e.)

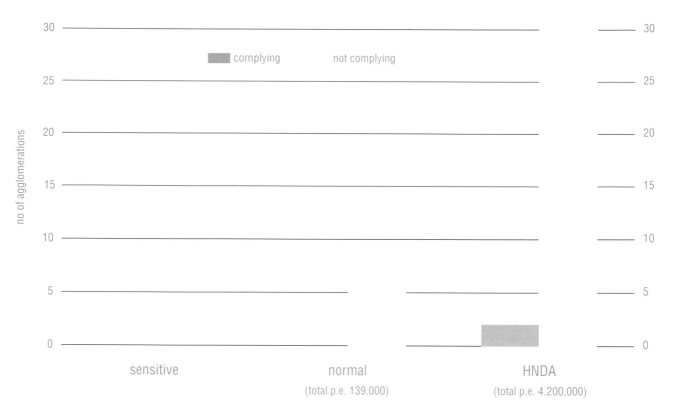

Source: EPU, SOAEFD

Chart 5.2b   UWWT - Freshwater and Estuary Discharges 1992
(discharges > 2,000 p.e.)

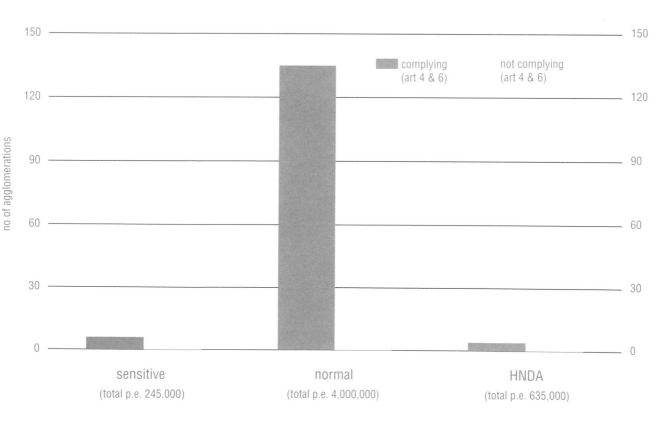

Source: EPU, SOAEFD

Table 5.8 — Disposal and reuse of sludge arising from Urban Waste Water Treatment, 1992

Authority	Quantity Disposed by Route expressed in tonnes of dry materials							Total
	Sludge Discharged to Sea		Sludge Reused		Sludge Disposed			
	Pipelines	Ships	Soil/Agriculture	Other	Landfill	Incineration	Other	
Borders RC			2,000					2,000
Central RC			300	250	2,450	900	500	4,400
Dumfries & Galloway RC			1,087		2,047			3,134
Fife RC			3,000					3,000
Grampian RC	3,000		3,000					6,000
Highland RC	244		912	60	306			1,522
Lothian RC		13,200			1,200			14,400
Strathclyde RC	840	46,365	2,000		120			49,325
Tayside RC			4,375					4,375
Orkney IC								
Shetland IC	935							935
Western Isles IC								
SCOTLAND	5,019	59,565	16,674	310	6,123	900	500	89,091

Source: EPU, SOAEFD

Table 5.9 — Sewage sludge licensed for disposal in Scottish waters, 1989-1993

	Licence issued	Licence quantity	Dumped wet	Contaminant levels (tonnes) dumped						
				Cadmium	Chromium	Copper	Mercury	Nickel	Lead	Zinc
1989	2	2,300,000	1,940,575	0.46	53	32	0.17	3	24	58
1990	2	3,000,000[1]	1,946,430	0.27	34	30	0.16	3	18	39
1991	2	3,500,000	1,984,035	0.236	34.801	41.038	0.103	2.718	19.616	44.325
1992	2	7,000,000	1,984,525	0.211	29.91	36.259	0.097	2.384	17.805	40.035
1993	2	3,000,000	1,946,340	0.187	18.101	25.813	0.074	2.948	17,887	34.760

Source: EPU, SOAEFD

(1)   Increase due to greater water dilution of sludge prior to loading.

Table 5.10 — Dredged material licensed for disposal in Scottish waters, 1989-1993

	Licence issued	Licence quantity	Dumped wet	Contaminant levels (tonnes)						
				Cadmium	Chromium	Copper	Mercury	Nickel	Lead	Zinc
1989	27	4,252,950	3,154,756	1.1	106	106	1.3	40	141	313
1990	21	3,031,960	2,109,114	0.8	61	59	0.8	36	116	210
1991	26	10,214,505	2,788,611	0.629	69.72	52,771	0.686	22.102	78.87	166.525
1992	35	13,487,050	4,026,861	0.504	82.513	71.149	0.782	28.178	90.669	197.104
1993	26	3,174,050	2,025,525	0.320	55.223	36.919	0.752	16.344	45.629	103.137

Source: SOAEFD

Table 5.11 — Local authority capital expenditure on sewerage and sewage treatment 1987/88-1993/94

£ thousands

Authority	1987-88	1988-89	1989-90	1990-91	1991-92	1992-93	1993-94
Borders	1,206	1,453	1,073	1,899	1,912	2,465	2,912
Central	2,918	2,886	2,254	5,968	5,242	7,066	7,239
Dumfries & Galloway	1,419	1,995	2,063	2,821	3,617	3,889	4,148
Fife	3,823	4,905	5,488	6,724	8,188	10,041	10,651
Grampian	9,095	7,772	5,484	8,429	8,167	11,768	12,398
Highland	2,744	3,612	4,424	5,578	5,530	8,667	12,801
Lothian	5,727	6,652	10,112	11,110	12,321	12,918	16,401
Strathclyde	19,639	20,563	27,094	27,060	30,680	43,896	49,473
Tayside	4,224	5,764	5,485	7,257	12,101	12,209	13,591
Orkney	371	213	329	354	1,465	2,248	3,313
Shetland	571	130	471	203	603	1,483	1,647
W Isles	878	583	1,140	1,096	769	1,320	1,230
Total Sewerage	52,615	56,528	65,417	78,499	90,595	117,970	135,804

Source: EPU, SOAEFD

Table 5.12 — Water pollution events arising from agricultural practice, 1985-1994

Source of pollution	1985	1986	1987	1988	1989	1990	1991	1992	1993	1994
Total	763	478	713	572	462	535	521	400	546	542
Cattle, pigs and poultry	35	37	51	50	51	37	41	47	46	60
Slurry Store	62	39	67	74	66	57	41	39	59	50
Dungstead	30	17	27	31	17	12	15	39	28	33
Dairy Premises	30	24	15	25	25	22	34	16	29	30
Milk Bottling Plant	3	2	-	-	3	-	-	-	-	-
Sheep Dipper Unit	4	6	7	8	13	18	22	13	4	11
Vegetable Washing Unit	3	3	5	5	8	6	7	4	1	7
Silage Effluent	503	241	428	282	173	281	273	136	231	203
Chemicals/Fertilisers	5	19	12	19	17	8	12	10	15	7
Run-off from land	28	32	31	33	36	29	18	26	40	29
Waste Treatment	2	2	-	-	-	1	-	1	3	2
Farm Tip	13	13	19	9	9	4	8	11	12	14
Oil	8	12	9	16	18	24	13	15	18	27
Stream Cleaning	13	14	14	8	6	2	8	5	10	14
Miscellaneous	24	19	28	12	20	33	29	38	50	55

Source: SOAEFD

Map 5.5 Water Treatment Works, 1991 (see notes, paragraph 5.7)

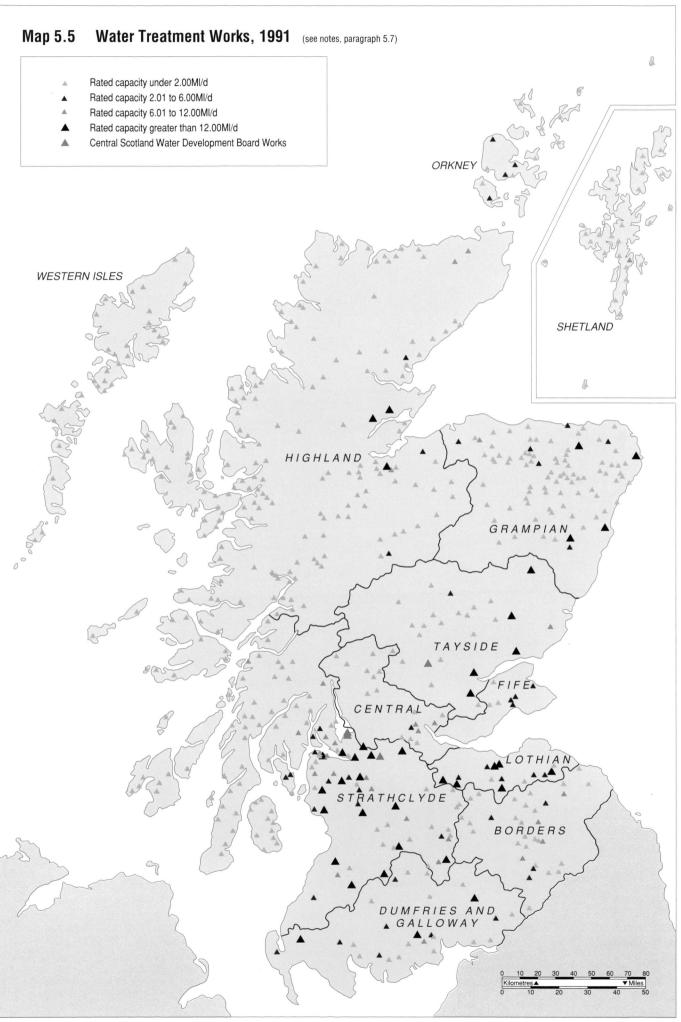

Rated capacity under 2.00Ml/d
Rated capacity 2.01 to 6.00Ml/d
Rated capacity 6.01 to 12.00Ml/d
Rated capacity greater than 12.00Ml/d
Central Scotland Water Development Board Works

WESTERN ISLES

ORKNEY

SHETLAND

HIGHLAND

GRAMPIAN

TAYSIDE

FIFE

CENTRAL

LOTHIAN

STRATHCLYDE

BORDERS

DUMFRIES AND
GALLOWAY

Kilometres ▲
Miles ▼

Source: EPU, SOAEFD

Map 5.6   River Classification, Central Scotland, 1990

(see notes, paragraph 5.8)

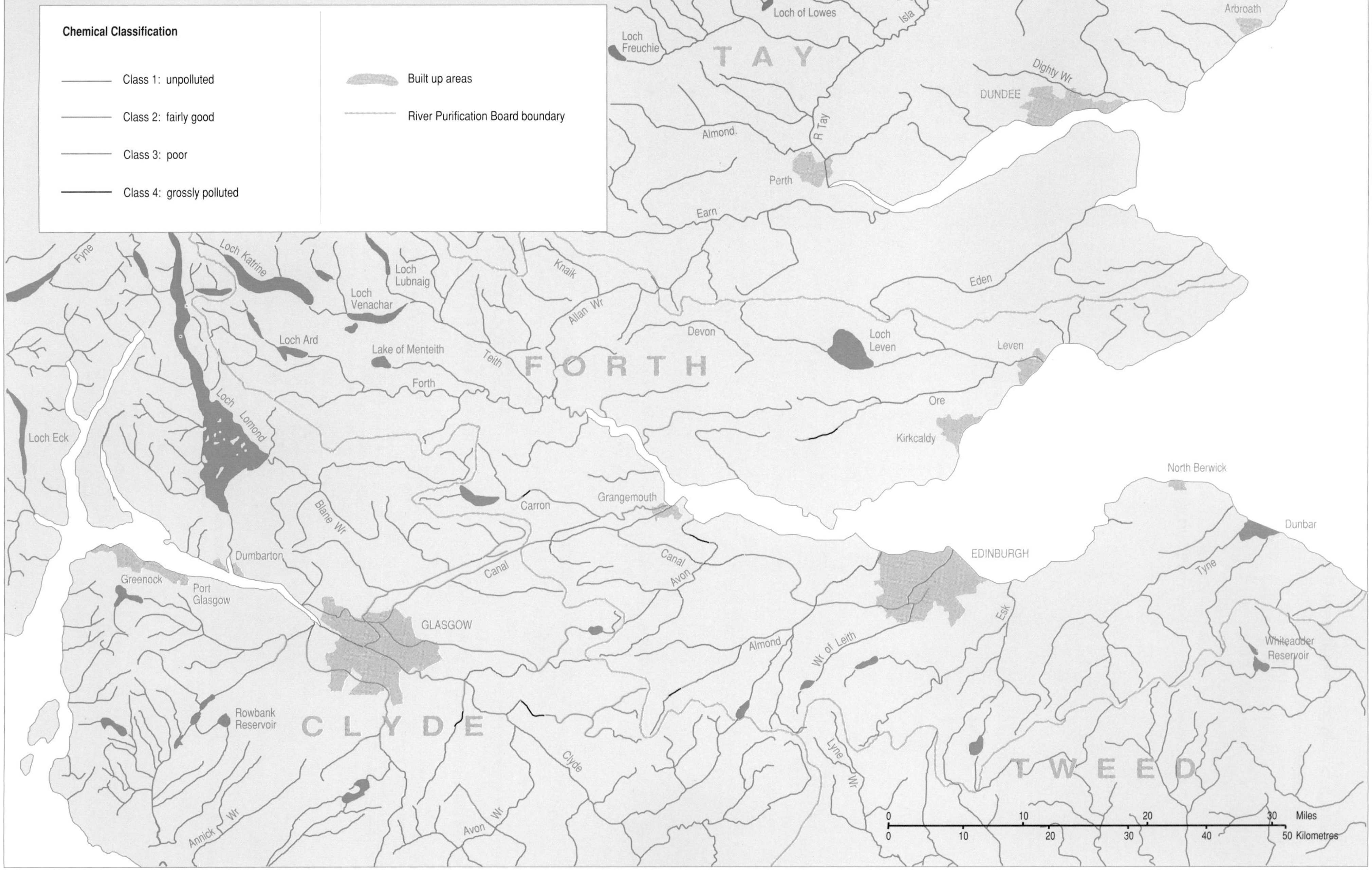

Chemical Classification

— Class 1: unpolluted

— Class 2: fairly good

— Class 3: poor

— Class 4: grossly polluted

Built up areas

River Purification Board boundary

Arbroath

Dean Wr

Digity Wr

DUNDEE

Isla

Loch of Lowes

T A Y

Loch Freuchie

Almond.

R Tay

Perth

Earn

Eden

Leven

Ore

Kirkcaldy

Loch Leven

Knaik

Allan Wr

Devon

F O R T H

Teith

Loch Lubnaig

Loch Venachar

Lake of Menteith

Forth

Loch Ard

Loch Katrine

Loch Lomond

Blane Wr

Dumbarton

Carron

Grangemouth

Canal

Avon

Canal

GLASGOW

C L Y D E

Clyde

Port Glasgow

Greenock

Rowbank Reservoir

Arnick Wr

Avon

Wr

North Berwick

Dunbar

Whiteadder Reservoir

Tyne

EDINBURGH

ESK

Wr of Leith

Almond

Lyne

Wr

T W E E D

Loch Eck

Fyne

Miles

Kilometres

0   10   20   30   40   50

0   10   20   30

Source: EPU, SOAEFD

HMSO Cartographic Centre 95071331

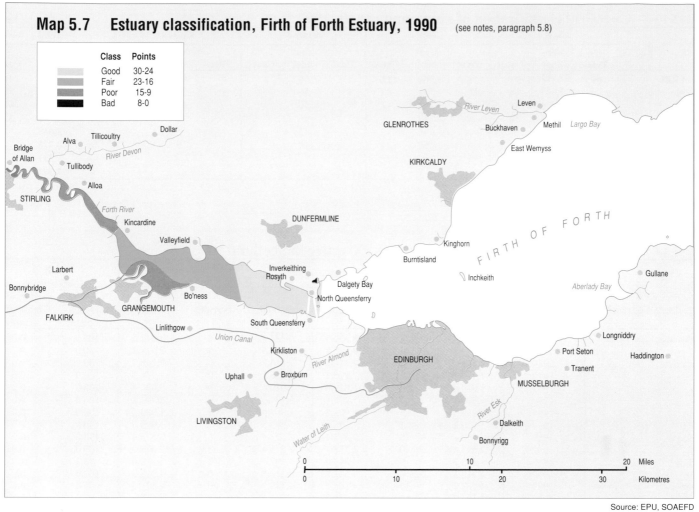

Map 5.7   Estuary classification, Firth of Forth Estuary, 1990   (see notes, paragraph 5.8)

Class	Points
Good	30-24
Fair	23-16
Poor	15-9
Bad	8-0

Dollar
Tillicoultry
Alva
Bridge of Allan
River Devon
Tullibody
Alloa
STIRLING
Forth River
Kincardine
Valleyfield
DUNFERMLINE
Larbert
Bonnybridge
Bo'ness
Inverkeithing
Rosyth
Dalgety Bay
North Queensferry
FALKIRK
GRANGEMOUTH
South Queensferry
Linlithgow
Union Canal
Kirkliston
River Almond
Uphall
Broxburn
EDINBURGH
LIVINGSTON
Water of Leith
River Esk
Dalkeith
Bonnyrigg
MUSSELBURGH
GLENROTHES
River Leven
Leven
Buckhaven
Methil
Largo Bay
East Wemyss
KIRKCALDY
Kinghorn
Burntisland
Inchkeith
FIRTH OF FORTH
Aberlady Bay
Gullane
Longniddry
Port Seton
Haddington
Tranent

0		10		20	Miles
0	10	20	30		Kilometres

Source: EPU, SOAEFD

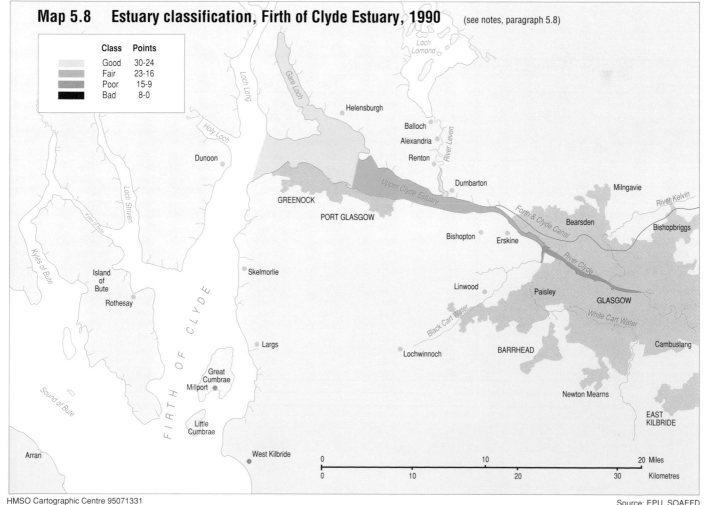

Map 5.8   Estuary classification, Firth of Clyde Estuary, 1990   (see notes, paragraph 5.8)

Class	Points
Good	30-24
Fair	23-16
Poor	15-9
Bad	8-0

Loch Lomond
Loch Long
Gare Loch
Holy Loch
Helensburgh
Balloch
Alexandria
River Leven
Renton
Dunoon
Loch Striven
GREENOCK
Upper Clyde Estuary
Dumbarton
Milngavie
River Kelvin
PORT GLASGOW
Forth & Clyde Canal
Bearsden
Bishopbriggs
Kyles of Bute
Bishopton
Erskine
River Clyde
Skelmorlie
Island of Bute
Linwood
Paisley
GLASGOW
Rothesay
Black Cart Water
White Cart Water
FIRTH OF CLYDE
Largs
Lochwinnoch
BARRHEAD
Cambuslang
Great Cumbrae
Millport
Sound of Bute
Newton Mearns
Little Cumbrae
EAST KILBRIDE
Arran
West Kilbride
Kyles of Bute

0		10		20	Miles
0	10	20	30		Kilometres

HMSO Cartographic Centre 95071331

Source: EPU, SOAEFD

Table 5.13 Chemical classification of rivers and canals, 1990
km

	Class 1			Class 2			Class 3			Class 4			Total		
	Tidal	Non-tidal	Canal	Tidal	Non-tidal	Canal	Tidal	Non-tidal	Canal	Tidal	Non-tidal	Canal	Tidal	Non-tidal	Canal
Total RPB	199	49,181	71	21	1,060	122	4	229	4	-	69	-	224	50,539	197
Clyde	23	9,947	18	12	534	80	4	56	-	-	17	-	39	10,554	98
Forth	-	2,906	21	-	298	42	(1)	150	4	-	44	-	-	3,398	67
Highland	125	13,858	32	6	43	-	(1)	6	-	(1)	1	-	131	13,908	32
North East	7	8,615	-	1	46	-	-	5	-	-	1	-	8	8,667	-
Solway	2	4,891	-	-	69	-	-	12	-	(1)	6	-	2	4,978	-
Tay	36	6,189	-	2	62	-	-	(1)	-	-	-	-	38	6,251	-
Tweed	6	2,775	-	-	8	-	-	-	-	-	-	-	6	2,783	-

(1)   Indicates a length between 0 and 0.5 km

Source: EPU, SOAEFD

Table 5.14 Compliance with EC Freshwater Fish Directive in Scotland

RPB	Year	Designations (Length in Km)			Compliance (Length in Km)			% Age of Designations	
		Salmonid	Cyprinid	Total	Salmonid	Cyprinid	Total	Overall compliance	Overall failure to comply
Highland	1989	8,377.5	0	8,377.5	8,377.5	0	8,377.5	100.0	0.0
	1992	8,577.5	0	8,577.5	8,577.5	0	8,577.5	100.0	0.0
North East	1989	7,146.2	0	7,146.2	7,146.2	0	7,146.2	100.0	0.0
	1992	7,976.1	0	7,976.1	9,976.1	0	7,976.1	100.0	0.0
Tay	1989	5,020.4	0	5,020.4	5,020.4	0	5,020.4	100.0	0.0
	1992	5,794.1	0	5,794.1	5,794.1	0	5,794.1	100.0	0.0
Forth	1989	1,869.5	33.7	1,903.2	1,869.5	33.7	1,903.2	100.0	0.0
	1992	1,959.8	33.7	1,993.5	1,959.8	33.7	1,993.5	100.0	0.0
Tweed	1989	2,573.4	0	2,573.4	2,573.4	0	2,573.4	100.0	0.0
	1992	2,573.4	0	2,573.4	2,573.4	0	2,573.4	100.0	0.0
Solway	1989	4,313.3	0	4,313.3	3,799.6	0	3,799.6	88.1	11.9
	1992	4,313.3	0	4,313.3	4,313.3	0	4,313.3	100.0	0.0
Clyde	1989	4,767.2	39	4,806.2	4,549.3	30	4,579.3	95.4	4.6
	1992	5,194.7	39	5,233.7	5,085.4	30	5,115.4	97.9	2.1
Scotland	**1989**	**34,067.5**	**72.7**	**34,140.2**	**33,335.9**	**63.7**	**33,399.6**	**97.9**	**2.1**
	1992	**36,388.9**	**72.7**	**34,461.6**	**36,279.6**	**63.7**	**36,343.3**	**99.7**	**0.3**

Source: EPU, SOAEFD

Table 5.15 Bathing Waters Directive, Scottish Results

Bathing Water	1988	1989	1990	1991	1992	1993	1994	1995
Nairn (East Beach)	Fail	Pass	Fail	Pass	Pass	Pass	Pass	Pass
Cullen	Pass	Pass	Pass	Pass	Pass	Pass	Pass	Pass
Fraserburgh	Fail	Pass	Pass	Pass	Pass	Pass	Pass	Pass
Aberdeen	Pass	Pass	Pass	Pass	Pass	Pass	Pass	Pass
Montrose	Pass	Pass	Pass	Pass	Pass	Pass	Pass	Pass
Arbroath	Fail	Fail	Fail	Fail	Pass	Pass	Pass	Pass
Carnoustie	Pass	Fail	Pass	Fail	Pass	Pass	Pass	Pass
St Andrews (West Sands)	Pass	Pass	Pass	Pass	Pass	Pass	Pass	Pass
Kinghorn (Pettycur)	Pass	Pass	Pass	Fail	Fail	Pass	Pass	Pass
Aberdour (Silversands)	Pass	Pass	Fail	Fail	Fail	Pass	Pass	Pass
Gullane	Pass	Pass	Pass	Pass	Pass	Pass	Pass	Pass
Yellowcraigs	Pass	Pass	Fail	Pass	Pass	Pass	Pass	Pass
North Berwick (Milsey Bay)	Fail	Pass	Pass	Pass	Pass	Pass	Pass	Pass
Dunbar (Belhaven)	Pass	Pass	Pass	Pass	Pass	Pass	Pass	Pass
Pease Bay	Pass	Pass	Pass	Pass	Pass	Pass	Pass	Pass
Sandyhills	Pass	Pass	Fail	Pass	Pass	Pass	Fail	Pass
Girvan	Fail	Pass	Fail	Pass	Fail	Pass	Fail	Fail
Turnberry	Fail	Fail	Fail	Fail	Fail	Fail	Fail	Fail
Ayr (South Beach)	Fail	Fail	Fail	Fail	Fail	Fail	Fail	Fail
Prestwick	Fail	Fail	Fail	Fail	Fail	Fail	Fail	Pass
Troon (South Beach)	Fail	Pass	Pass	Pass	Pass	Pass	Pass	Pass
Irvine-Gailes (New Town)	Fail	Fail	Fail	Fail	Fail	Fail	Fail	Pass
Saltcoats/Ardrossan (South Beach)	Fail	Fail	Fail	Pass	Fail	Fail	Fail	Fail
Total Annual Passes	12	16	12	15	15	18	16	19
Total Annual Fails	11	7	11	8	8	5	7	4

Source: EPU, SOAEFD

Chart 5.3   EC Bathing Water Directive: Identified Bathing Waters
            Passing/Imperative Standards 1988-95

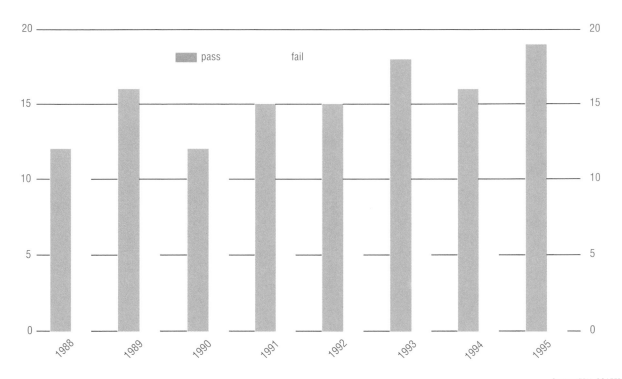

Source: EPU, SOAEFD

Table 5.16(a) Bathing Waters Survey - 1993 Results

Bathing Water	Pass/Fail	Total Coliforms		Faecal Coliforms	
		Number of Samples	Number failing to conform	Number of samples	Number failing to conform
Nairn	Pass	23	1	23	0
Cullen	Pass	20	0	20	0
Fraserburgh	Pass	20	1	20	1
Aberdeen	Pass	20	0	20	0
Montrose	Pass	23	0	23	0
Arbroath	Pass	23	0	23	0
Carnoustie	Pass	23	1	23	1
St Andrews (West Sands)	Pass	23	0	23	0
Kinghorn (Pettycur)	Pass	23	0	23	0
Aberdour (Silversands)	Pass	23	0	23	0
Gullane	Pass	23	0	23	0
Yellowcraigs	Pass	23	0	23	0
North Berwick (Milsey Bay)	Pass	23	1	23	1
Dunbar (Belhaven)	Pass	23	0	23	0
Pease Bay	Pass	20	0	20	0
Sandyhills	Pass	20	0	20	0
Girvan	Pass	22	0	22	1
Turnberry	Fail	22	1	22	4
Ayr (South Beach)	Fail	22	3	22	5
Prestwick	Fail	22	0	22	4
Troon (South Beach)	Pass	22	0	22	1
Irvine (New Town)	Fail	22	1	22	3
Saltcoats (South Beach)	Fail	22	0	22	3

Source: EPU, SOAEFD

Table 5.16(b) Bathing Waters Survey - 1994 Results

Bathing Water	RPB	Pass/Fail	Total Coliforms		Faecal Coliforms	
			Number of Samples	Number failing to conform	Number of samples	Number failing to conform
Nairn	Highland	Pass	20	0	20	0
Cullen	North East	Pass	20	0	20	0
Fraserburgh	North East	Pass	20	0	20	0
Aberdeen	North East	Pass	20	0	20	1
Montrose	Tay	Pass	23	0	23	0
Arbroath	Tay	Pass	23	0	23	0
Carnoustie	Tay	Pass	23	0	23	0
St Andrews (West Sands)	Tay	Pass	21	0	22	0
Kinghorn (Pettycur)	Forth	Pass	21	0	21	0
Aberdour (Silversands)	Forth	Pass	21	0	21	0
Gullane	Forth	Pass	21	0	21	0
Yellowcraigs	Forth	Pass	21	0	21	0
North Berwick (Milsey Bay)	Forth	Pass	21	0	21	1
Dunbar (Belhaven)	Forth	Pass	21	0	20	0
Pease Bay	Tweed	Pass	22	0	22	0
Sandyhills	Solway	Fail	20	0	20	4
Girvan	Clyde	Fail	22	0	22	5
Turnberry	Clyde	Fail	22	2	22	5
Ayr (South Beach)	Clyde	Fail	22	1	22	2
Prestwick	Clyde	Fail	22	0	22	4
Troon (South Beach)	Clyde	Pass	22	0	22	1
Irvine (New Town)	Clyde	Fail	22	1	22	2
Saltcoats (South Beach)	Clyde	Fail	22	2	22	4

Source: EPU, SOAEFD

Table 5.16(c) Bathing Waters Survey - 1994 Results

Bathing Water	RPB	Pass/Fail	Total Coliforms					Faecal Coliforms				
			Number of Samples	Median	Range Min	Range Max	Number failing to conform	Number of samples	Median	Range Min	Range Max	Number failing to conform
Nairn	Highland	Pass	20	235	1	880	0	20	84	0	830	0
Cullen	North East	Pass	20	65	4	500	0	20	36	7	300	0
Fraserburgh	North East	Pass	20	300	66	2,140	0	20	144	32	1,240	0
Aberdeen	North East	Pass	20	104	5	3,640	0	20	46	2	2,760	1
Montrose	Tay	Pass	23	36	0	250	0	23	9	0	150	0
Arbroath	Tay	Pass	23	290	27	4,200	0	23	90	0	920	0
Carnoustie	Tay	Pass	23	400	18	9,800	0	23	120	0	1,000	0
St Andrews (West Sands)	Tay	Pass	21	9	0	770	0	22	5	0	180	0
Kinghorn (Pettycur)	Forth	Pass	21	70	2	598	0	21	64	<2	589	0
Aberdour (Silversands)	Forth	Pass	21	34	6	500	0	21	26	2	196	0
Gullane	Forth	Pass	21	72	<2	600	0	21	46	<2	532	0
Yellowcraigs	Forth	Pass	21	86	2	1,500	0	21	56	<2	1,500	0
North Berwick (Milsey Bay)	Forth	Pass	21	164	<2	4,300	0	21	66	<2	3,800	1
Dunbar (Belhaven)	Forth	Pass	21	8	<2	260	0	20	4	<2	88	0
Pease Bay	Tweed	Pass	22	34	1	1,300	0	22	16	0	1,300	0
Sandyhills	Solway	Fail	20	1,150	49	6,600	0	20	510	18	5,000	4
Girvan	Clyde	Fail	22	255	3	8,900	0	22	132	1	6,300	5
Turnberry	Clyde	Fail	22	175	2	12,000	2	22	210	2	7,600	5
Ayr (South Beach)	Clyde	Fail	22	580	30	30,000	1	22	05	20	20,000	2
Prestwick	Clyde	Fail	22	365	6	6,800	0	22	195	4	6,100	4
Troon (South Beach)	Clyde	Pass	22	53	<1	9,600	0	22	30	1	8,000	1
Irvine (New Town)	Clyde	Fail	22	260	7	14,600	1	22	155	5	11,200	2
Saltcoats (South Beach)	Clyde	Fail	22	300	16	26,000	2	22	125	19	18,000	4

Source: EPU, SOAEFD

Table 5.16(d) Bathing Waters Survey - 1994 Results

Bathing Water	RPB	Number of Samples (Number of Non-Complying Samples)							
		pH	Transp-arency	Salmon-nella	Entero viruses	Colour	Mineral Oils	Surface Active Substances	Phenols
Nairn	Highland	20(0)	20(0)*	0(0)	0(0)	20(0)*	20(0)	20(0)	20(0)
Cullen	North East	0(0)	20(0)	0(0)	4(0)	20(0)	20(0)	20(0)	20(0)
Fraserburgh	North East	0(0)	20(0)	0(0)	4(0)	20(0)	20(0)	20(0)	20(0)
Aberdeen	North East	0(0)	20(0)*	0(0)	4(1)	20(0)*	20(0)	20(0)	20(0)
Montrose	Tay	0(0)	23(0)*	0(0)	0(0)	23(0)	23(0)	23(0)	23(0)
Arbroath	Tay	0(0)	23(0)*	0(0)	0(0)	23(0)	23(0)	23(0)	23(0)
Carnoustie	Tay	0(0)	23(0)*	0(0)	0(0)	23(0)	23(0)	23(0)	23(0)
St Andrews (West Sands)	Tay	0(0)	22(0)	0(0)	0(0)	22(0)	22(0)	22(0)	22(0)
Kinghorn (Pettycur)	Forth	0(0)	21(1)	0(0)	0(0)	21(0)	21(0)	21(0)	21(0)
Aberdour (Silversands)	Forth	0(0)	21(2)	0(0)	0(0)	21(0)	21(0)	21(0)	21(0)
Gullane	Forth	0(0)	21(1)	0(0)	0(0)	21(0)	21(0)	21(0)	21(0)
Yellowcraigs	Forth	0(0)	21(0)	0(0)	0(0)	21(0)	21(0)	21(0)	21(0)
North Berwick (Milsey Bay)	Forth	0(0)	21(0)	0(0)	0(0)	21(0)	21(0)	21(0)	21(0)
Dunbar (Belhaven)	Forth	0(0)	21(0)	0(0)	0(0)	21(0)	21(0)	21(0)	21(0)
Pease Bay	Tweed	22(0)	22(0)	0(0)	0(0)	22(0)	22(0)	22(0)	22(0)
Sandyhills	Solway	20(0)	0(0)*	0(0)	0(0)	20(0)	20(0)	20(0)	20(0)
Girvan	Clyde	20(0)	22(2)	0(0)	4(1)	22(0)	22(0)	22(0)	22(0)
Turnberry	Clyde	20(0)	22(3)	0(0)	0(0)	22(0)	22(0)	22(0)	22(0)
Ayr (South Beach)	Clyde	20(0)	22(1)	0(0)	0(0)	22(0)	22(0)	22(0)	22(0)
Prestwick	Clyde	20(0)	22(2)	0(0)	0(0)	22(0)	22(0)	22(0)	22(0)
Troon (South Beach)	Clyde	20(0)	22(0)	0(0)	0(0)	22(0)	22(0)	22(0)	22(0)
Irvine (New Town)	Clyde	20(0)	22(0)	0(0)	0(0)	22(0)	22(0)	22(0)	22(0)
Saltcoats (South Beach)	Clyde	20(0)	22(0)	0(0)	0(0)	22(0)	22(0)	22(0)	22(0)

Source: EPU, SOAEFD

NOTE: *Denotes waiver granted because of geographical conditions.

117

Map 5.9   Location of Identified Bathing Waters in Scotland

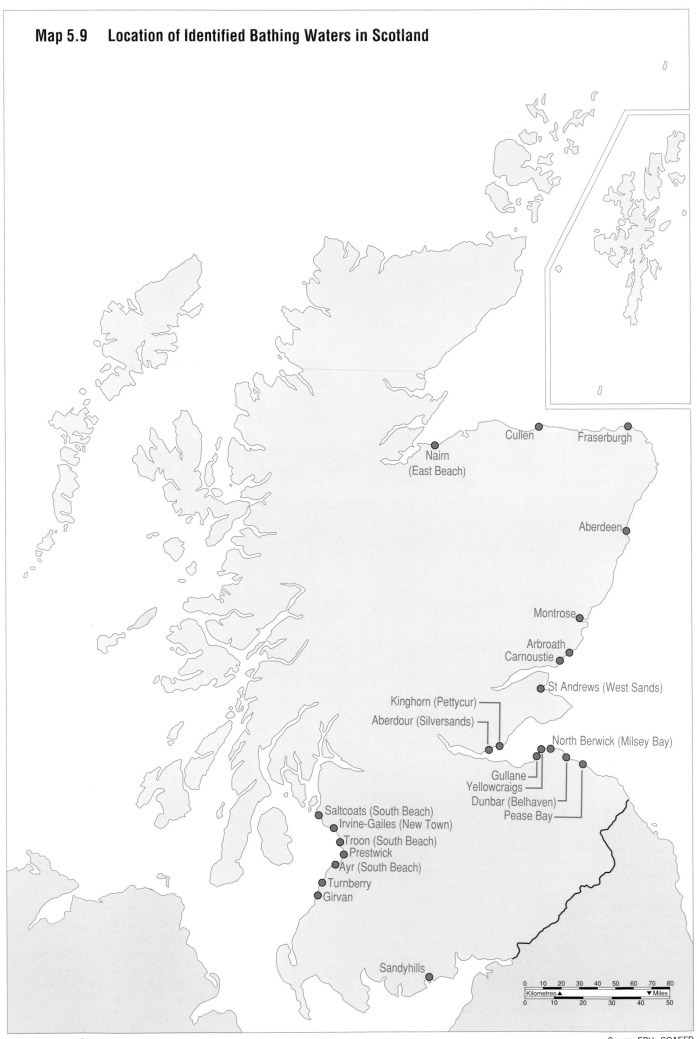

Cullen

Fraserburgh

Nairn
(East Beach)

Aberdeen

Montrose

Arbroath
Carnoustie

St Andrews (West Sands)

Kinghorn (Pettycur)

Aberdour (Silversands)

North Berwick (Milsey Bay)

Gullane
Yellowcraigs
Dunbar (Belhaven)
Pease Bay

Saltcoats (South Beach)
Irvine-Gailes (New Town)
Troon (South Beach)
Prestwick
Ayr (South Beach)
Turnberry
Girvan

Sandyhills

0 10 20 30 40 50 60 70 80
Kilometres ▲
▼ Miles
0   10   20   30   40   50

Source: EPU , SOAEFD

Table 5.17   **Harmonised monitoring, by determinands, 1993**   annual average

River	Determinands						
	Instantaneous flow (m³/sec)	PH (ph units)	BOD[1] (mg/IO) (inhibited)	Nitrate (mg/IN)	Dissolved oxygen (mg/IO)	Ammoniacal nitrogen (mg/IN)	Suspended solids (mg/I)
Clyde	53.04	7.5	3.9	1.4	9.6	0.9	16.2
Forth	55.41	7.3	1.6	-	10.5	0.1	6.8
Lochy	27.8	6.4	0.9	0.1	11.4	0.0	0.9
Nith	32.2	7.5	2.4	1.1	11.7	0.1	5.4
Spey	60.5	6.2	0.6	0.4	12.1	0.0	1.6
Tay	179.8	7.4	2.2	0.6	12.1	0.0	2.1
Tweed	99.4	7.9	2.6	1.9	12.3	0.1	3.8

Source: Department of the Environment

1) BOD - biochemical oxygen demand.

Chart 5.4   Harmonised monitoring[1], 1976 - 1993

(a) Instantaneous flow (cumecs)

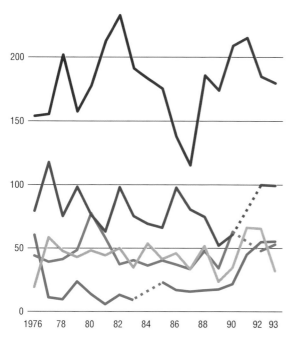

(b) Nitrate (mg/litre as nitrogen)

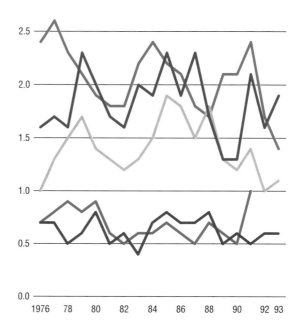

(c) Suspended solids (mg/litre)

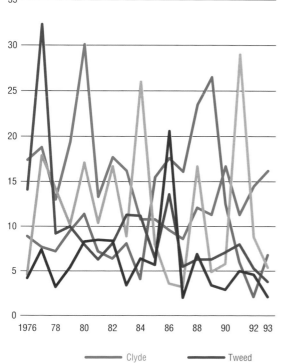

(d) Dissolved oxygen (average) (mg/litre as oxygen)

——— Clyde   ——— Tweed   ——— Forth   ——— Tay   ——— Nith

(1) figures are annual averages

Source: Department of the Environment

119

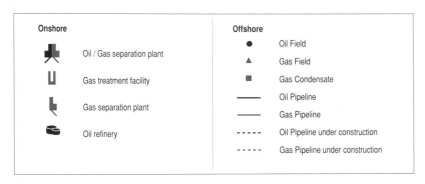

Map 5.10 Oil and Gas Developments, January 1995 (see notes, paragraph 5.16)

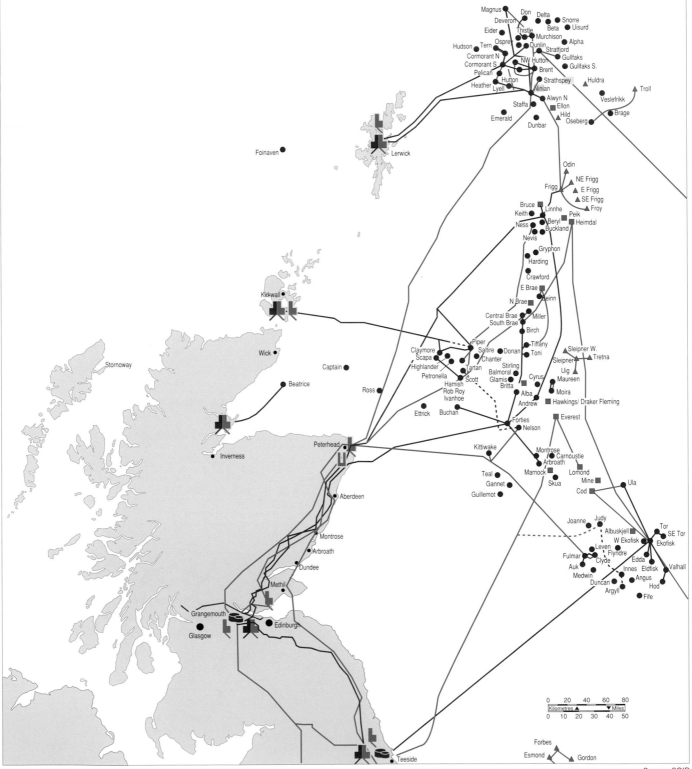

Source: SOID

Table 5.18　**Oil fields in production in the UK sector of the Northern North Sea, 1991-1994**

million tonnes

Field[1]	Operator	Discovery date	Reserve[5] estimate	Oil production[7]			
				1991	1992	1993	1994
Total				**83.0**	**85.2**	**90.0**	**115.4**
Alwyn N	Total	1975	29.0	4.0	3.6	2.9	1.9
Alba	Chevron	1984	50.7	0.0	0.0	0.0	2.3
Angus[2]	Amerada Hess	1987	1.4	0.0	1.2	0.2	0.0
Arbroath	Amoco	1969	17.9	1.6	1.7	1.6	1.5
Argyll[4]	Hamilton	1971	9.7	0.2	0.2	0.0	0.0
Auk	Shell	1971	15.7	0.4	0.4	0.4	0.5
Balmoral	Sun Oil	1975	13.3	1.3	1.3	1.0	0.8
Beatrice	BP	1976	20.9	1.0	0.7	0.6	0.5
Beinn	Marathon	1987	3.0	0.0	0.0	0.1	0.2
Beryl	Mobil	1972	204.1	4.6	5.1	4.6	4.2
Brae Central	Marathon	1976	9.0	0.6	0.8	0.6	0.5
Brae East	Marathon	1980	38.6	0.0	0.0	-	2.7
Brae North	Marathon	1975	21.0	2.6	1.8	1.1	0.8
Brae South	Marathon	1972	40.0	0.9	0.6	0.5	0.5
Brent	Shell	1971	262.3	8.5	10.8	10.9	9.5
Bruce	BP	1974	23.0	0.0	0.0	0.9	2.1
Buchan	BP	1974	14.6	0.8	0.7	0.5	0.6
Chanter	Elf Enterprise	1985	1.4	0.0	0.0	0.2	0.1
Claymore	Elf Enterprise	1974	77.0	2.6	2.3	2.4	2.2
Clyde	BP	1978	17.5	1.7	1.2	0.9	0.7
Cormorant N	Shell	1974	57.4	1.7	1.4	1.7	2.1
Cormorant S	Shell	1972	29.2	1.0	1.0	0.7	0.9
Cyrus[3]	BP	1979	4.4	0.3	0.1	0.0	0.0
Deveron	BP	1972	2.2	0.0	0.1	0.1	-
Don	BP	1976	1.9	0.3	0.2	0.2	0.2
Donan	BP	1987	3.3	0.0	0.3	0.5	0.4
Dunbar	Total	1973	15.8	0.0	0.0	0.0	-
Duncan[4]	Hamilton	1981	2.5	-	-	0.0	0.0
Dunlin	Shell	1973	55.0	1.3	1.3	1.1	1.0
Eider	Shell	1976	14.4	1.7	1.6	1.6	1.2
Emerald	Midland & Scottish Energy	1981	2.3	0.0	0.4	0.9	0.6
Everest	Amoco	1982	4.6	0.0	0.0	0.1	0.2
Forties	BP	1970	330.7	8.2	7.6	5.8	6.0
Fulmar	Shell	1975	75.8	5.0	4.0	2.6	2.0
Gannet A	Shell	1978	9.0	0.0	0.0	-	0.6
Gannet B	Shell	1979	4.4	0.0	0.0	0.1	0.1
Gannet C	Shell	1982	8.1	0.0	-	1.3	1.4
Gannet D	Shell	1987	4.0	0.0	-	0.3	0.3
Glamis	Sun Oil	1982	2.3	0.5	0.2	0.2	0.3
Gryphon	Kerr McGee	1987	14.7	0.0	0.0	0.2	1.7
Hamish	Amerada Hess	1988	0.5	0.1	0.1	-	-
Heather	Unocal	1973	14.0	0.5	0.4	0.4	0.3
Highlander	Texaco	1976	10.4	0.7	0.5	0.4	0.4
Hudson	Amerada Hess	1987	11.7	0.0	0.0	0.8	1.5
Hutton	Oryx	1973	25.3	0.9	1.1	1.1	1.2
Hutton N W	Amoco	1975	15.5	0.4	0.5	0.5	0.3
Ivanhoe	Amerada Hess	1975	7.9	1.2	1.3	1.3	0.9
Kittiwake	Shell	1981	6.7	1.3	1.3	1.4	1.5
Leven	BP	1981	1.0	0.0	0.1	0.2	0.1
Linnhe[4]	Mobil	1988	0.2	-	0.0	0.0	0.0
Lomond	Amoco	1972	1.6	0.0	0.0	0.1	1.9
Lyell	Oryx	1975	5.1	0.0	0.0	0.4	0.8
Machar	BP	1975	8.1	0.0	0.0	0.0	0.6
Magnus	BP	1974	106.3	6.4	6.7	6.7	6.8
Maureen	Phillips	1973	28.0	1.7	1.2	0.9	0.8
Medwin	BP	1989	0.1	0.0	0.0	0.0	0.1
Miller	Britoil	1983	35.3	0.0	2.8	5.7	6.4
Moira	Philips	1988	0.6	0.2	0.1	0.1	0.1
Montrose	Amoco	1971	12.8[6]	0.1	0.1	0.1	0.2
Murchison (UK)	Oryx	1975	35.8[8]	1.1	1.3	0.8	0.6
Nelson	Enterprise	1988	64.1	0.0	0.0	0.0	5.1
Ness	Mobil	1986	5.4	0.4	0.3	0.3	0.2
Ninian	Chevron	1974	157.0	4.2	3.3	3.3	3.2
Osprey	Shell	1974	12.9	0.9	1.4	1.6	1.3
Petronella	Texaco	1975	5.4	0.5	0.5	0.5	0.4
Piper	Elf Enterprise	1973	135.5	0.0	0.0	2.6	3.8
Rob Roy	Amerada Hess	1984	13.5	1.7	1.7	1.7	1.9
Saltire	Elf Enterprise	1988	12.0	0.0	0.0	0.7	1.8
Scapa	Elf Enterprise	1975	14.5	1.3	1.4	1.4	1.2
Scott	Amereda Hess	1984	71.9	0.0	0.0	1.5	8.0
Staffa	Lasmo	1985	0.8	0.0	0.3	0.2	0.1
Statfjord (UK)	Statoil	1975	75.8[6]	4.6	3.2	3.8	4.5
Strathspey	Texaco	1975	11.2	0.0	0.0	0.3	1.4
Tartan	Texaco	1975	14.1	0.7	0.4	0.3	0.6
Tern	Shell	1975	40.8	2.6	3.6	3.3	3.7
Thistle	Britoil	1973	55.3	0.7	1.0	0.9	0.7
Tiffany	Agip	1977	16.8	0.0	0.0	0.2	1.8
Toni	Agip	1979	5.3	0.0	0.0	-	0.6

Source: Department of Trade and Industry

'0' 　= None '-'= less than half the final digit ie less than 0.1.
(1) 　Includes offshore condensate fields in production.
(2) 　The Angus field was abandoned in 1993.
(3) 　The Cyrus field was abandoned in April 1992 but is due to resume production in 1997.
(4) 　Production from the Argyll, Duncan and Linnhe fields ceased during 1992.
(5) 　Operator's own estimated of proven recoverable reserves (million tonnes)
(6) 　Total reserves of field excluding Norwegian Sector.
(7) 　Figures are rounded to the nearest 100,000 tonnes.

Table 5.19 Fields under development in the UK sector of the northern North Sea, 1994 — Million Tonnes

Field	Operator	Discovery Date	Reserve Estimate(1)	Planned Production Start Date
Andrew	BP	1974	15.77mt	1996
Armada Complex	British Gas E&P	Hawkins 1980, Drake/Fleming 1982	34.00bcm (gas)	1997
Birch	Lasmo	1985	4.04mt (oil)	1995
			2.19mt (gas)	
			0.36mt (natural gas liquids)	
Blenheim	Acro	1990	3.03mt	1995
Brittannia	Brittannia Operator Ltd	1975	72.2bcm (gas)	1998
Captain	Texaco	1977	44.5mt	1996
Carnoustie	Amoco	1980	0.1mt	1995
Douglas	Hamilton	1990	11.6mt	1995
Fife	Amerada Hess	1991	4.56mt	1995
Foinaven	BP	1990	26.67mt	1996
Guillemot A	Shell	1979	6.2mt	1996
Harding	BP	1988	26.5mt	1996
Joanne	Phillips	1981	13.00bcm (gas)	1996
			4.5mt (hydrocarbon liquid)	
Judy	Phillips	1985	8.9bcm (gas)	1996
			3.5mt (hydrocarbon liquid)	
Pelican	Shell	1975	7.5mt	1996
Teal	Shell	1989	4.8mt	1996
Teal South	Shell	1992	1.1mt	1998

Source: Department of Trade and Industry

(1) See footnote (1) to Table 5.20.
(2) bcm = million cubic metres

Table 5.20 Oil pollution incidents reported, marine zones polluted and extent of pollution, 1985-1994

	1985	1986	1987	1988	1989	1990	1991	1992	1993	1994
Incidents - total	**178**	**247**	**336**	**368**	**425**	**484**	**434**	**327**	**370**	**311**
West Scotland	11	13	18	19	15	30	25	32	33	45
Orkney/Shetland	26	33	21	30	26	26	40	19	39	31
East Scotland	50	46	43	50	77	75	120	93	106	79
Offshore North Sea[1]	91	165	254	269	307	353	249	183	192	156
Zones polluted										
Open sea[1]	97	170	264	285	327	372	264	196	234	179
Tidal river/estuary	7	8	2	3	6	19	21	22	14	17
Bay/nearshore	13	4	13	8	8	17	11	17	15	24
Beach/shore	9	15	18	17	19	17	22	14	32	24
Port	55	50	39	55	65	59	84	78	75	67
Other	..	-	-	-	-	-	-	-	-	-
Extent of pollution[2]										
More than 1.6km - shore	5	5	5	5	11	7	8	4	9	5
- sea	5	-	3	3	9	6	13	11	9	3
1.6km or less - shore	12	35	18	13	17	12	17	15	34	19
- sea	62	15	46	60	86	107	137	111	89	100
Not reported	..	..	..	..	..	..	125	92	37	28

Source: ACOPS

(1) Includes all offshore North Sea spills.
(2) Information not available on offshore North Sea spills.

Table 5.21 Source and amount of oil spilled, 1984-1993

	1984	1985	1986	1987	1988	1989	1990	1991	1992	1993
Source										
Coastal tanker/VLCC/ULCC[1]	25	20	22	11	16	16	12	18	10	13
Non tanker ship	21	23	20	19	28	38	32	66	52	71
Wreck/offshore oil installation[2]	66	91	161	257	253	293	346	238	179	183
Oil pipeline/terminal/jetty	9	12	6	6	6	9	7	12	8	3
Industrial premises/sewers/outfalls/other	9	10	10	15	11	14	25	39	25	30
Not known	29	22	28	28	54	55	62	61	53	70
Amount spilled										
Excluding offshore North Sea										
455 litres or less	34	40	31	20	30	31	29	50	46	49
456 litres to 1 tonne	5	5	-	5	5	5	7	6	4	9
More than 1 tonne to 50 tonnes	14	10	10	6	8	13	13	18	7	11
More than 50 tonnes	-	4	-	1	-	-	1	-	3	2
Not known	40	28	41	50	56	69	81	125	84	107
Offshore North Sea spills										
455 litres or less	29	45	84	138	177	192	225	147	107	141
456 litres to 1 tonne	15	25	39	59	37	35	42	46	32	15
1 tonne to 50 tonnes	19	18	37	40	36	59	79	52	37	34
More than 50 tonnes	3	1	2	2	2	5	3	-	-	-
Not known	-	2	3	15	17	16	4	14	7	2

Source: ACOPS

(1) VLCC - very large crude carrier and ULCC - ultra large crude carrier.
(2) Includes all offshore North Sea installations.

Table 5.22 Causes of oil spills and operations undertaken, 1993[1]

Operation	1993
	Operation in Progress/Circumstances Spillage
Total	**179**
Loading cargo/ballast	10
Bunkering	17
Discharging cargo/ballast	5
Pumping bilges	9
Stranding/ground/wreck/collison	16
Cleaning tanks	3
Other	6
Not known	113
	Causes of Oil Spillages
Total	**207**
Human error	58
Equipment failure	43
Not known	106

Source: ACOPS

(1) The figures are frequencies for each of the categories shown and more than one entry may have been made for each case of pollution.

Table 5.23 Expenditure on clean up, 1991-1993[1]

Expenditure by reporting organisations	1991 West Scotland	1991 Orkney/ Shetland	1991 East Scotland	1992 West Scotland	1992 Orkney/ Shetland	1992 East Scotland	1993 West Scotland	1993 Orkney/ Shetland	1993 East Scotland
Man hours reported	220	250	1,830	-	-	390	70	10	1,500
Total expenditure (£)	2,200	99,300	49,500	300	-	31,700	2,000	671,800	13,900
- of which clean up	-	96,200	46,400	100	-	27,900	1,200	16,800	8,600
materials	100	500	1,100	-	-	-	-	-	800
other	2,100	2,600	2,000	200	-	3,800	800	655,000	4,500
Expenditure by others	-	600	5,000	-	-	-	-	-	15,100
Expenditure recovered from polluters	100	87,000	-	-	-	-	-	-	-

Source: ACOPS

(1) Expenditure information not available on offshore North Sea spills.

Map 5.11   Oil Spill Incidents 1993 (see table 5.22)

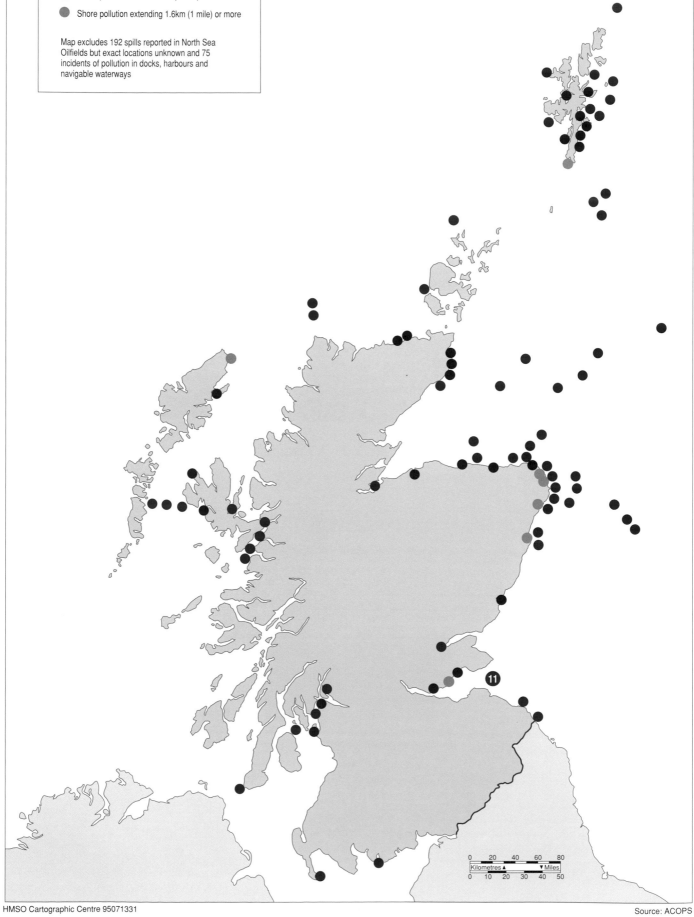

Pollution in estuaries and at sea

⑪ Multiple incidence of oil pollution

Shore pollution under 1.6km (1 mile)

Shore pollution extending 1.6km (1 mile) or more

Map excludes 192 spills reported in North Sea
Oilfields but exact locations unknown and 75
incidents of pollution in docks, harbours and
navigable waterways

Source: ACOPS

Chart 5.5   Oil Spill Incidents by Zone, 1994 [1]

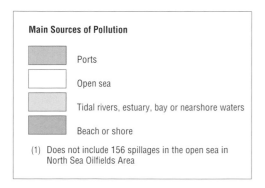

Main Sources of Pollution

Ports

Open sea

Tidal rivers, estuary, bay or nearshore waters

Beach or shore

(1) Does not include 156 spillages in the open sea in North Sea Oilfields Area

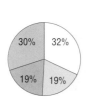

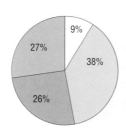

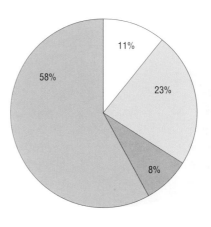

Orkney and Shetland
31 Incidents

West Scotland
45 Incidents

East Scotland
79 Incidents

Source: ACOPS

Chart 5.6   Oil Spill Incidents by Source, 1994 [1]

**Environmental Zones Polluted
(total reports for each enumeration area)**

Vessel source pollution (tankers, non-tanker vessels and disturbance of wrecks)

Other sources (including pipelines, terminals, jetties, industrial premises, sewers and outfalls)

Unknown or not reported

(1) Does not include 156 spillages in the open sea in North Sea Oilfields Area

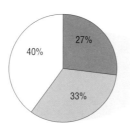

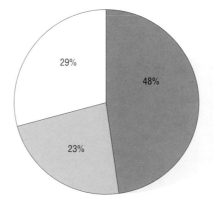

Orkney and Shetland
31 Incidents

West Scotland
45 Incidents

East Scotland
79 Incidents

Source: ACOPS

conservation

6 conservation

6.1   This section deals with statutory designations in terms of conservation. There is information on protected species, on fishing, and on the distribution selected mammals in Scotland. The cultural heritage is represented by scheduled ancient monuments, listed buildings, designated conservation areas, and a national record of historic gardens and designed landscapes.

DESIGNATED AND PROTECTED AREAS

6.2   Scottish Natural Heritage (SNH) have the responsibility of advising the Secretary of State and public agencies on policies for, and the management of, the natural heritage and countryside of Scotland. The aim of SNH is to secure the conservation and enhancement of the natural environment in a sustainable way, and to foster understanding and enjoyment of the countryside.

6.3   National Scenic Areas (NSAs) are areas of outstanding landscape value defined by SNH and designated by the Secretary of State (table 6.3). Country Parks are established by local authorities to provide facilities for outdoor activities, which may be grant aided by SNH (table 6.4). Regional Parks are large areas of countryside partly devoted to recreation, currently designated by Regional Councils with the support of SNH (table 6.5).

6.4   Green Belts are defined in local authority development plans to control development adjacent to large urban areas. The aim is to prevent urban sprawl and to safeguard the countryside around towns. There are currently 6 Green Belts designated in local authority plans (table 6.6).

6.5   Under the terms of the Wildlife and Countryside Act 1981, SNH designates Sites of Special Scientific Interest (SSSI) for reason of their flora, fauna, geological or physiographic interest, and specifies operations likely to damage that interest (tables 6.2, 6.9(a) and map 6.2). Tables 6.10(a)(b) and (c) show damage to SSSIs. The categories of damage are as follows:

Sites lost: damage which will result in the denotification of the whole SSSI.

Partial loss: damage which will result in the denotification of part of the SSSI.

Long-term damage: damage causing a lasting reduction in the special interest.

Short-term damage: damage from which the special interest could recover.

SNH are empowered by Section 15 of the Countryside Act 1968 to enter into agreements with the owners, leasees, and the occupiers of land designated as SSSIs to safeguard the nature conservation of the sites (table 6.11(a) and (b)).

6.6   Areas of national importance are declared as National Nature Reserves (NNR's by SNH (tables 6.2, 6.9(a) and map 6.2), and local authorities can establish Local Nature Reserves in consultation with SNH to protect areas of local interest (tables 6.2 and 6.9(b) and map 6.2). SNH are also responsible for marine nature conservation and have published a list of Marine Consultation Areas (tables 6.2 and 6.8) where consultation is required on developments affecting the marine environment.

6.7   Preferred Coastal Conservation Zones are designated coastal areas where there is a presumption against major development (table 6.1 and map 6.1)

6.8   Special Protection Areas (SPAs) are classified by the Secretary of State for Scotland to comply with international obligations under the European Community Wild Birds Directive which requires certain species of birds and their habitats to be protected. The Ramsar Convention requires wetlands of international importance to be classified to safeguard their wetland habitat and protect wildfowl. In the UK, SPAs and Ramsar sites have SSSI status, and development will be strictly controlled where it is likely to damage the bird or wetland interests. (table 6.2 and map 6.2). UNESCO World Heritage Convention requires areas of universal nature conservation, landscape or cultural importance to be designated as a world heritage site. St Kilda is the only existing site in Scotland; other sites are proposed for nomination, including the Cairngorms.

6.9   The Royal Society for the Protection of Birds (RSPB) the Scottish Wildlife Trust, The Wildfowl & Wetlands Trust, The Woodland Trust, The National Trust for Scotland and other non-governmental organisations, contribute to landscape and nature conservation by managing land owned, leased, or held by agreement (table 6.12). Many of their properties are also SSSIs.

6.10   Table 6.13 shows the annual membership of selected voluntary environmental organisations. The Royal Zoological Society of Scotland is an independent charity, promoting conservation of species, environmental education, scientific study and recreation.

THE SPECIAL GRANTS (ENVIRONMENTAL) PROGRAMME

6.12   The Special Grants (Environmental) Programme (table 6.16) was introduced in April 1987, and is designed to assist voluntary environmental organisations in improving their overall capability and effectiveness in carrying out either practical environmental conservation or improvement work, environmental education or training, co-ordination of voluntary environmental organisations or co-ordination or rural land use and environmental issues. The programme consists of 2 parts: (a) assistance for organisations carrying out strategic Government initiatives on the environment and (b) funding for projects which help to further Government environmental policy.

To be eligible for funding, organisations are required to operate in more than one local authority district; however exceptions are made for innovative projects in less populated Highland or Island areas.

6.13   Environmentally Sensitive Areas (ESAs) (tables 6.1, 6.7, and map 6.1) are areas of ecological and scenic value within which farmers are encouraged to adopt appropriate farming practices to conserve the natural beauty and nature conservation interest in the land, and to protect any historic or archaeological features. ESAs are designated by the Secretary of State for Scotland on the advice of SNH and the recommendation of the Scottish Office Agriculture, Environment and Fisheries Department (SOAEFD).

ENVIRONMENTAL ASSESSMENT

6.14   If a proposed development is deemed likely to have significant environmental effects, then an environmental assessment (EA) should be carried out. This is a process whereby information about the impact on the environment of a particular project is collected and assessed, before it is decided whether or not the project should be authorised. The information is presented in an Environmental Statement which is a publicly available document, prepared by the developer.

CULTURAL HERITAGE

6.15   Statutory responsibility for the protection of Scotland's built heritage - through the scheduling of monuments and the listing of buildings - lies with Historic Scotland, an executive agency of the Secretary of State. Historic Scotland's principal activities are to protect, conserve and promote the built heritage of Scotland. The agency's activities are funded by Central Government and income from commercial operations associated with presentation of the monuments.

6.16   Chart 6.3 details Historic Scotland's gross spend by activity, and table 6.19 shows income and expenditure. Table 6.20 details Historic Scotland's key performance targets. The Secretary of State sets key performance measures for the agency. Each measure is concerned with an important and measurable aspect of Historic Scotland's work, particularly those which have a substantial impact on its customers or which involve a significant investment of staff and other sources.

ANCIENT MONUMENTS

6.17   The 6008 scheduled monuments (map 6.3(b)) are those monuments recognised to be of national importance and protected against deliberate or accidental damage by being "scheduled" under the Ancient Monuments and Archaeological Areas Act 1979. The 330 ancient monuments in the care of the Secretary of State are shown on map 6.3(c).

A list of ancient monuments is published by Historic Scotland. The Secretary of State has to give consent for any works to be carried out which affect a scheduled monument or for the use of a metal detector. He also has to be consulted about development proposals which may affect the site of an ancient monument. Some monuments, scheduled and unscheduled, are the subject of management agreements and grants may be available to their owners. The Secretary of State also provides advice and guidance on how archaeological remains and discoveries should be protected and dealt with under the planning system.

PROTECTED BUILDINGS

6.18   Buildings are listed as being of special architectural or historic interest. Table 6.17 records the number of listed buildings by category. The categories are defined as follows:

Category A: Buildings of national or international importance, whether architectural or historic, or fine little altered examples of some particular period, style or building type.

Category B: Buildings of regional or more than local importance, or major examples of some particular period, style or building type which may have been altered.

Category C (statutory):   Buildings of local importance; lesser examples of any period, style or building type, as originally constructed or altered; and simple traditional buildings which group well with others in categories A and B or are part of a planned group such as an estate or industrial complex.

Listing protects against unauthorised works of alteration, extension or demolition, and ensures careful consideration of development or demolition proposals.

PROPERTIES IN CARE

6.19   Some 330 ancient monuments and historic buildings are in the care of the Secretary of State and open to the public. Historic Scotland are responsible for ensuring their sound conservation and maintenance and for encouraging members of the public to visit them.

CONSERVATION AREAS

6.20   Local authorities are required to designate areas, as distinct from buildings, as being of architectural or historic interest. Authorities also publish policies and proposals for the preservation and enhancement of conservation areas. The national importance of any conservation area is recognised by its classification as Outstanding by the Secretary of State. Table 6.14 provides details of the number of conservation areas and those classified as Outstanding.

GARDENS AND DESIGNED LANDSCAPES.

6.21   Gardens and designed landscapes provide an important resource for recreation and tourism. The inventory of Gardens and Designed Landscapes in Scotland, published in 1988, provides a systematically obtained record of 275 existing historic gardens and designed landscapes as a basis for research and policy formulation. Table 6.15 gives a breakdown on the number of Inventory sites by region. Work is now in hand to extend the number of recorded sites.

Planning authorities are required to consult the Secretary of State on any planning application which is likely to have an effect on an Inventory site.

6.22   The National Trust for Scotland is an independent charity which promotes the preservation of buildings and landscape and encourages public enjoyment of these through ownership and management of properties. (map 6.3(a) and table 6.18.)

SPECIES AT RISK AND PROTECTED SPECIES.

6.23 The International Union for the Conservation of Nature (IUCN) has defined three categories of threatened species which indicate the degree of threat.

Endangered species: those in danger of extinction and whose survival is unlikely if current circumstances persist.

Vulnerable species: those which are believed likely to become endangered if current circumstances persist.

Rare species: those with small world populations that are not at present endangered or vulnerable, but are at risk.

6.24   Scotland supports significant populations of some of the species on the EC Habitats and Species Directive Council (Council Directive 92/43/EEC) on the conservation of natural habitats and of wild fauna and flora, including notably, otter, freshwater pearl, mussel, bottle nosed dolphin, the marsh fritillary butterfly and the only known site in Scotland for the green shield moss. In addition, many scarce or threatened species are either endemic to Scotland, such as the Scottish primrose, the Scottish crossbill, (our only endemic bird) and the moss Pictus Scoticus, or are restricted to Scotland in the UK, such as the New Forest burnet moth, pygmy weed, and alpine sow-thistle. Some rare species, such as the blue heath, (a member of the heather family) which occurs in snow beds in Scottish Mountains, may be valuable indicators of, and be threatened by, climate change.

Many species of plants and animals are fully or partially (eg during the closed season) protected by Government legislation (table 6.22). Despite the legal protection given to species, extinctions still occur. The rare fish vendace were lost this century from their only two Scottish locations in Dumfriesshire and now only occur in two English lakes. A recent SNH funded survey has failed to locate the endangered tadpole shrimp at its only known locality in Scotland.

Grey and Common Seals

6.25   The Sea Mammal Research Unit (SMRU) of the Natural Environment Research Council (NERC) carries out annual surveys of the grey and common seal population to meet the requirements of the Conservation of Seals Act 1970 (table 6.23).

Red and Grey Squirrel Distribution

6.26   Maps 6.4(a) and (b) were prepared from information supplied by the Biological Records Centre, Environmental Information Centre, Institute of Terrestrial Ecology, Monks Wood.

Fox Distribution

6.27   Map 6.5 was also derived from data supplied by the Biological Records Centre. The number of foxes in many parts of Scotland has increased during the last 30 years, spreading to areas where they were previously absent such as the North East. Exact figures are difficult to obtain, but recent studies suggest foxes are probably at their scarcest in the highlands with a density of less than 1 per 10km, at somewhat greater densities in lowland agricultural areas, and most numerous in parts of suburban Edinburgh (around 3 adults per km^2) and Glasgow. Additional information can be found in the following papers:

A study of fox populations in Scotland from 1971 to 1976 (Journal of Applied Ecology (17) pages 7-19)

Distribution and density of fox breeding dens and the effects of management (Journal of Applied Ecology(23) pages 531-538.

6.28   Maps 6.6(a)-(d) show the distribution of red, roe, fallow and sika deer in Scotland. They are based on distribution data held by the Biological Records Centre from records supplied by the British Deer Society and the Mammal Society. The numbers of each species in Scotland according to figures from the Red Deer Commission are as follows:

300,000	red deer (including 30,000 in woodlands)
200,000	roe deer
10,000	sika deer
1,000 -2,000	fallow deer

BADGER DISTRIBUTION

6.29   Map 6.7(a) was also derived from data supplied by the Biological Records Centre. The badger has been recorded throughout mainland Scotland and the Isle of Arran, but not from the Inner or Outer Hebrides, Orkney or Shetland. It appears to be absent from most areas of high moorland and mountains. A recent review of badgers suggests that numbers have probably increased during the present century, almost certainly due to a reduction in persecution by gamekeepers. Although widespread in Scotland the numbers of individuals in social groups are sometimes smaller than in other parts of Great Britain. Additional information can be found in the following books and paper:

Changes in the sizes of groups and ranges of the European badger (Meles meles L.) in an area of Scotland (Journal of Animal Ecology (56) pages 351-364)

The history, distribution, status and habitat requirements of the badger in Britain, by P. Cresswell, S. Harris, and D. J. Jefferies, published by the Nature Conservancy Council, Peterborough (1990).

The social badger: ecology and behaviour of a group living carnivore (Meles, meles) by H Kruuk, published by Oxford University Press (1989).

COMMON FROG DISTRIBUTION

6.30   Map 6.7(b) was also derived from data supplied by the Biological Records Centre. The common frog has been recorded throughout mainland Scotland. It has been introduced to the Isle of Lewis, Shetland and Orkney, although the records from Orkney have not been received and therefore have not been mapped (see below for additional information on Orkney). Other apparent absences, at least from mainland Scotland, are probably the result of a lack of records rather than a real absence of frogs, except in the very highest mountainous areas.

Amphibia 1994 (Orkney Field Club Bulletin 1995, pages 55-56)

MERCURY CONCENTRATIONS IN FISH

6.31   Mercury is a trace metal of particular concern in aquatic monitoring due to the possibility of its incorporation in the aquatic food chain and its transfer to man via marine foodstuff. Fish exporters require a certificate containing a statement of the mercury content of their produce. A regular survey to monitor mercury concentration in fish was initiated in 1976. Until 1993, species of particular importance were sampled every 6 months (in spring and autumn). Changes in EC Legislation have resulted in a review of this monitoring strategy. A new scheme was initiated in 1993 which decreases the effort on mercury and examines additional metals including cadmium and lead. A report on the results is due in 1996. Areas sampled reflect the main sources of each species, but some flexibility is retained in obtaining samples as the availability of some species at each sampling area at specific times cannot be guaranteed. Further details of the programme are available in the SOAEFD report "A revised scheme for monitoring trace metals in Fish and Shellfish landed at Scottish Ports". The most recent data is summarised in (tables 6.24 and 6.25).

SALMON AND SEA TROUT CATCHES

6.32   Section 15 of the Salmon and Freshwater Fisheries Protection (Scotland) Act 1951 provides for the collection of returns from proprietors and occupiers of salmon fishings (table 6.26). The figures quoted are the reported catch: no allowance is made for non-returns or gaps in the roll of proprietors and occupiers. The weather, timing of salmon runs and the amount and quality of fishing effort can all affect the size of salmon catches. As these factors may vary from year to year a difference in catch does not necessarily indicate a difference in the abundance of the stock which provides the catch. Further information is available in the annual statistical bulletin: "Scottish Salmon and Trout Catches", published by SOAEFD.

FISH AND SHELLFISH FARMING

6.33   SOAEFD have statutory responsibility for fish and shellfish farms under the Diseases of Fish Acts of 1937 and 1983. The legislation requires all fish and shellfish farms to register with SOAEFD. Annual surveys of all registered shellfish, rainbow trout and salmon farming business are carried out by the Department, and the results published in their series of Annual Reports (tables 6.27 - 6.29). The Crown Estate are responsible for granting sea bed leases for marine fish and shellfish farms (table 6.30 and map 6.8)

FISH LANDINGS AND VESSELS

6.34.   Statistics on sea fish landings in Scotland (maps 6.9(a)-(d), tables 6.31 - 6.33) are collated by the 21 District Fishery Offices of SOAEFD Sea Fisheries Inspectorate. The data on weight and value are obtained from market sales notes completed at the first sale of the fish, additional information on fishing grounds, days at sea, hours fished, is obtained from the vessels' European Community Log Books. The various species of fish are grouped on three main categories; demersal (ie whitefish) pelagic (eg herring and mackerel) and shellfish. For pelagic species, the direct sales by UK vessels to foreign containers or factory vessels (klondykers) for immediate report are immediate export are included in the figures as landings.

6.35   Data on vessels (table 6.32) are obtained by fishing officers at the district fishery offices. All vessels actively engaged in commercial fishing and registered under the Merchant Shipping Act 1988, are recorded.

6.36   Many statutory rules and regulations govern fishing operations in the interests of the conservation of fish stocks and the safety of life at sea. Licences are required to catch certain species, and there are various regulations relating, amongst other things, to the fishing gear that may be used (eg minimum mesh sizes) hygiene standards, safety and the presentation and quantity of fish which may be landed. The European Commission sets annual Total Allowable Catches for species requiring protection, based on scientific assessments of the state of the stocks; these are allocated to member states (table 6.33).

6.37   The RSPB receives information on type of incidents and any resulting deaths concerning owls and birds of prey and have published details in their report "Death by Design" from which table 6.35 is derived. The Society also produces an annual report on Offences against Wild birds each October. This report details offences reported to the RSPB Investigations Section. In 1995 the Society also produced a report analysing bird of prey persecution in Scotland in 1994. SOAEFD also produces figures on known deaths of owls and birds of prey (table 6.36). This data is not directly comparable with that in table 6.35 because of differences in data collected and classification systems used. Table 6.34 shows incidents of persecution involving wild birds.

Map 6.1   Landscape Conservation, designated areas 1995

National Scenic Areas

○   Country Parks

▭   Regional Parks

Environmentally Sensitive Areas

Greenbelts

Preferred Coastal Conservation Zone

St Kilda

Kilometres ▲
0 10 20 30 40 50 60 70 80

▼ Miles
0   10   20   30   40   50

HMSO Cartographic Centre 95071331

Source: Rural Affairs Division, SOAEFD

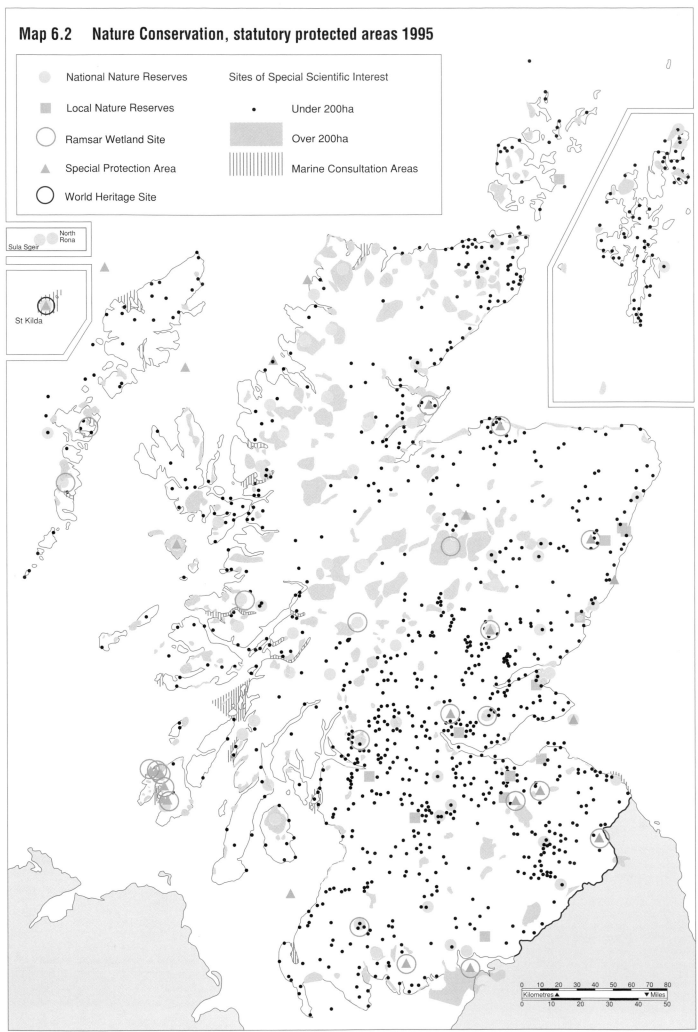

Map 6.2 Nature Conservation, statutory protected areas 1995

National Nature Reserves

Local Nature Reserves

Ramsar Wetland Site

Special Protection Area

World Heritage Site

Sites of Special Scientific Interest

Under 200ha

Over 200ha

Marine Consultation Areas

Sula Sgeir North Rona

St Kilda

Source: Scottish Natural Heritage

Table 6.1   Landscape conservation, designated areas, March 1995

Status	Number of sites	Area (hectares)
National scenic areas	40	1,001,800
Country parks	36	6,426
Regional parks	4	26,125
Environmentally sensitive areas	10	143,921
Green Belts	6	155,851
Preferred coastal conservation zones	26	7,546[2]

Source: Rural Affairs Division, SOAEFD

1) Including water area of lochs.
2) Length in kilometres.

Table 6.2   Nature conservation, statutory protected areas, March 1995

Status	Number of sites	Area (hectares)
National nature reserves	71	113,320
Local nature reserves	17	3,385
Sites of special scientific interest	1,381	865,582
Special protection area[1][2][4]	42	79,982
'Ramsar' wetland sites[1][3][4]	27	53,439
Marine Consultation Areas	29	111,797

Source: Rural Affairs Division, SOAEFD

1) In the UK all SPA and 'Ramsar' sites have SSSI status.
2) Designated under EC Birds Directive, see introductory notes, paragraph 6.8.
3) Designated under 'Ramsar' convention, see introductory notes, paragraph 6.8.
4) Includes 2 sites to be amalgamated into a larger site.

Chart 6.1a   National Nature Reserves, 1995

Main Habitats Represented on National Nature Reserves

Habitat type

- Coastlands
- Uplands
- Open waters
- Peatlands
- Woodlands
- Lowlands

Areas Declared as National Nature Reserves

Hectares

- Owned
- Leased
- Under NRA
- Under S.35(1)(c)

NRA = Nature Reserve Agreement
S.35(1)(c) = Land held and managed by an approved body and declared
under Section 35(1)(c) of the Wildlife & Countryside Act 1981

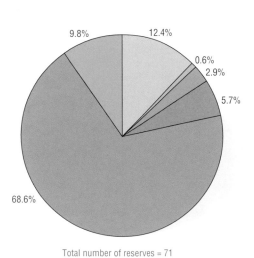

9.8%   12.4%
0.6%
2.9%
5.7%
68.6%

Total number of reserves = 71

0%
30%
67%   3%

Total area = 113,320 hectares

Source: Scottish Natural Heritage

141

Table 6.3   **National Scenic Areas by region, 1995**

Region	Number of sites	Area (hectares)
Scotland	**40**	**1,017,300**
Borders	2	15,900
Central	3	19,800
Dumfries and Galloway	3	19,800
Grampian	2	62,000
Highland	16	539,600
Strathclyde	9	137,000
Orkney	1	14,800
Shetland	7	15,600
Western Isles	3	115,600

Source: Rural Affairs Division, SOAEFD

Table 6.4   **Country Parks by region, 1995**

Region	Number of sites	Area (hectares)
Scotland	**36**	**6,426**
Central	3	335
Fife	3	489
Grampian	4	276
Lothian	7	1,568
Strathclyde	14	3,283
Tayside	5	475

Source: Rural Affairs Division, SOAEFD

Table 6.5   **Regional Parks by region, 1995**

Region	Location	Area (hectares)	Designated
Scotland		86,184	
Fife	Fife Regional Park	6,526	July 1986
Lothian	Pentland Hills	9,158	September 1986
Strathclyde/Central	Loch Lomond	44,200	March 1988
Strathclyde	Clyde Muirshiel	26,300	October 1990

Source: Rural Affairs Division, SOAEFD

Table 6.6   **Green Belts 1995**

Location	Area (hectares)
Total	156,224
Aberdeen	23,039
Ayr/Prestwick	3,024
Clackmannan	973
Falkirk/Grangemouth	3,388
Glasgow	109,933
Lothian	15,866

Source: SODD

Table 6.7 Environmentally Sensitive Areas, July 1993

Site		Date	Area(ha)
1. Breadalbane	revised	1992	181,207
2. Loch Lomond	revised	1992	49,687
3. Machair (Western Isles)	revised	1993	18,110
4. Stewarty	revised	1993	60,312
5. Central Borders (inc Whitlaw Eildon)	revised	1993	35,125
6. Central Uplands		1993	273,317
7. Western S Uplands		1993	220,500
8. Cairngorms Straths		1993	236,138
9. Shetland Islands		1993	146,478
10. Argyll Islands		1993	264,050
Total Designed Area		**1993**	**1,491,285**

Source: SOAEFD

Table 6.8 Marine Consultation Areas by region, 1994

Region	Number of sites	Area (hectares)
Scotland	**29**	**111,797**
Borders	1	4,838
Dumfries and Galloway	1	4,160
Highland	8	20,873
Strathclyde	8	53,936
Shetland	4	433
Western Isles	7	27,557

Source: Rural Affairs Division, SOAEFD

Table 6.9(a) National Nature Reserves and SSSI by region[1]

LA Region	SSSI No[2]	SSSI Area (ha)	NNR No[3]	NNR Area
Scotland	**1,382**	**865,617**	**71**	**113,320**
Borders	89	25,696	3	105
Central	85	20,806	1	1,687
Dumfries and Galloway	92	64,528	5	9,966
Fife	52	7,279	3	596
Grampian	111	57,357	6	16,389
Highland	328	465,963	28	68,195
Lothian	59	8,416	1	69
Strathclyde	263	89,321	11	2,959
Tayside	148	57,356	6	8,811
Orkney	31	20,404	0	0
Shetland	76	15,737	3	1,307
Western Isles	48	32,753	4	3,237

Source: Scottish Natural Heritage

1) All figures are as at 31 March 1995
2) Where sites lie in more than one Local Authority Region they are assigned to the region within which the greatest apportionment of area lies.
3) Where sites span more than one Local Authority Region they are noted under the region in which the associated SSSI is assigned in the Scottish Natural Heritage Coredata database.

Table 6.9(b) Local Nature Reserves

Area (ha)

Site Name	Local Authority	
Aberlady	East Lothian DC	582
Castle and Hightae Lochs	Annandale and Eskdale DC	109
Eden Estuary	North East Fife DC	891
Gladhouse Reservoir	Midlothian DC	201
Gartmorn Dam	Clackmannan DC	44
Straiton Pond	Edinburgh DC	5
Arnhall Moss	Gordon DC	10
Montrose Basin	Angus DC	1,024
Mull Head	Orkney DC	243
Perchy Pond	Motherwell DC	41
Den of Maidencraig	Aberdeen DC	15
Donmouth	Aberdeen DC	36
Paisley Moss	Renfrew DC	4
Drumbreck Marsh	Cumbernauld and Kilsyth DC	19
Corstorphine Hill	Edinburgh DC	67
Hermitage of Braid/Blackford Hill	Edinburgh DC	59
Scotstown Moor	Aberdeen DC	34

Source: Scottish Natural Heritage

Chart 6.1b   Main Habitats represented on SSSI's 1995

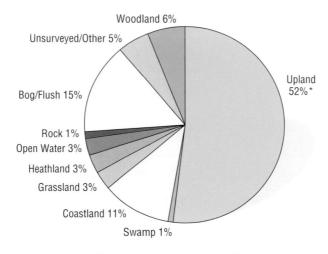

Woodland 6%

Unsurveyed/Other 5%

Upland
52% *

Bog/Flush 15%

Rock 1%
Open Water 3%

Heathland 3%

Grassland 3%

Coastland 11%

Swamp 1%

* Sites surveyed by the Upland Survey Team

Source: Scottish Natural Heritage

144

Table 6.10(a)   Damage to Sites of Special Scientific Interest, 1995[1]

Cause of Damage to SSSI[2][3][4][5][6]	Term of Damage	No of SSSI	Area (ha)	Length (m) if linear
Agricultural Activities	Long	1	150	0
	Short	4	41.2	0
Forestry Activities	Long	1	0.5	0
	Short	0	0.0	0
Statutory Undertakers	Long	0	0	0
	Short	1	0	1,200
Recreational	Long	1	0	500
	Short	1	0	3,000
Miscellaneous Activities	Long	1	2.5	0
(including pollution, unauthorised tipping and burning)	Short	13	541.4	1,050
TOTAL	Long	4	153	500
	Short	19	582.6	5,250

Source: Scottish Natural Heritage

1)   1 April 1994 to 31 March 1995.

2)   See introductory notes, paragraph 6.5 for definition of categories.

3)   On one SSI, cases of short term damage fell into more than one of the categories given above. The totals given at the foot of the table are therefore lower than the sum of the individual entries.

4)   Damage due to insufficient management is not recorded.

5)   No sites were either partly or completely lost as a result of damage sustained.

6)   Does not include cases of chronic damage (eg not caused by acidification and over-grazing)

Table 6.10(b)   Damage records by interest feature and severity 1986-1995 [1][2][3][4]

Feature	Term of Damage		Total
	Long Term	Short Term	
Woodland	17	60	77
Grassland	20	40	60
Heathland	7	31	38
Bog	12	32	44
Fen	6	19	25
Water	5	14	19
Coastlands	19	25	44
Geological	3	5	8
Species	6	8	14

Source: Scottish Natural Heritage

1)   Summation of cases reported by SNH and its predecessor bodies in their Annual Reports

2)   Damage due to insufficient management is not recorded.

3)   No sites were either partly or completely lost as a result of damage sustained.

4)   Does not include cases of chronic damage (eg not caused by acidification and over-grazing)

Table 6.10(c)   Damage records by category and severity of damage 1986-1995[1][3]

Category of Damage[2][4]	Short Term	Long Term	Totals
Construction	3	5	8
Roads & Tracks	8	6	14
Cable & Pipeline	7	2	9
Peat/Turf Removal	6	4	10
Extraction of minerals	1	7	8
Dumping	9	8	17
Regrading	8	5	13
Livestock	16	5	21
Arable	-	2	2
Pesticide/Herbicide	3	1	4
Burning	33	3	36
Vehicle Damage	23	2	25
Planting	3	6	9
Felling	10	1	11
Scrub control/mowing	5	-	5
Water Levels	17	7	24
Pollution	9	-	9
Misc Damage	12	3	15

Source: Scottish Natural Heritage

1)   Summation of cases reported by SNH and its predecessor bodies in their Annual Reports

2)   Damage due to insufficient management is not recorded.

3)   No sites were either partly or completely lost as a result of damage sustained.

4)   Does not include cases of chronic damage (eg not caused by acidification and over-grazing)

Table 6.11(a)   **Sites with Section 15 Management Agreements with SNH, 1995**[1][2]

Region	Number of Agreements	No of SSSIs with Agreements	Total Area (Hectares)
Scotland	**565**	**319**	**132,478**
Borders	14	13	5,524
Central	17	15	5,313
Dumfries and Galloway	49	32	5,560
Fife	15	12	658
Grampian	30	20	1,251
Highland	170	85	85,405
Lothian	10	9	328
Orkney Isles	41	13	4,089
Shetland Isles	37	15	3,842
Strathclyde	121	55	18,553
Tayside	47	41	1,644
Western Isles	14	9	310

Source: Scottish Natural Heritage

(1)   At 11 October. See paragraph 6.5 for definitions.
(2)   Figures may not sum to total due to rounding.

Table 6.11(b)   **Section 15 Management Agreements by habitat type, 1995**

Habitat Type	Total*
Unspecified/other	10
Arable/artificial	7
Bog/flush	171
Bracken/herb	2
Coastland	66
Grassland	84
Heathland	106
Marine	1
Open water	31
Rock	17
Swamp, fen and inundation communities	22
Woodland	131

Source: Scottish Natural Heritage

NB. As some agreements cover more than one habitat type, the total number of cases above exceeds the total number of management agreements presented in Table 6.11(a).

Chart 6.2   Annual trends in Section 15 management agreements numbers and areas 1995

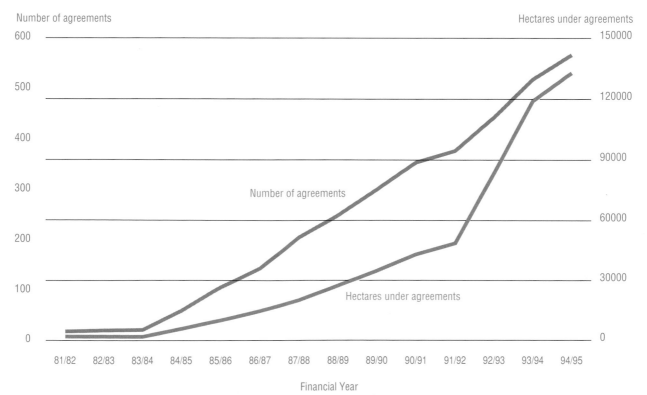

Source: Scottish Natural Heritage

Table 6.12   Nature conservation, non-statutory protected areas, 1994

Protecting body	Number of Sites			Area (hectares)		
	Owned	Leased	Administered under agreement	Owned	Leased	Administered under agreement
Forestry Commission[1]	23	-	-	163,964	-	-
Royal Society for the Protection of Birds	35	10	6	35,407	5,826	1,778
Scottish Wildlife Trust	50	10	42	4,629	6,995	7,044
The Wildfowl & Wetlands Trust[2]	1	1	-	222	338	-
The Woodland Trust[3]	61	1	16	1,735	18	28
The National Trust for Scotland	51	-	-	75,000	-	-

Source: Protecting body in table

[1] Forest nature reserves and forest parks. Borders park extends into England. Forest parks are shown on map 2.5(a), they are designated primarily to recreational purposes and are not officially classed as "protected areas" in their entirety.
[2] Figures for one site only which is split between 2 categories.
[3] 309 sites covering 332 hectares are administered under agreement for the UK as a whole but no figures for Scotland only are available.

Table 6.13   Membership of selected voluntary environmental organisations, 1988-1993

Region	1988	1989	1990	1991	1992	1993
The National Trust for Scotland	179,000	197,000	218,000	234,500	237,000	235,000
Royal Society for the Protection of Birds	35,000	50,000	55,000	52,200	55,500	63,000
Royal Zoological Society of Scotland	11,015	11,649	11,873	12,485	12,801	13,158
Scottish Wildlife Trust	9,796	9,876	10,913	10,411	10,651	11,200

Source: Organisation in table

Table 6.14   Conservation Areas 1994

Region/Islands Area	Number of Designated Conservation Areas	of which those classified Outstanding
Scotland	**581**	**215**
Borders	40	12
Central	52	10
Dumfries and Galloway	37	14
Fife	47	21
Grampian	50	20
Highland	28	11
Lothian	84	35
Strathclyde	167	60
Tayside	65	26
Orkney	6	3
Shetland	3	1
Western Isles	2	2

Source: Historic Scotland

Table 6.15   Historic Gardens and Designed Landscapes, 1993

Region/Islands Area	Inventory sites
Scotland	**275**
Borders	30
Central	13
Dumfries and Galloway	20
Fife	15
Grampian	34
Highland	23
Lothian	44
Strathclyde	49
Tayside	46
Orkney	1
Shetland	-
Western Isles	-

Source: Historic Scotland

Table 6.16   Awards made under Special Grants (Environmental) Programme, 1990/91-1994/95   £ thousand

Organisation	1990/91	1991/92	Grant allocated 1992/93	1993/94	1994/95
Total	**200.0**	**274.0**	**320.0**	**334.0**	**400.0**
Age Concern Orkney	-	-	3.3	-	-
Association for the Protection of Rural Scotland	2.5	2.2	2.0	2.0	6.0
Association of Community Technical Aid Centres	-	-	-	-	-
Association of Deer Management Groups	-	-	-	-	6.0
Ayrshire Architectural Heritage Trust	-	-	4.5	-	-
Biological Recording in Scotland Campaign	-	-	-	-	7.0
Buchan Countryside Group	2.5	2.2	2.0	-	4.0
Central Scotland Countryside Trust	12.0	-	-	-	-
Central Scotland Woodlands	-	-	-	5.0	-
Centre for Environmental Interpretation	-	-	4.0	5.7	-
Centre for Human Ecology	4.0	5.0	6.5	7.0	-
Community Service Volunteers	7.5	7.0	6.5	6.0	24.1
Council for Scottish Archaeology	8.0	15.0	16.5	17.0	16.0
Easter Ross Rights of Way Society	-	-	-	-	1.1
Environment Centre	6.0	7.0	4.5	-	-
Friends of the Earth	-	14.0	17.0	10.0	-
Garden History Society	-	-	4.5	4.5	4.0
Habitat Scotland	-	-	3.0	3.0	4.0
Heartland Radio Association	-	1.5	2.0	1.8	2.0
Heritage Education Trust	-	-	1.5	1.5	1.5
Heather Trust	-	-	1.5	6.0	9.0
Heatwise	-	-	-	-	6.0
Highland Forum	10.0	9.0	11.0	12.0	18.0
HT Scotland	-	-	-	-	2.4
John Muir Trust	5.0	4.5	4.0	2.0	-
Keep Scotland Beautiful	-	1.5	-	-	-
Landwise Glasgow	-	-	-	-	5.0
Locus Breadalbane	2.0	1.8	2.5	1.8	-
Lothian and Edinburgh Environmental Partnership	-	3.0	3.5	3.0	4.9
National Society for Clean Air	-	3.9	3.5	3.0	4.4
Planning Aid for Scotland	-	-	-	8.0	10.0
Reclaimers (Tayside)	-	-	1.0	-	-
Reforesting Scotland	-	-	-	-	7.0
Royal Society for the Protection of Birds	11.0	10.0	9.0	15.6	20.0
Royal Zoological Society of Scotland	4.0	3.5	3.0	-	-
Rural Forum	-	15.0	14.0	13.0	16.0
Scottish Allotments & Garden Society	-	-	-	0.5	-
Scottish Association of Agriculture	-	3.0	-	5.9	7
Scottish Community Education Council	-	-	-	1.5	-
Scottish Conservation Projects Trust	35.0	27.8	25.0	40.0	42.0
Scottish Ecological Design Association	4.0	2.0	1.9	1.4	1.2
Scottish Ecological Consultants	4.0	2.0	2.0	-	-
Scottish Environmental Education Council	14.0	27.0	33.0	37.0	40.0
Scottish Environmental Forum	-	-	3.0	6.0	8.0
Scottish Field Studies Association	8.0	7.5	3.0	-	-
Scottish Field School of Archaeology	1.5	-	3.0	-	-
Scottish Historic Buildings Trust	11.0	13.0	11.7	11.7	11.7
Scottish Native Woodlands Campaign	6.0	6.0	9.5	8.5	8.0
Scottish Rights of Way Society	2.5	5.0	7.0	5.0	7.0
Scottish Scenic Trust	2.0	2.0	1.8	1.8	1.5
Scottish Wildlife and Countryside Link	10.0	9.5	9.0	10.0	12.0
Scottish Wildlife Trust	25.0	28.0	28.0	36.1	33.5
Shetland Amenity Trust	-	-	33.2	-	-
Skye Forum	-	-	3.7	5.0	-
Slide Workshop Scotland	-	-	-	-	2.0
Strathclyde Historic Buildings Trust	2.5	7.0	6.3	-	-
Sustrans	-	5.0	15.0	13.5	7.5
Tay Ringing Group	-	-	-	4.0	-
Tayside Scrap Store Project	-	-	-	1.4	1.5
Touchstone	-	4.7	7.0	2.0	2.0
Tree Wise	-	-	-	-	7.0
Uist and Barra Amenity Group	-	2.0	-	-	-
Ventura Scotland	-	2.2	2.0	4.0	3.8
Water of Leith Trust	6.0	5.0	10.0	5.8	6.0
West Galloway Fisheries Trust	-	1.0	1.4	2.4	1.5
Wise Group - Treewise	-	-	-	6.0	5.0
Woodland Trust	-	-	-	-	6.0
World Wide Fund for Nature	-	-	-	-	5.0
Youth Clubs Scotland	-	-	-	-	10.0

Source: Rural Affairs Division, SOAEFD

Figures may not sum to total due to rounding.

Table 6.17   Protection of buildings and archaeological sites, 1994

Species	Listed Buildings[1] As at 31 March 1995			
	Category A	Category B	Category C(S)[2]	Total
Scotland	**3,098**	**25,199**	**13,135**	**41,513**
Borders	149	1,028	730	1,907
Central	107	1,022	741	1,870
Dumfries and Galloway	223	1,843	1,382	3,448
Fife	174	3,159	949	4,282
Grampian	365	3,415	2,610	6,390
Highland	174	1,599	1,110	2,883
Lothian	823	4,088	1,473	6,465
Strathclyde	728	4,840	2,165	7,733
Tayside	316	3,708	1,764	5,788
Orkney	16	264	64	344
Shetland	8	79	63	150
Western Isles	5	154	84	253

Source: Historic Scotland

[1] For definition of categories A, B and C(S) see introductory notes, paragraph 6.18.

[2] S = Statutory. A small number of non-statutory not included; these will be considered for statutory listing during the current re-survey of lists.

Table 6.18   Features of properties owned by the National Trust for Scotland, 1995[1]

Total number of properties	Number of properties with				
	Interesting building	Garden	Countryside	Viewpoints	Walks and trails
113	65	30	60	45	48

Source: National Trust for Scotland

[1] Several features may be available at any single property.

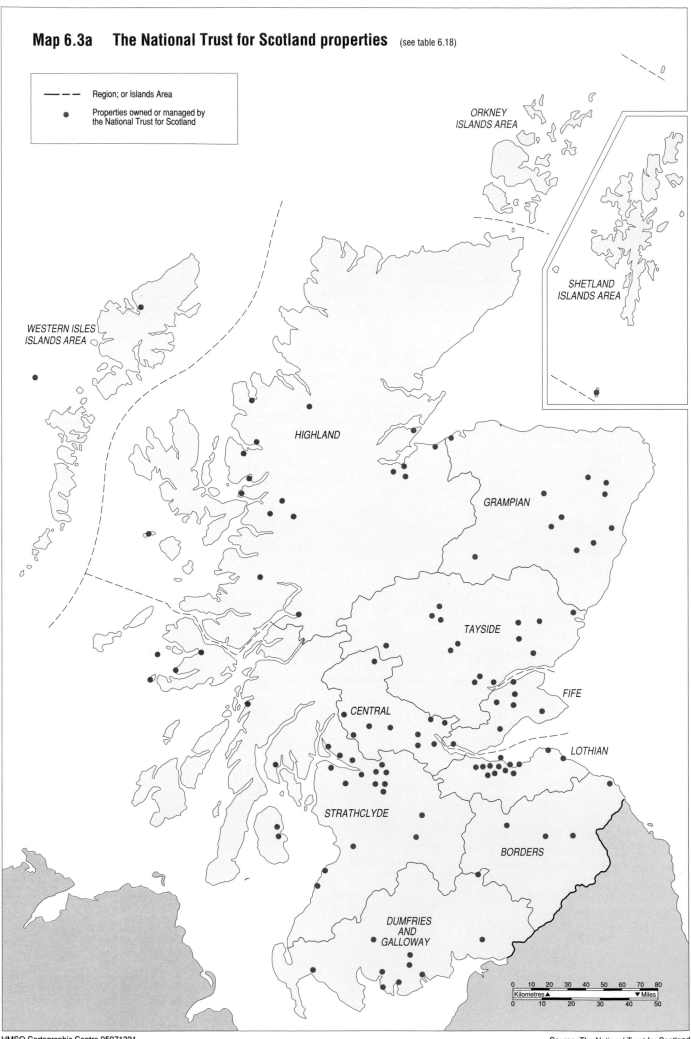

Map 6.3a The National Trust for Scotland properties (see table 6.18)

Region; or Islands Area

Properties owned or managed by
the National Trust for Scotland

ORKNEY
ISLANDS AREA

SHETLAND
ISLANDS AREA

WESTERN ISLES
ISLANDS AREA

HIGHLAND

GRAMPIAN

TAYSIDE

FIFE

CENTRAL

LOTHIAN

STRATHCLYDE

BORDERS

DUMFRIES
AND
GALLOWAY

Kilometres ▲
0 10 20 30 40 50 60 70 80

▼ Miles
0 10 20 30 40 50

Source: The National Trust for Scotland

Historic Scotland: Operating Account for the year ending 31 March 1995

	1993-94 £000s	1994-95 £000s
Income		
Income from Properties in Care	6,731	7,455
Other Income	152	235
Sub Total	**6,883**	**7,690**
Loss on Sale of Fixed Asset	-2	-25
Total	**6,881**	**7,665**
Expenditure		
Cost of Goods Sold	1,049	1,103
Grants	11,900	11,323
Archaeology	1,587	1,671
Employment Costs	12,074	12,273
Operational Activities	8,894	9,225
Other Costs	4,335	4,108
Depreciation	556	964
Total	**40,395**	**40,667**
Operating Deficit	**33,514**	**33,002**
Interest on Capital	-404	-437
Net Operating Deficit	**33,918**	**33,439**

Source: Historic Scotland

Map 6.3b   Scheduled monuments

Prehistoric Sites
Roman Sites
Post Roman Sites
Industrial Sites

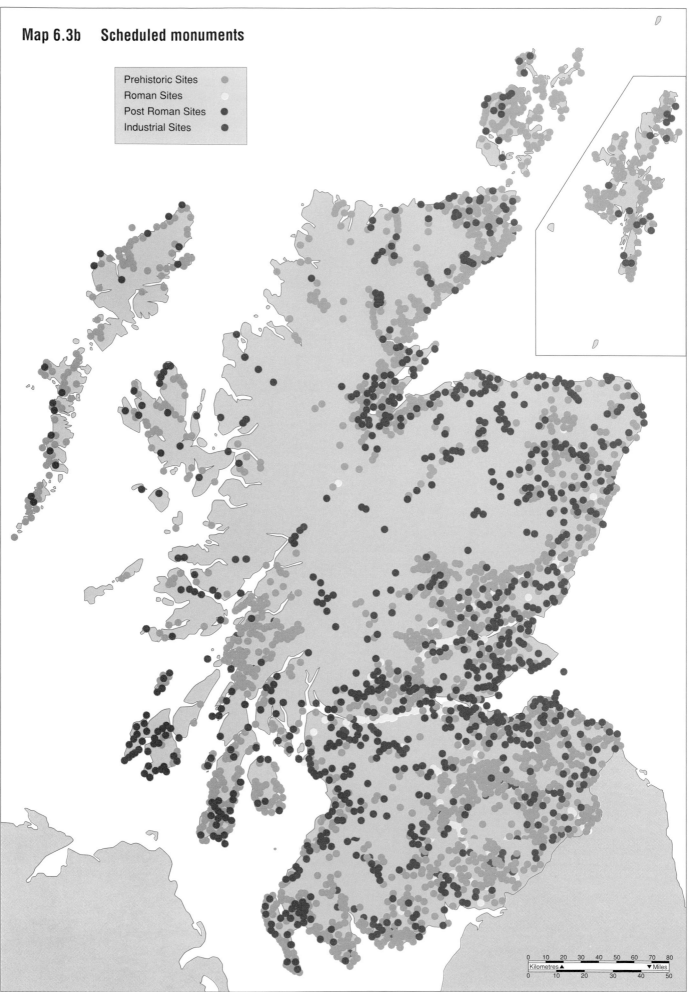

Kilometres ▲
0 10 20 30 40 50 60 70 80

▼ Miles
0   10   20   30   40   50

Source: Historic Scotland

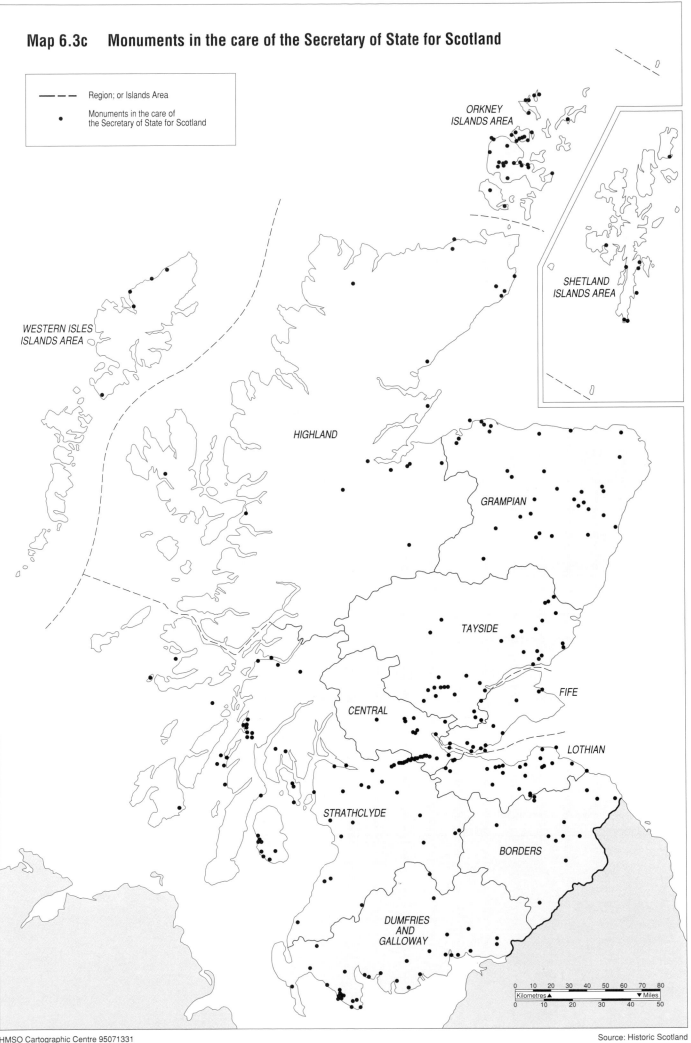

Map 6.3c   Monuments in the care of the Secretary of State for Scotland

- — - — Region; or Islands Area

• Monuments in the care of
the Secretary of State for Scotland

ORKNEY
ISLANDS AREA

SHETLAND
ISLANDS AREA

WESTERN ISLES
ISLANDS AREA

HIGHLAND

GRAMPIAN

TAYSIDE

FIFE

CENTRAL

LOTHIAN

STRATHCLYDE

BORDERS

DUMFRIES
AND
GALLOWAY

0 10 20 30 40 50 60 70 80
Kilometres ▲
▼ Miles
0   10   20   30   40   50

Source: Historic Scotland

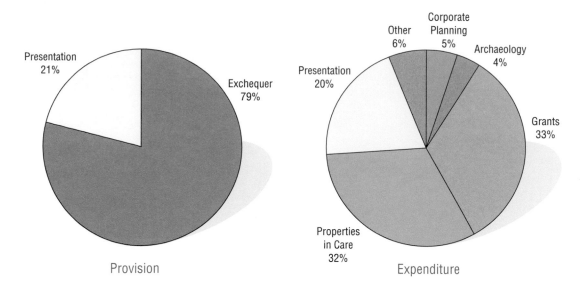

Source: Historic Scotland

Table 6.20   **Historic Scotland: Key Performance Targets, 1993-94 and 1994-95**

	1993-94 Target	1993-94 Achieved	1994-95 Target	1994-95 Achieved
Protecting Scotland's built heritage:				
Monuments scheduled, (includes rescheduled or descheduled)	340	395	350	351
Listed building survey units	150	150	150	151
Historic building repair grants awarded	135	149	137	140
Conservation of monuments in care	reduce maintenance backlog	achieved	reduce maintenance backlog	achieved
Promoting and Presenting Built Heritage:				
Visitors to monuments in care (million)	2.4	2.4	2.4	2.3
Total income (£ million)	£7.5	£8.0	£7.9	£8.8
Agency Management:				
Value for money savings on maintenance of monuments in care (per cent)	3.5	4.2	3.5	4.5

Source: Historic Scotland

Table 6.21   Environmental statements sent to the Secretary of State under planning legislation - 30 September 1995

Development Project	Number	Totals
Schedule 1[1]		
Radioactive Waste Disposal	3	
Integrated Chemical Installation	3	
Road/Rail/Airport	3	
Trading Port/Inland Waterway	1	
Special Waste Treatment	5	
Special Waste Landfill	7	(16)
Total Schedule 1		**22**
Schedule 2[2]		
Agriculture		
Poultry Rearing	3	
Land Reclamation	1	(4)
Extractive Industry		
Unclassified	1	
Extracting Peat	3	
Extracting Minerals (non metaliferous or energy producing)	34	
Extracting coal or lignite	15	
Extracting Natural Gas	2	
Extracting Ores	1	
Open-cast minerals (non metaliferous or energy producing)	3	(59)
Energy Industry		
Unclassified	2	
Production of electricity	2	
Installation for carrying gas steam or hot water	1	
Industrial Briquetting of Coal and Lignite	1	
Wind Farms	16	(22)
Food Industry		
Slaughter of animals	1	(1)
Textile, Leather, Wood and Paper Industries		
Manufacture of pulp paper and board	2	(2)
Rubber Industry		
Elastomer manufacture/treatment	1	(1)
Infrastructure Projects		
Industrial estate	12	
Urban development project	13	
Ski lift or cable car	4	
Road harbour aerodrome	4	
Dam or other installation	1	
A Tramway or railway for passenger transport	4	
Oil or gas pipeline	2	
Yacht Marina	4	(44)
Other Projects		
Holiday village/hotel complex	14	
Racing or test track	1	
Disposal of controlled waste	26	
Waste water treatment plant	6	
Depositing sludge	1	(48)
Total Schedule 2		**181**
Schedule 1 and 2 Total		**203**

Source: Planning Services Division, SODD

(1)   Environmental assessment is mandatory.
(2)   Environmental assessment required if the project is likely to have significant environmental effects
( )   Sub-totals

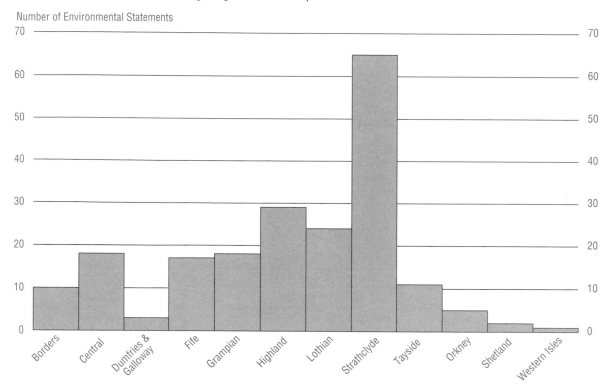

Chart 6.3b   Environmental Statements sent to the Secretary of State
              Under Planning Legislation - September 1995

Number of Environmental Statements

Source: Planning Services, SODD

Table 6.22   **Species at risk and protected species, 1994** [1]

Species group	Total number of known species	Number endangered	Number vulnerable	Number rare	Number fully protected	Number partially protected
Vascular plants	1,560	7	19	54	26	-
Lower Plants	2,367[2]	-	-	-	34	-
Freshwater fish	42[3]	1	2	2	3[3]	1
Amphibians	6	-	2	-	2	4
Reptiles	3[4]	-	-	-	-	-
Birds	200	4	9	36	200	-
Mammals breeding on land	40	1	6	-	9	13
Invertebrates	30,000[5]	66[6]	78	184	5	9

Source: Scottish Natural Heritage

(1)   See introductory notes, paragraph 6.22 for definitions of risk categories.
(2)   Data includes only bryophytes (mosses and liverworts), Lichens and charophytes (algae).
(3)   Figures include one extinct and all introduced species.
(4)   Excludes 5 species of marine turtles recorded in British water.
(5)   Figures based on UK distribution.
(6)   Figures exclude 132 species which are not clearly defined.

Table 6.23   **Estimated population of grey and common seals, 1993**

Grey seals		Common seals	
Area	**Estimated Population**	**Area**	**Estimated Population**
Scotland	**105,500**	**Scotland**	**26,447**
Inner Hebrides	10,800	East coast Scotland	1,730
Isle of May	5,100	NE, N & W Coast Scotland and Inner Hebrides	8,331
Mainland Scotland and South Ronaldsay[1]	3,900	Orkney	7,873
Orkney	38,700	Outer Hebrides	2,278
Outer Hebrides	43,600	Shetland	6,227
Shetland[1]	3,400	Dumfries & Galloway	8

Source: NERC: Sea Mammal Research Unit

(1)   Estimates taken from surveys in previous years.

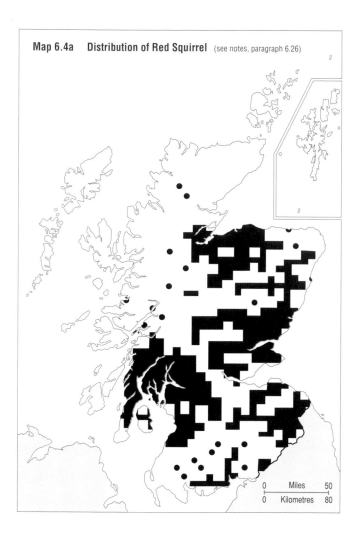

Map 6.4a Distribution of Red Squirrel (see notes, paragraph 6.26)

| Miles | 0 | 50 |
| Kilometres | 0 | 80 |

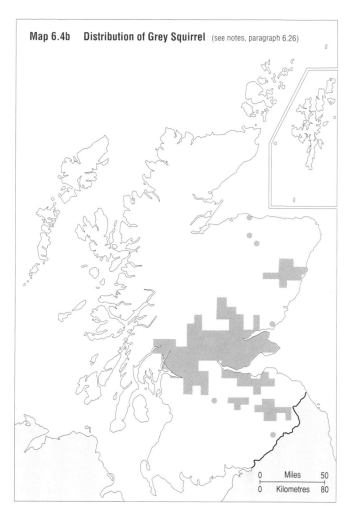

Map 6.4b Distribution of Grey Squirrel (see notes, paragraph 6.26)

| Miles | 0 | 50 |
| Kilometres | 0 | 80 |

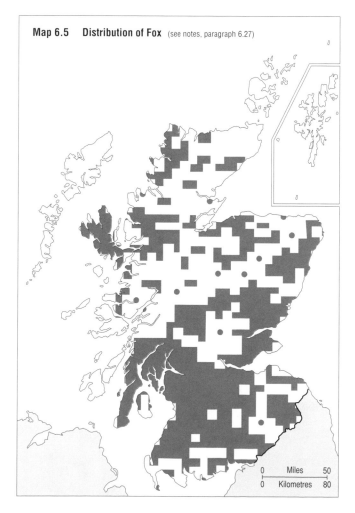

Map 6.5 Distribution of Fox (see notes, paragraph 6.27)

| Miles | 0 | 50 |
| Kilometres | 0 | 80 |

HMSO Cartographic Centre 95071331

Source: Biological Records Centre, ITE

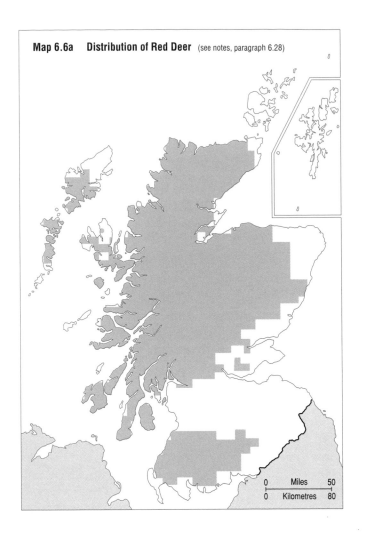

Map 6.6a **Distribution of Red Deer** (see notes, paragraph 6.28)

Miles 0 — 50
Kilometres 0 — 80

Map 6.6b **Distribution of Roe Deer** (see notes, paragraph 6.28)

Miles 0 — 50
Kilometres 0 — 80

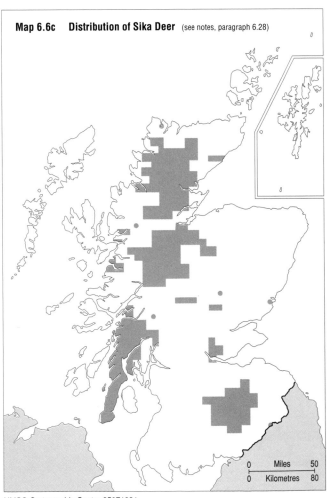

Map 6.6c **Distribution of Sika Deer** (see notes, paragraph 6.28)

Miles 0 — 50
Kilometres 0 — 80

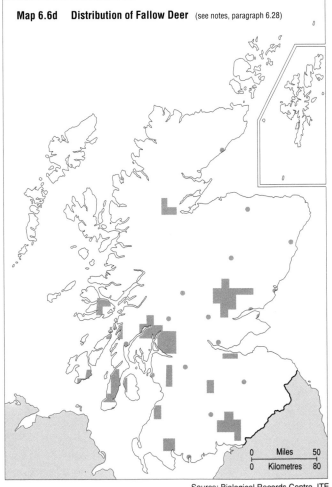

Map 6.6d **Distribution of Fallow Deer** (see notes, paragraph 6.28)

Miles 0 — 50
Kilometres 0 — 80

HMSO Cartographic Centre 95071331

Source: Biological Records Centre, ITE

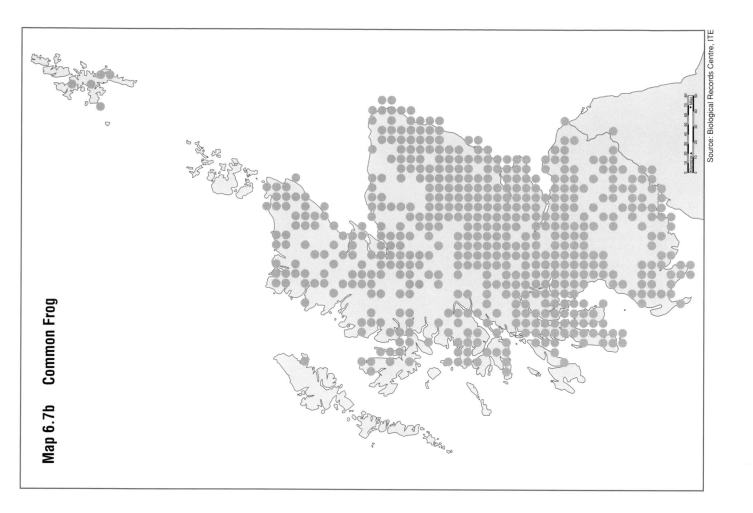

Map 6.7b   Common Frog

Source: Biological Records Centre, ITE

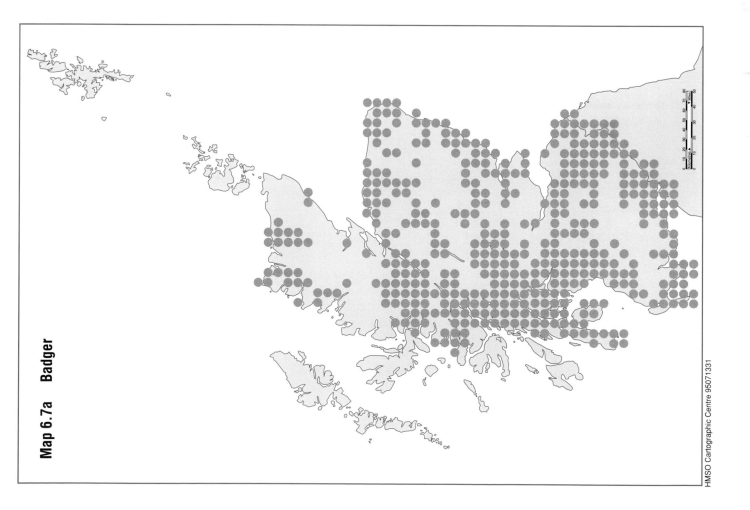

Map 6.7a   Badger

HMSO Cartographic Centre 95071331

Table 6.24   **Mercury concentrations in selected species of fish, 1989-1993**[1]   mg/kg wet weight

Type of Fish		1989	1990	1991	1992	1993
Angler	number sampled	14	15	24	19	32
	range of concentration	0.02-0.12	0.02-0.07	0.005-0.07	0.02-0.12	0.04-0.24
	mean concentration	0.07	0.05	0.07	0.06	0.10
Nephrops (large)	number sampled	3	2	6	4	2
	range of concentration	0.06-0.08	0.05-0.08	0.07-0.28	0.05-0.09	0.03-0.15
	mean concentration	0.07	0.07	0.14	0.06	0.08
Whiting	number sampled	10	9	10	15	20
	range of concentration	0.03-0.09	0.03-0.09	0.04-0.08	0.02-0.10	0.03-0.06
	mean concentration	0.06	0.06	0.06	0.05	0.04

Source: SOAEFD

(1)   Figures taken from the Autumn survey.

Table 6.25   **Mercury concentrations in fish, 1993**   mg/kg wet weight

Species	Range of concentration	Mean concentration
Demersal		
Angler (tails)	0.04-0.24	0.10
Haddock	<0.01-0.09	0.04
Pelagic		
Herring	<0.01-0.17	0.06
Kipper	<0.01-0.03	0.03
Whiting	0.03-0.06	0.04
Shellfish		
Nephrops	0.03-0.15	0.08
Squid	<0.01-0.03	0.02

Source: SOAEFD

Table 6.26   **Scottish salmon and sea trout catches, 1992 and 1993**[1]

Method of Catching	Salmon and grilse				Sea trout			
	number (thousand)		weight (tonnes)		number (thousand)		weight (tonnes)	
	1992	1993	1992	1993	1992	1993	1992	1993
Total								
Road and line	82.9	79.5	293.9	283.2	34.3	33.5	34.5	31.9
Net and coble	44.9	33.0	140.4	108.0	19.9	19.7	26.5	24.5
Fixed engine	56.7	53.8	165.2	155.4	10.3	6.3	11.1	6.7

Source: SOAEFD

(1)   Figures may not sum to total due to rounding.

Table 6.27   Farmed Shellfish Production 1991-1993

	1991				1992				1993			
	Mussels (Tonnes)	Oysters (100s)	Scallops (100s)	Queens (100s)	Mussels (Tonnes)	Oysters (100s)	Scallops (100s)	Queens (100s)	Mussels (Tonnes)	Oysters (100s)	Scallops (100s)	Queens (100s)
Scotland	**1,052.1**	**58,118**	**20,592**	**18,413**	**971.0**	**41,729**	**15,343**	**26,653**	**838.7**	**47,690**	**8,120**	**34,080**
Highland	238.9	1,984	19,734	6,396	295.0	2,887	10,235	15,402	291.6	6,470	5,070	27,910
Strathclyde	740.8	45,543	435	11,200	560.1	33,970	4,527	10,505	337.7	20,520	2,420	6,050
Orkney	22.4	9,656	423	815	45.0	2,965	388	743	50.0	19,330	500	110
Shetland	9.4	-	-	-	10.8	-	-	-	1.9	-	-	-
Western Isles	40.6	-	-	2	60.1	80	1	3	157.5	460	-	-
Dumfries and Galloway	-	925	-	-	-	1,827	192	-	90.0	-	130	-
Lothian	-	10	-	-	-	-	-	-	-	-	-	-

Source: SOAEFD

Table 6.28   Farmed Salmon Production 1991-1993   tonnes

	1991				1992				1993			
Region	Annual Salmon Production	Grilse	Pre Salmon	Salmon	Annual Salmon Production	Grilse	Pre-Salmon	Salmon	Annual Salmon Production	Grilse	Pre-Salmon	Salmon
Scotland	**40,593.0**	**7,449.2**	**13,577.1**	**19,567.1**	**36,101.0**	**6,723.3**	**14,649.7**	**14,728.0**	**48,691**	**12,740**	**20,077**	**15,875**
Highland	15,022.7	4,007.7	4,000.0	7,015.0	13,980.1	3,351.9	5,790.8	4,837.4	20,279	7,177	7,303	5,800
Orkney	1,329.1	118.1	407.1	803.9	1,046.2	163.4	412.2	470.6	1,245	212	428	605
Shetland	10,614.0	826.2	4,321.8	5,466.0	10,678.9	851.2	4,635.7	5,192.0	11,659	1,246	6,013	4,400
Strathclyde	8,004.8	1,549.6	2,447.3	4,007.9	6,458.3	1,154.3	2,108.0	3,196.0	8,675	2,107	3,366	3,202
Western Isles	5,622.4	947.6	2,400.8	2,274.0	3,937.5	1,202.5	1,703.0	1,.032.0	6,834	1,998	2,968	1,868

Source: SOAEFD

Table 6.29   Farmed Rainbow Trout Production 1991-1993   tonnes

	1991		1992		1993	
Region	Table[1]	Re-Stocking	Table[1]	Re-Stocking	Table	Re-Stocking
Scotland	**2,908.9**	**425.3**	**3,455.0**	**708.0**	**3,516**	**506**
Border	294.0	6.0	339.0	26.0	338	8
Central and Fife	551.6	96.0	595.0	101.0	627	84
Dumfries and Galloway	784.6	146.5	855.0	114.0	849	124
Grampian	11.4	14.0	17.0	26.0	18	22
Highland	379.9	20.8	577.0	230.0	268	34
Lothian	32.0	56.0	-	54.0	11	45
Strathclyde	654.5	63.0	646.0	90.0	1,024	124
Tayside	200.9	23.0	426.0	67.0	381	65
Western Isles	-	-	-	-	-	-

Source: SOAEFD

1)   Fish reared for the table market.

Table 6.30   Seabed Leases for fish farming in Scotland, at April 1995

Areas	Formal Leases Issues			% By Areas
	Salmon Farming	Shellfish Farming	Total Leases	
Lochaber	20	27	47	9
Skye	22	38	60	12
Ross-shire	27	40	67	13
Sutherland	10	16	26	5
Total Highland	**79**	**121**	**200**	**39**
Argyll	46	78	124	24
South West	2	2	4	1
Western Isles	55	29	84	17
Orkney	18	7	25	5
Shetland	65	8	73	14
Total Scotland	**265**	**245**	**510**	**100**

Source: Crown Estate Office

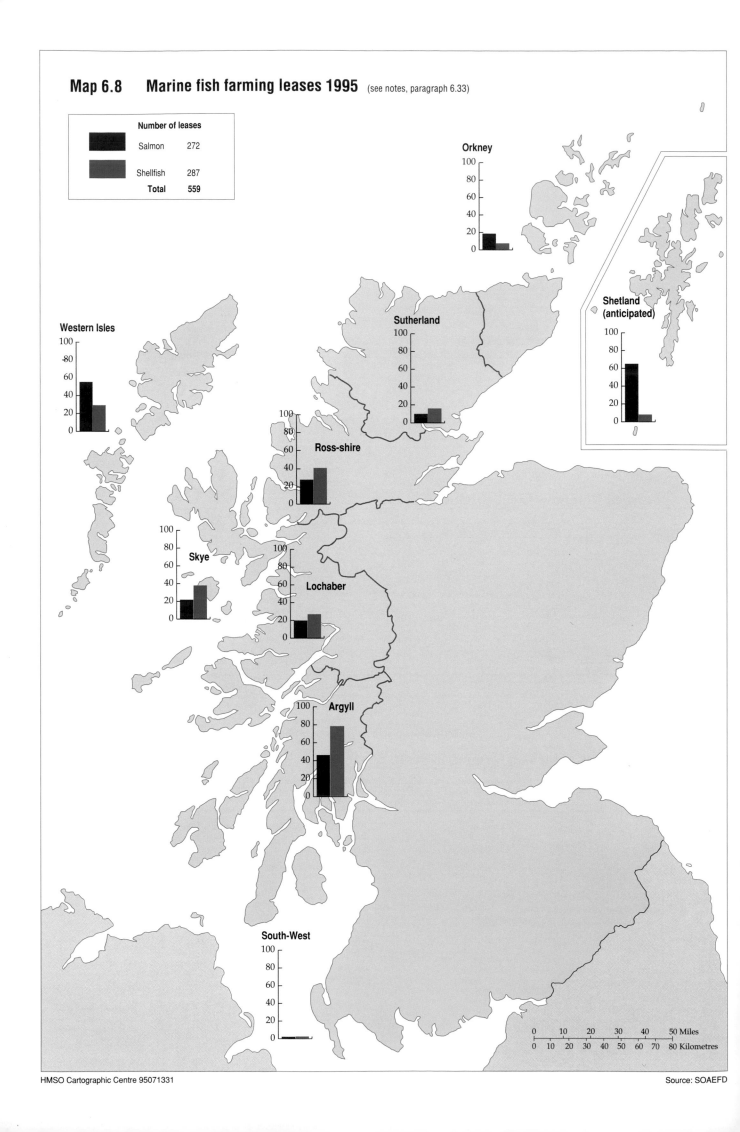

Map 6.8   Marine fish farming leases 1995 (see notes, paragraph 6.33)

Number of leases

■	Salmon	272
■	Shellfish	287
	Total	**559**

Orkney

Shetland
(anticipated)

Western Isles

Sutherland

Ross-shire

Skye

Lochaber

Argyll

South-West

| 0 | 10 | 20 | 30 | 40 | 50 Miles |
| 0 | 10 | 20 | 30 | 40 | 50 | 60 | 70 | 80 Kilometres |

HMSO Cartographic Centre 95071331

Source: SOAEFD

Map 6.9   Landings, in Scotland by United Kingdom vessels, of four important species, 1994

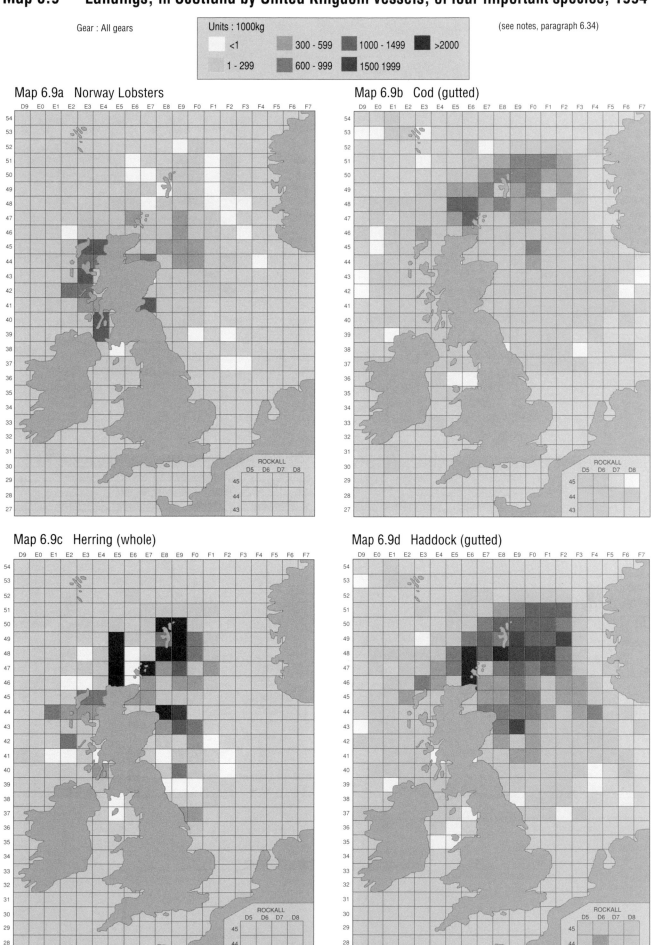

Gear : All gears

Units : 1000kg

<1	300 - 599	1000 - 1499	>2000
1 - 299	600 - 999	1500 1999	

(see notes, paragraph 6.34)

Map 6.9a   Norway Lobsters

Map 6.9b   Cod (gutted)

Map 6.9c   Herring (whole)

Map 6.9d   Haddock (gutted)

Source: Marine Laboratory, Aberdeen

Table 6.31 Fish landings in Scotland by UK vessels, 1987-1993[1]

| Species | Weight (thousand tonnes)[2] | | | | | | | Value in 1993[3] | |
	1987	1988	1989	1990	1991	1992	1993	Total (£m)	Average (£/tonne)
All species total	**574.9**	**554.9**	**510.6**	**458.4**	**432.4**	**442.4**	**463.2**	**260.7**	**562.8**
Demersal total	**263.8**	**252.6**	**208.3**	**178.5**	**171.4**	**162.1**	**184.3**	**167.2**	**1,220.9**
Cod	54.3	43.0	35.7	35.8	32.6	30.7	29.8	34.0	1,142.4
Dogfish	5.9	5.9	5.9	5.7	6.2	7.0	4.8	4.5	943.8
Haddock	94.0	91.2	68.6	46.4	43.3	43.0	69.3	49.8	719.2
Monkfish	6.6	7.3	8.4	8.9	8.8	9.3	10.5	25.9	2,473.9
Plaice	6.7	6.9	6.1	6.5	7.8	7.4	5.6	5.8	1,032.0
Saithe	13.2	12.1	10.0	10.1	11.3	8.7	8.1	3.4	422.9
Sandeels	21.7	30.2	24.6	17.0	8.3	4.1	2.9	0.1	42.1
Whiting	40.5	34.9	28.8	29.4	32.9	31.8	32.8	17.5	533.8
Other	21.0	21.1	20.2	18.7	20.2	20.1	20.6	26.1	1,267.0
Pelagic total	**272.2**	**257.9**	**257.3**	**239.3**	**215.0**	**234.2**	**233.6**	**29.2**	**119.3**
Herring	96.3	87.5	95.0	93.5	88.0	83.9	81.7	9.0	109.9
Mackerel	170.4	161.3	150.2	138.0	118.2	141.6	145.6	19.6	134.5
Other pelagic	5.5	9.1	12.1	7.8	8.8	8.7	6.3	0.7	0.1
Shellfish total	**38.9**	**44.4**	**45.0**	**40.6**	**45.9**	**46.1**	**45.3**	**64.2**	**1,418.2**
Edible crabs	5.2	6.1	5.6	4.7	5.9	5.2	5.2	4.5	860.4
Norway lobsters	16.5	19.2	18.1	16.9	18.0	17.7	19.4	36.5	1,879.0
Periwinkles	2.1	2.2	2.4	1.5	2.1	1.8	1.7	1.1	6.29.9
Queen scallops	5.4	3.7	5.1	5.1	4.9	5.5	6.3	2.5	391.3
Scallops	4.8	4.2	4.7	4.2	3.9	5.1	5.6	8.7	1,558.2
Other shellfish	5.0	9.0	9.1	8.2	11.1	10.8	7.1	10.9	1,535.2

Source: SOAEFD

(1) Figures may not sum to total due to rounding.
(2) The standard landed weight for demersal fish (excluding Norway pout and sandeels) is the weight of the gutted fish with head; for other species (including shellfish) it means the whole fish.
(3) Value at the first sale of the fish.

Table 6.32 Fishing vessels by base district and landings by UK vessels by landing district, 1994[1]

| District | Vessels in district | | | Landings by UK vessels into district[2] | | | | |
| | | | | Weight (thousand tonnes)[3] | | | | Value[4] |
	Under 30'	30' and over	Total	Demersal	Pelagic	Shellfish	Total	£m
Scotland								
Eyemouth	1,542	1,486	2,994	189.0	223.8	45.2	458.1	278.0
Pittenweem	57	90	147	3.3	+	1.3	4.6	6.6
Arbroath	58	60	118	1.0	+	1.2	2.1	3.1
Aberdeen	61	36	97	0.3	+	0.8	1.1	1.7
Peterhead	37	32	69	23.5	6.7	1.4	31.6	26.3
Fraserburgh	47	120	167	73.4	44.0	1.1	118.4	73.6
Macduff	62	135	197	13.8	10.7	4.7	29.2	23.3
Buckie	22	77	99	1.8	-	1.3	3.0	4.4
Lossiemouth	20	73	93	1.1	+	1.6	2.7	2.0
Wick	99	39	138	16.0	+	2.3	18.4	20.9
Orkney	124	73	197	0.8	+	2.0	2.8	4.3
Shetland	102	95	197	20.5	130.8	1.2	152.6	29.9
Stornoway	292	101	393	1.6	+	5.0	6.6	10.6
Kinlochbervie	12	10	22	15.5	+	0.7	16.2	16.1
Lochinver	12	22	34	5.1	+	0.9	6.1	7.7
Ullapool	35	34	69	1.2	27.2	1.1	29.5	6.8
Mallaig	156	94	250	5.0	3.3	4.8	13.1	14.7
Oban	106	53	159	1.2	+	4.5	5.8	8.3
Campbeltown	134	84	218	0.4	0.7	4.5	5.5	8.5
Ayr	84	129	213	2.2	0.3	4.4	6.9	7.5

Source: SOAEFD

(1) The base district of a vessel is the district of residence of the skipper or the majority of owners.
(2) Figures may not sum to total due to rounding.
(3) See note (2) table 6.31.
(4) See note (3) table 6.31.
+ less than 100 tonnes

Table 6.33 **Fish Landings by UK vessels:**
Total Allowable Catches, UK quotas and uptake (liveweight), 1991-1993

Stock Species	1991			1992			1993		
	Total Allowable Catch	UK Quota	Uptake	Total Allowable Catch	UK Quota	Uptake	Total Allowable Catch	UK Quota	Uptake
Demersal									
Anglers (Monks)	..	..	..	..	..	..	27,840	7,390	6,894
Atlantic Redfish	63,820	1,400	500	62,320	3,300	1,050	62,320	800	727
Cod	232,521	70,460	67,545	232,801	70,417	66,689	216,227	74,785	67,699
Flatfish	1,000	680	0	1,000	680	20	1,000	680	53
Greenland Halibut	..	..	..	..	..	..	5,300	700	824
Haddock	71,680	50,280	53,552	79,250	53,930	54,048	158,700	93,780	86,642
Hake	39,940	7,570	7,458	41,170	7,570	7,213	42,710	7,640	7,250
Ling/Blue Ling	3,600	205	6	3,600	205	6	3,600	205	23
Megrim	20,728	3,800	3,243	20,270	3,730	3,584	23,840	4,040	3,723
Norway Pout	..	..	..	..	..	..	69,000	2,500	-
Plaice	219,550	39,255	34,505	221,150	43,192	36,951	191,450	47,405	35,433
Pollack (Lythe)	15,100	2,840	2,068	15,100	2,840	1,970	15,100	2,840	2,267
Saithe	168,400	19,371	19,234	147,000	16,765	15,554	128,400	14,840	15,354
Sandeel	..	..	..	..	..	..	131,000	7,500	4,538
Sole	35,225	4,260	4,461	35,225	3,715	3,798	39,075	3,435	3,433
Whiting	184,000	46,887	46,689	174,500	11,800	44,617	159,200	47,380	46,065
Pelagic									
Blue Whiting	499,200	11,000	3,983	451,500	190,500	30,355	481,500	11,000	2,384
Herring	158,400	110,070	111,621	376,190	110,870	107,152	522,000	106,450	107,114
Horse Mackerel	348,000	-	-	378,000	212,000	84.8	310,000	-	13,542
Mackerel	428,670	199,160	111,070	488,670	232,480	196,957	544,200	256,010	246,892
Spat	67,000	3,240	4,450	67,000	3,240	8,545	126,000	6,300	5,123
Shellfish									
Norway Lobster	32,500	19,970	33,772	44,000	30,285	24,982	44,600	18,870	28,750
Other Species	9,510	3,489	8,763	10,460	3,889	3,730	10,210	3,690	3,529

Source: SOAEFD

Table 6.34 **Wild bird persecution: Total number of incidents in Scotland from 1985-1994**

Type of Occurrence	1985	1986	1987	1988	1989	1990	1991	1992	1993	1994
Shooting & destruction of birds of prey	26	40	34	51	83	69	98	85	110	117
Poisoning	12	26	39	50	85	55	60	60	63	53
Taking, sale or illegal possession of birds of prey	13	18	23	36	52	41	50	50	90	73
Egg collecting	37	49	52	37	45	41	37	58	31	40
Taxidermy	1	4	3	1	8	6	5	11	13	11
Photography & disturbance	9	4	10	8	15	11	15	14	11	10
Import and export	0	1	1	2	2	0	3	3	3	8
Selling of eggs	0	0	1	1	2	4	3	0	1	1
Shooting & destruction (ex birds of prey)	18	40	32	34	41	30	28	38	28	33
Taking, sale or illegal possession (ex birds of prey)	16	14	6	7	9	6	12	18	11	10
Suspicious circumstances (new category 1993)	-	-	-	-	-	-	-	-	9	12
Miscellaneous	1	2	5	3	7	6	10	17	16	26
Total	**133**	**198**	**206**	**230**	**349**	**269**	**321**	**354**	**386**	**394**

Source: RSPB

Table 6.35 **Known persecution incidents and deaths of owls and birds of prey by region 1990-1994** [1]

Area	Poisoned		Shot		Trapped		Total Incidents	Total Deaths	Nests Destroyed (inc eggs & young)
	Incidents	Deaths	Incidents	Deaths	Incidents	Deaths			
Scotland	**92**	**70**	**93**	**45**	**28**	**8**	**213**	**122**	**124**
Borders	4	2	10	4	5	1	19	7	12
Central	12	3	-	4	-	-	12	7	6
Dumfries & Galloway	5	3	8	1	5	-	18	4	5
Fife	10	1	2	1	1	-	13	1	-
Grampian	8	10	13	7	2	2	23	19	8
Highland	29	28	26	12	3	2	58	42	29
Lothian	3	1	7	2	-	-	10	3	3
Strathclyde	9	11	12	11	5	-	26	22	42
Tayside	12	9	14	3	7	3	33	15	19
Western Isles	-	2	1	-	-	-	1	2	-

Source: RSPB

(1)   Cumulative total.

Table 6.36   **Known deaths of owls and birds of prey by cause, 1993**

Species	Cause of death					Total
	Trauma	Disease	Starvation	Poisoned	Unknown	
Total	**11**	**2**	**5**	**20**	**36**	**74**
Barn Owl	1	-	-	-	-	1
Buzzard	2	-	1	18	17	38
Golden Eagle	1	-	-	1	2	4
Goshawk	-	-	-	-	1	1
Kestrel	1	1	4	-	3	9
Merlin	-	-	-	-	1	1
Peregrine falcon	-	-	-	-	3	3
Red kite	-	-	-	1	3	4
Tawny owl	2	1	-	-	2	5
Osprey	1	-	-	-	-	1
Sparrow hawk	3	-	-	-	3	6
Sea eagle	-	-	-	-	1	1

Source: SOAEFD

radioactivity

7 radioactivity

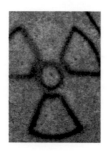

NOTES

7.1   This section deals with general environmental monitoring for radioactivity, and the routine monitoring of radioactive waste disposals from nuclear sites.

DISPOSALS FROM NUCLEAR SITES AND ENVIRONMENTAL MONITORING FOR DISCHARGES

7.2   Tables 7.1 to 7.3 show radioactive waste disposals from nuclear sites in Scotland. Responsibility for the control of radioactive waste disposal rests with the Chief Inspector of HM Industrial Pollution Inspectorate and disposal is prohibited except in accordance with an authorisation. Authorisations are granted only after the operator's proposals have been examined to ensure that radioactive waste is not being produced unnecessarily and that there is a justifiable need to dispose. A certificate is issued containing limitations and conditions designed to achieve compliance with relevant national and international standards including the dose limits for members of the public recommended by the International Commission on Radiological Protection. The certificates contain the requirement that records be kept of radioactive discharges and that the techniques employed for measuring the radioactivity of discharges are subject to the agreement of the Chief Inspector. In addition, samples of waste are collected and analysed by external laboratories to provide independent checks on the operator's results. The Scottish Office Agriculture Environment and Fisheries Department (SOAEFD) statistical bulletin "Radioactive Waste Disposals from Nuclear Sites in Scotland: 1990 to 1994" (Env 1995/3) gives further details.

7.3   Tables 7.4 and 7.5(a) and (b) deal with the regular programme of monitoring, undertaken by operators as a condition of authorisation, to check the environmental effects of disposals from nuclear sites. Similar monitoring surveys are undertaken on behalf of SOAEFD as an independent check on the operator's results. Combined with information on the habits of groups affected by discharges, measurements made on certain materials provide the means of quantifying the radiation exposure of the population and hence the basis for comparing the effects of the discharge with the national standards of radiological safety. More detail is contained in the SODD statistical bulletin "Environmental Monitoring for Radioactivity in Scotland, 1989 to 1991" (Env/1994/5).

7.4   Radiation of natural origin is responsible for most of the exposure to the population. According to the latest review by the National Radiological Protection Board (NRPB), some 85 per cent of the annual dose in the United Kingdom arises from natural sources, the main components of which are cosmic rays, terrestrial gamma rays, the short-lived decay products of radon and long-lived radionuclides in the body from diet. The situation is similar for Scotland (chart 7.1). The short-lived decay products of radon-222, often called radon daughters, are the most important source and account for almost half of the overall dose from natural radiation, they also cause the highest doses to individual people. In 1990, NRPB recommended to Government that the Action Level for radon in homes should be 200 becquerels per cubic metre of air (Bqm-3) and suggested a comprehensive control strategy based on the concept of Radon Affected Areas. These are specified as areas where one per cent or more of homes exceed the Action Level. The Government accepted this advice and continued the work it had already begun on radon. The Scottish Office Environment Department (now SODD) commissioned the NRPB to carry out surveys of radon levels in Scottish dwellings.

7.5   A survey to review the available data on radon in homes in Scotland from work undertaken by NRPB (Radon in Dwellings in Scotland: 1995 Review, NRPB M569) has been completed. A report will be published in the spring. Previously, NRPB advised SODD that parts of the districts of Caithness, Sutherland, Gordon and Kincardine and Deeside qualified as Radon Affected Areas and published contoured maps showing the percentage of homes above the Action Level (map 7.2) (Radon Affected Areas: Scotland Doc NRPB 4, No 4, 1-8). Subsequently, arrangements have been made by SODD for home owners within the Radon Affected Areas to qualify for free radon measurements from NRPB.

7.6   A survey of indoor gamma-ray dose rates was also undertaken by NRPB in homes in Scotland. The gamma-ray dose rate was found to be relatively low and fairly constant across the country and action to control exposure was not considered necessary. Further details are given in " Natural Radiation Exposure in UK Dwellings." (NRPB R190-May 1988).

7.7   Gamma radiation levels outdoors in Great Britain were measured by NRPB staff. The intention was to make at least one measurement in every readily accessible 10km square of the Ordnance Survey Grid and over 3,100 measurements were made covering 90 per cent of the 2,400 or so 10km grid squares in Great Britain. To achieve total coverage, the missing values were infilled using special mathematical techniques. In general, the gamma-ray dose rate varies within a 10km grid square and individual measurements are of limited value. A smoothing routine was therefore used to produce a more representative value for each square. Map 7.3(a) uses the infilled data and thus emphasises local detail while map 7.3(b) uses infilled doubly-smoothed data revealing general underlying patterns. Greater detail is given in "Gamma-radiation Levels Outdoors in Great Britain" (NRPB R191-February 1989).

7.8   As part of the National Response Plan, introduced by the Government in 1987 to deal with the possible effects on the UK of nuclear incidents abroad such as that at Chernobyl, a network known as the Radioactive Incident Monitoring Network (RIMNET) was established to detect any unusual rise in radioactivity. The network is operated by the Department of the Environment. At present there are 27 RIMNET sites in Scotland and chart 7.3 summarises the monthly mean gamma dose rates at each site. Detailed results are published by the Department of the Environment in a series of statistical bulletins.

7.9   Programmes of general environmental monitoring are undertaken by AEA Technology, Harwell Laboratory and NRPB. The AEA Technology sampling points at Lerwick and Eskdalemuir (charts 7.4 to 7.6) are part of an international network of sites for monitoring radionuclides in air and rainwater. At the two Scottish sites, air is sampled continuously at 1m above the ground by passing quantities of air through filter papers. Rainwater samples are collected by funnels mounted over polythene bottles, and laboratory analysis of samples, is performed by gamma ray spectrometry. More information is contained in the AEA Technology series of reports "Radioactive Fallout in Air and Rain".

7.10   The NRPB operates an environmental surveillance programme in order to assess the intake of artificially produced radionuclides in the UK population. In Scotland, the programme includes the analysis of airborne dust and rainwater in Glasgow, and of samples of milk from a number of depots throughout the country. For the milk analysis, account is taken of the quantity of milk handled by each depot. Samples from 3 months are bulked to provide a quarterly sample which is analysed for strontium 90, caesium 137 and calcium (chart 7.7). Laboratory analysis is performed by radiochemical methods. Further details are contained in the NRPB series of reports entitled "Environmental Radioactivity Surveillance Programme".

7.11   Following the Chernobyl accident in April 1986, extensive monitoring surveys of its effect in Scotland were undertaken by the Scottish Office. Full details of Chernobyl monitoring in Scotland are given in two statistical bulletins "Chernobyl Accident, Monitoring for Radioactivity in Scotland" published by SODD April 1988 and SOAEFD in August 1990.

7.12   Map 7.4 shows concentration of caesium 137 in filtered sea water off Scotland. This monitoring is carried out by the Directorate of Fisheries Research, Ministry of Agriculture, Fisheries and Food, as part of a wider programme to verify the satisfactory control of liquid radioactive waste discharges to the aquatic environment. Further information about radioactive waste disposals can be obtained from statistical bulletins which are issued annually by SOAEFD-HMIPI.

Table 7.1   Discharges of liquid radioactive waste from nuclear sites, 1990-1994

Nature of radioactivity	1990	1991	1992	1993	1994
From Chapelcross Works *(terabecquerels)*[1]					
Tritium	0.28	1.87	0.70	0.50	0.49
Alpha emitters	0.0005	0.0002	0.0002	0.0005	0.0008
Beta emitters (excl tritium)	0.11	0.11	0.071	0.27	0.31
From Dounreay *(terabecquerels)*					
Alpha emitters (excl curium 242)	0.022	0.030	0.026	0.099	0.10
Beta emitters (excl tritium)	4.3	5.5	6.4	8.0	9.0
Tritium	0.3	0.82	2.9	1.0	3.2
Cobalt 60	0.023	0.040	0.025	<0.019	<0.01
Strontium 90	1.3	1.1	1.8	1.4	1.6
Zirconium 95 + niobium 95	<0.01	0.02	<0.012	<0.015	<0.012
Ruthenium 106	0.34	0.52	0.50	<0.81	0.35
Silver 110m	<0.01	0.035	<0.006	<0.0073	<0.0068
Caesium 137	2.2	3.5	3.1	3.8	4.7
Cerium 144	0.038	0.043	<0.024	<0.092	<0.026
Plutonium 241	0.72	0.57	0.044	1.3	0.94
Curium 242	0.019	0.0030	0.00094	<0.0013	<0.0007
From Hunterston *(terabecquerels)*					
A Station Tritium	0.52	0.25	0.17	0.36	0.20
Total alpha + beta (excl tritium)	0.32	0.28	0.21	0.29	0.21
B Station Tritium	353	257	245	362	423
Sulphur 35	2.5	1.5	1.7	2.1	1.5
Total alpha + beta (excl tritium and sulphur 35)	0.05	0.04	0.02	0.034	0.031
From Torness *(gigabecquerels)*[2]					
Tritium[3]	82	132	250	235	220
Sulphur 35[3]	0.081	0.044	0.048	0.021	0.019
Cobalt 60	0.029	1.5	3.5	1.4	0.26
Total beta (excluding tritium, sulphur 35 and cobalt 60)	1.8	5.5	11	8.4	1.2
Total alpha	<0.008	<0.009	<0.014	<0.012	0.008

Source: Her Majesty's Industrial Pollution Inspectorate, SOAEFD

(1)   1 terabecquerel = 10^{12} becquerels.
(2)   1 gigabecquerel = 10^{9} becquerels.
(3)   For Tritium and Sulphur 35 figures are in terabecquerel.

Table 7.2   Discharges of radioactive waste to the atmosphere from nuclear sites, 1990-1994

Nature of radioactivity	1990	1991	1992	1993	1994
From Chapelcross Works *(terabecquerels)*					
Tritium	1,900	1,400	1,500	1,500	1,600
Sulphur 35	0.012	0.013	0.022	0.021	0.022
Argon 41	2,900	3,000	3,000	3,200	3,200
From Dounreay[1] *(gigabecquerels)*[1]					
Alpha emitters (excl curium 242 and 244)	0.020	0.065	0.16	0.094	0.085
Beta emitters (excl tritium and krypton 85)	2.5	2.4	4.0	2.3	2.7
Tritium[2]	<0.13	0.11	0.31	<0.29	<0.029
Krypton 85[2]	350	528	448	640	647
Strontium 90	1.1	0.50	0.96	0.65	0.98
Ruthenium 106	0.46	0.30	0.15	0.30	0.15
Iodine 129	<0.12	0.16	0.12	<0.081	<0.068
Iodine 131 (organic and inorganic)	<0.07	0.031	0.021	<0.015	<0.027
Caesium 134	0.046	0.080	0.14	0.044	<0.051
Caesium 137	0.89	1.0	2.23	0.85	1.48
Cerium 144	0.20	0.44	0.44	<0.13	<0.071
Plutonium 241	<0.42	0.44	0.06	1.3	1.4
Curium 242	<0.005	0.010	0.017	<0.0060	<0.0032
Curium 244[3]	<0.006	0.007	0.008	<0.0024	<0.0032
From Hunterston *(terabecquerels)*					
A Station Tritium	0.46	0.13	0.069	0.035	0.031
Carbon 14	0.077	0.018	0.043	0.015	0.037
Sulphur 35	0.004	nd	nd	-	-
Argon 41	86	nd	nd	-	-
Beta particulate[4]	0.008	0.0016	0.0011	0.0036	0.0025
B Station Tritium	5.8	2.9	2.6	4.6	2.9
Carbon 14	1	0.94	0.84	0.99	1.1
Sulphur 35	0.097	0.061	0.051	0.15	0.059
Argon 41	60	29	21	30	30
Beta particulate[4]	0.13	0.049	0.12	0.18	0.13
From Torness *(terabecquerels)*					
Tritium	1.9	1.3	1.7	1.7	1.3
Carbon 14	0.64	0.42	0.35	0.55	0.49
Sulphur 35	0.050	0.040	0.030	0.021	0.021
Argon 41	5.6	5.3	3.8	5.0	8.1
Beta particulate[4]	0.045	0.027	0.013	0.026	0.071

Source: Her Majesty's Industrial Pollution Inspectorate, SOAEFD

(1)   From Dounreay Fuel Cycle Area, (1 gigabecquerel = 10^{9} becquerels).
(2)   For tritium and krypton 85 the unit is terabecquerels.
(3)   The discharge figures include any curium 243 present.
(4)   For beta particulate the units are gigabecquerels.

Table 7.3   Disposals of solid waste to Drigg, 1990-1994

			Annual disposals				
			1990	1991	1992	1993	1994
Chapelcross							
Volume		(cubic metres)[1]	235	75	39	96	125
Radioactivity: total beta/gamma		(gigabecquerels)	169	145	22	113	57
Dounreay[2]							
Volume		(cubic metres)	41	217	300	1,200	255
Radioactivity:		(gigabecquerels)					
	total alpha		3.7	23	27	20	21
	total beta/gamma		76	490	14	340	243
Hunterston							
Volume		(cubic metres)	168	251	228	223	223
Radioactivity:		(gigabecquerels)					
	Alpha emitters		0.011	0.021	0.011	0.002	0.011
	Beta/gamma emitters (except tritium and cobalt 60)		11	27	15	14	36
	Tritium		0.39	6.4	0.38	0.34	0.67
	Cobalt 60		1.7	3.9	2.6	2.6	5.7
Torness							
Volume		(cubic metres)[1]	57	nil	38	nil	57
Radioactivity:		(gigabecquerels)					
	Alpha emitters		nil	nil	0.0045	nil	nil
	Beta/gamma emitters (except tritium and cobalt 60)		0.40	nil	0.32	nil	0.98
	Tritium		0.0017	nil	0.0011	nil	0.0030
	Cobalt 60		0.13	nil	0.085	nil	0.28

Source: Her Majesty's Industrial Pollution Inspectorate, SOAEFD

1) Figures are the volumes of the waste and its packaging; they do not include the volume of the transport containers.
2) Disposals made to the approved area at Dounreay.

Table 7.4   Environmental monitoring by the operator for discharges to the atmosphere, 1986-1991

annual mean concentrations

Site	Material	Nature of Radioactivity	Location	1986	1987	1988	1989	1990	1991
Chapelcross	Milk[1]	Tritium	Inner farms	370	<330	370	<300	<310	<310
			Outer farms	<320	<300	<320	<300	<320	<300
		Carbon 14	Inner farms	43	46	48	48	68	12
			Outer farms	33	32	33	55	68	12
		Sulphur 35	Inner farms	0.95	<1.6	<1.4	<1.6	1.8	0.61
			Outer farms	1.2	1.7	<1.4	<1.9	<2.0	0.70
		Strontium 90	Inner farms	0.06	0.10	0.04	0.03	0.06	0.02
			Outer farms	0.06	0.10	0.04	0.04	0.05	0.01
		Caesium 134[2]	Inner farms	1.8	0.55	nd	nd	na	na
			Outer farms	1.7	0.58	nd	nd	na	na
		Caesium 137	Inner farms	3.8	1.9	0.27	0.26	0.10	0.09
			Outer farms	3.8	1.9	0.62	0.18	0.09	0.09
	Green vegetables[3]	Tritium	Near farms	1,300[4]	2,800	800	4,100	2,200	700
			Remote farms	500[4]	160	850	600	1,650	60
		Carbon 14	Near farms	300[4]	<25	74	10	6.0	3.2
			Remote farms	430[4]	<35	<110	7.0	5.0	3.0
		Strontium 90	Near farms	1.0[4]	0.55	0.20	0.60	<0.10	0.5
			Remote farms	0.60[4]	0.20	0.10	0.20	<0.10	0.10
Dounreay	Milk[1]	Strontium 90	Inner farms	0.24	0.29	0.22	0.24	0.20	na
			Outer farms	0.16	0.30	0.24	0.19	0.40	0.40
		Iodine 131	Inner farms	<0.23	<2.8	<0.30	<0.30	<0.30	na
			Outer farms	<3.9	<2.8	<0.30	<0.30	<0.30	<0.30
		Caesium 134[2]		<7.0	<5.1	<1.5	na	<1.0	<1.0
		Caesium 137	Inner farms	8.9	7.8	<5.8	<3.2	<1.0	na
			Outer farms	<9.2	<2.4	<5.5	<1.2	<1.0	<1.0
Hunterston	Milk[1]	Sulphur 35		0.90	1.0	0.46	0.81	0.43	0.26
		Strontium 89		<0.40	nd	nd	nd	nd	nd
		Strontium 90		0.14	0.13	0.10	0.14	0.10	0.072
		Iodine 131		<5.5	<0.40	<0.4	<0.4	<0.4	<0.4
		Caesium 134[2]		5.5	na	na	na	na	na
		Caesium 137[5]		12	4.7	1.3	0.94	0.81	0.85
Torness	Milk[1]	Sulphur 35		<1.0	<1.0	<1.0	<1.0	<1.0	<1.0
		Strontium 89		na	na	0.03	<0.11	na	na
		Strontium 90		<0.10	0.10	0.07	0.09	0.19	0.14
		Iodine 131		na	<0.40	<0.40	<0.40	<0.40	0.40
		Caesium 134		na	0.20	<0.15	<0.15	<0.16	<0.23
		Caesium 137		6.6	4.4	<0.25	<0.25	<0.22	<0.26

Source: Her Majesty's Industrial Pollution Inspectorate, SOAEFD

nd   not detected
na   not analysed.
1)   Becquerels per litre.
2)   Caesium 134 is not analysed as part of the statutory programme and the results given are based on special measurements undertaken as part of the Chernobyl monitoring for years up to 1987.
3)   Becquerels per kilogram (fresh weight).
4)   Based on limited sample.
5)   Includes any caesium 134 present from 1987 onwards.

Table 7.5 **Environmental monitoring by the operator for discharges to the sea, 1986-1991**

(a) Fish and shellfish monitoring — annual mean concentration, becquerels per kilogram (wet)

Site	Material	Nature of Radioactivity	1986	1987	1988	1989	1990	1991
Chapelcross	Flounder	Strontium 90	0.16	0.40	0.13	0.10	<0.10	<0.10
		Caesium 134	3.3	3.8	1.4	0.93	<0.18	<0.23
		Caesium 137	140	100	96	67	38	35
	Shrimps	Strontium 90	0.18	0.13	0.18	<0.10	<0.10	<0.13
		Caesium 134	1.8	0.60	0.33	0.28	<0.10	<0.10
		Caesium 137	33	29	22	17	13	10
	Sea Trout	Strontium 90	<0.1	0.45	0.20	0.10	<0.10	<0.10
		Caesium 134	1.5	1.6	1.0	0.25	<0.20	0.20
		Caesium 137	46	23	29	21	12	10
Dounreay	Winkles	Total alpha	8.8	<4.0	na	na	na	na
		Cobalt 60	8.8	<5.0	<4.4	<3.1	<3.3	<10
		Strontium 90	0.16	0.23	<0.1	<0.1	<0.1	<0.4
		Zirconium 95[1]	<1.5	<80	<80	<43	<50	<20
		Ruthenium 106[2]	<44	<40	<69	<55	<56	<55
		Silver 110m	56	89	160	75	<66	39
		Antimony 125	nd	nd	nd	nd	nd	nd
		Caesium 137	<8.5	<20	<5.0	<8.8	<10	<10
		Cerium 144	<1.0	nd	<50	<30	<30	<50
Hunterston	Fish	Total beta	120	120	120	100	ns	ns
		Caesium 137	40	27	13	9.6	ns	ns
	Shellfish[3]	Total beta	110	52	60	7.0	87	110
		Caesium 137	7.3	4.0	6.0	3.0	3.7	3.0
Torness	Winkles	Total beta	46	41	87	55	58	58
		Cobalt 60	nd	nd	nd	nd	nd	0.34
		Ruthenium 106	na	na	0.86	nd	nd	nd
		Silver 110m	nd	2.4	2.3	0.51	nd	nd
		Caesium 134	nd	nd	nd	<0.1	nd	nd
		Caesium 137	1.2	0.75	0.52	0.49	0.31	<0.54
	Fish (cod)	Total beta	75	89	83	92	100	100
		Cobalt 60	nd	nd	nd	nd	nd	nd
		Ruthenium 106	na	na	nd	nd	nd	nd
		Silver 110m	nd	nd	nd	nd	nd	nd
		Caesium 134	nd	0.18	0.15	<0.1	nd	nd
		Caesium 137	4.9	3.8	1.9	1.5	2.2	6.3

(b) Foreshore dose rate measurements — annual mean dose rates, micrograys per hour

Site	Location	Measurements	1986	1987	1988	1989	1990	1991
Chapelcross[4]	Beaches	Gamma dose rate	0.25	0.25	0.15	0.16	0.14	0.18
	Stake nets	Gamma dose rate	0.21	0.23	0.12	0.11	0.12	0.16
Dounreay[4]	General foreshore	Gamma dose rate at 1m	0.08	0.08	0.09	0.08	0.10	0.08
	Rocky areas	Gamma dose rate at 1m	0.12	0.12	0.17	0.10	0.11	0.09
	Salmon nets	Beta/gamma dose rate on surface of nets[5]	0.02	0.05	0.03	0.03	0.09	0.02
Hunterston[6]	Little Brigurd	Gamma dose rate	0.11	0.11	0.11	0.10	0.09	0.09
	Burnfoot	Gamma dose rate	0.10	0.11	0.10	0.10	0.10	0.09
	Ardneil Bay	Gamma dose rate	0.09	0.10	0.10	0.10	0.10	0.09
Torness[6]	Coldingham Bay	Gamma dose rate	0.062	0.063	0.067	0.067	0.065	0.065
	Pettico Wick	Gamma dose rate	0.089	0.095	0.098	0.090	0.100	0.087
	Hirst Rocks Beach	Gamma dose rate	0.088	0.094	0.095	0.087	0.089	0.093
	Pease Bay	Gamma dose rate	0.067	0.069	0.070	0.071	0.070	0.073
	Thorntonloch	Gamma dose rate	0.056	0.063	0.062	0.064	0.057	0.061
	Skateraw Harbour	Gamma dose rate	0.057	0.062	0.064	0.065	0.061	0.060
	Chapel Point/Barn's Ness	Gamma dose rate	0.056	0.064	0.067	0.062	0.062	0.065
	White Sands	Gamma dose rate	0.056	0.062	0.062	0.066	0.062	0.063
	Belhaven Bay (South)	Gamma dose rate	0.058	0.063	0.066	0.064	0.065	0.063
	Tyne Sands	Gamma dose rate	0.084	0.080	0.083	0.083	0.081	0.072

Source: Her Majesty's Industrial Pollution Inspectorate, SOAEFD

ns   not sampled
na   not analysed
nd   not detected.
(1)   Includes any niobium 95 present.
(2)   Includes any ruthenium 193 present.
(3)   Samples were available during June-October only in 1986, during June-August only in 1987 and during July-August only in 1991.
(4)   The measured dose rate includes a contribution of at least 0.10 micrograys per hour from natural radiation.
(5)   The dose rates on the nets have been corrected for the background count rate of the instrument used.
(6)   The measured dose rate includes a contribution of a least 0.05 micrograys per hour from natural radiation.

Table 7.6   Radon measurements by postcode area 1995

Postcode areas		Number of dwellings	Average radon level (Bq m³)	Highest value (Bq m³)	Number above Action Level
Total		**4,268**	**478**	**5,294**	**214**
AB	Aberdeen	2,539	69	1,600	144
DD	Dundee	63	34	180	0
DG	Dumfries	167	34	150	0
EH	Edinburgh	41	21	100	0
FK	Falkirk	46	20	51	0
G	Glasgow	73	15	58	0
IV	Inverness	55	33	160	0
KA	Kilmarnock	20	12	37	0
KW	Kirkwall[1]	1,016	78	2,200	69
KY	Kirkcaldy	77	17	51	0
ML	Motherwell	16	16	52	0
PA	Paisley	25	18	55	0
PH	Perth	46	37	130	0
TD	Galashiels	42	54	290	1
ZE	Lerwick	42	20	180	0

Source: NRPB

1)   Embraces Caithness and part of Sutherland.

Chart 7.1   Annual doses from all sources of radiation

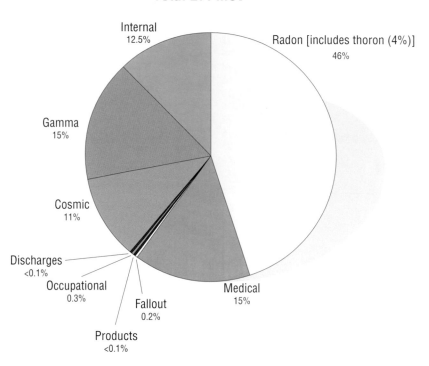

Total 2.4 mSv

Internal
12.5%

Radon [includes thoron (4%)]
46%

Gamma
15%

Cosmic
11%

Discharges
<0.1%

Occupational
0.3%

Fallout
0.2%

Products
<0.1%

Medical
15%

Source: NRPB

Chart 7.2   Indoor radon concentration: overall distribution

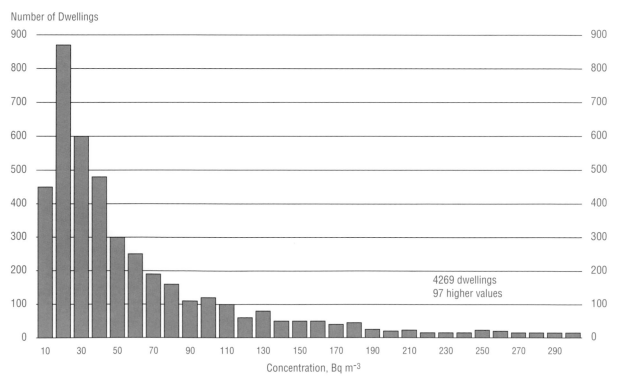

Number of Dwellings

4269 dwellings
97 higher values

Concentration, Bq m⁻³

Source: NRPB

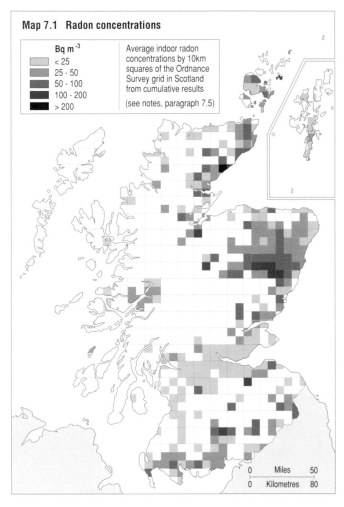

Map 7.1 Radon concentrations

Bq m⁻³

	< 25
	25 - 50
	50 - 100
	100 - 200
	> 200

Average indoor radon concentrations by 10km squares of the Ordnance Survey grid in Scotland from cumulative results

(see notes, paragraph 7.5)

Miles 0 — 50
Kilometres 0 — 80

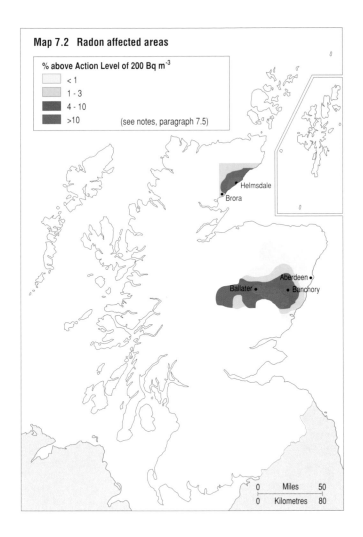

Map 7.2 Radon affected areas

% above Action Level of 200 Bq m⁻³

	< 1
	1 - 3
	4 - 10
	>10

(see notes, paragraph 7.5)

Helmsdale
Brora

Aberdeen
Ballater
Banchory

Miles 0 — 50
Kilometres 0 — 80

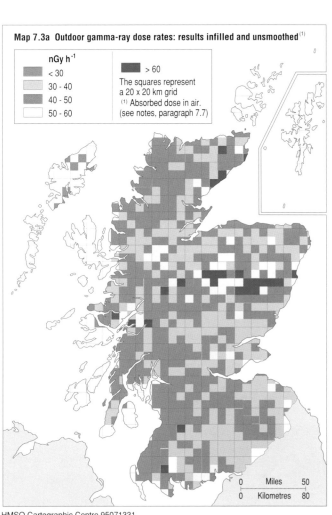

Map 7.3a Outdoor gamma-ray dose rates: results infilled and unsmoothed [1]

nGy h⁻¹

	< 30		> 60
	30 - 40		
	40 - 50		
	50 - 60		

The squares represent a 20 x 20 km grid
[1] Absorbed dose in air.
(see notes, paragraph 7.7)

Miles 0 — 50
Kilometres 0 — 80

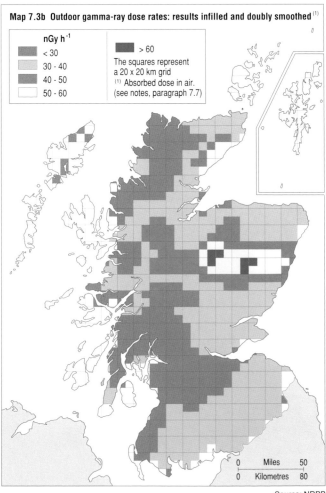

Map 7.3b Outdoor gamma-ray dose rates: results infilled and doubly smoothed [1]

nGy h⁻¹

	< 30		> 60
	30 - 40		
	40 - 50		
	50 - 60		

The squares represent a 20 x 20 km grid
[1] Absorbed dose in air.
(see notes, paragraph 7.7)

Miles 0 — 50
Kilometres 0 — 80

Source: NRPB

Chart 7.3 Monthly mean Gamma-Radiation dose rates: by sites 1991 - 1994

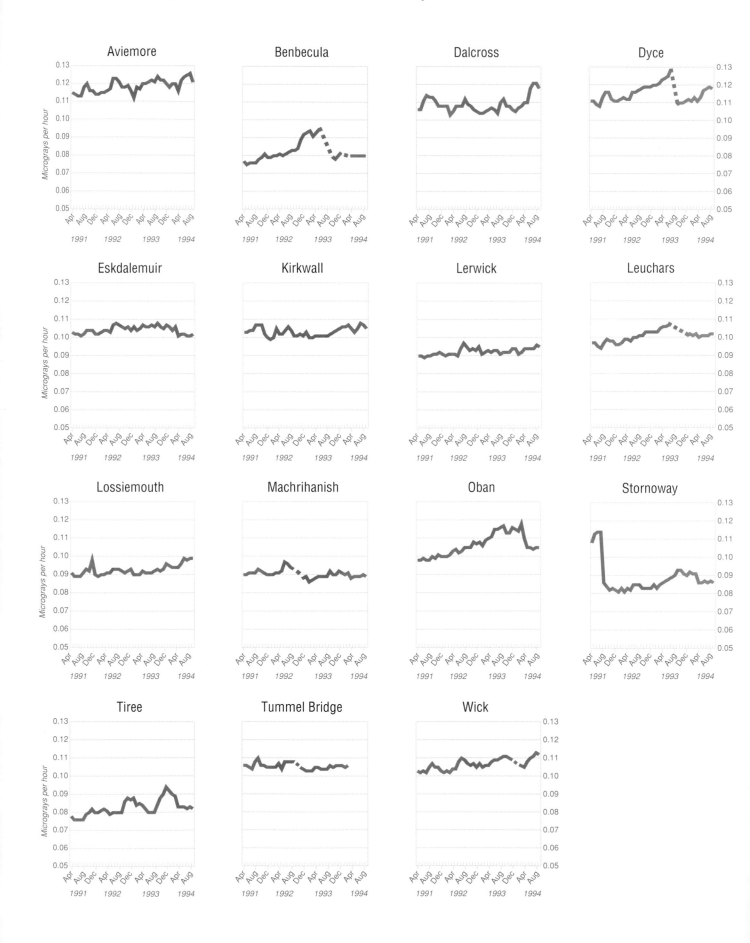

Source: HMIPI, SOAEFD

Chart 7.4   Concentration of caesium 137 in air at Lerwick and Eskdalemuir, 1961 to 1993 [1]

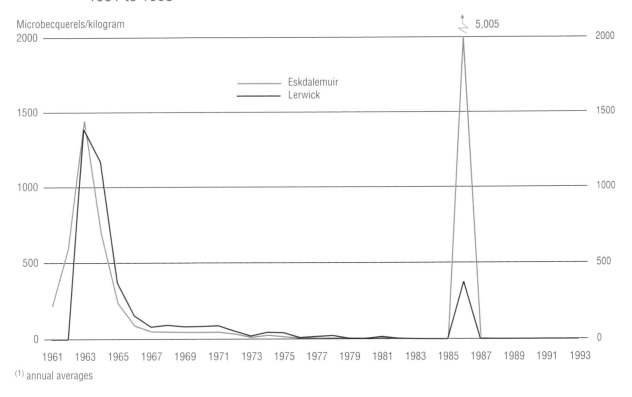

Microbecquerels/kilogram

—— Eskdalemuir
—— Lerwick

5,005

[1] annual averages

Source: AEA Technology

Chart 7.5   Concentration of caesium 137 in rain and yearly deposited caesium 137 at Lerwick and Eskdalemuir, 1965 to 1993 [1]

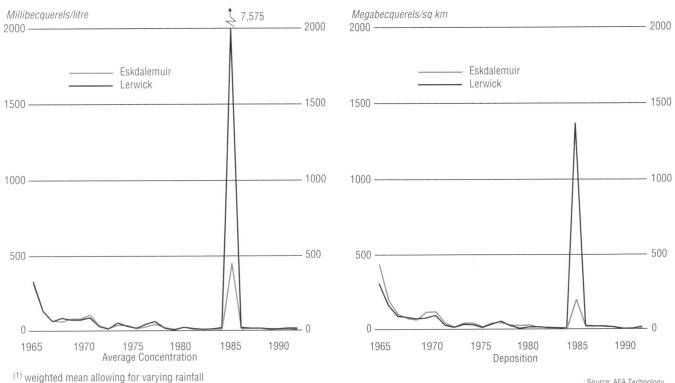

Millibecquerels/litre

7,575

—— Eskdalemuir
—— Lerwick

Average Concentration

Megabecquerels/sq km

—— Eskdalemuir
—— Lerwick

Deposition

[1] weighted mean allowing for varying rainfall

Source: AEA Technology

Chart 7.6 Concentration of tritium in rainwater at Eskdalemuir, 1966 to 1993 [1]

Becquerels/litre

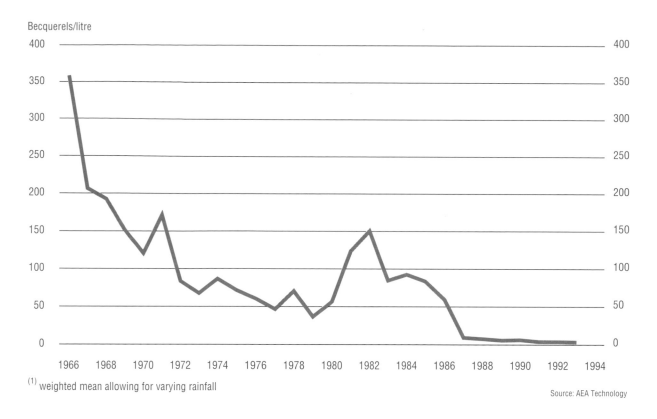

[1] weighted mean allowing for varying rainfall

Source: AEA Technology

Chart 7.7 Activity concentrations in milk, Scotland 1959 to 1993 [1]

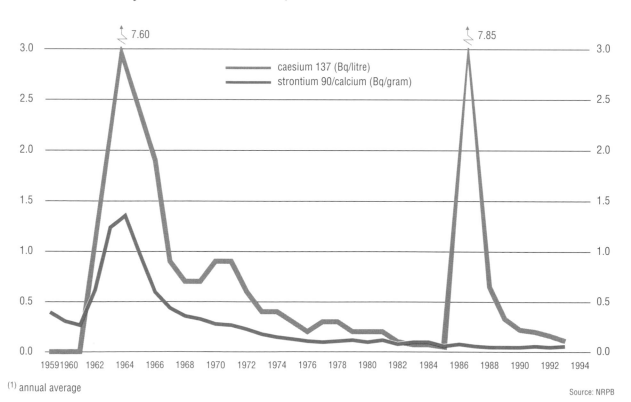

caesium 137 (Bq/litre)
strontium 90/calcium (Bq/gram)

[1] annual average

Source: NRPB

Map 7.4　Concentrations of caesium 137 in filtered water, 1993

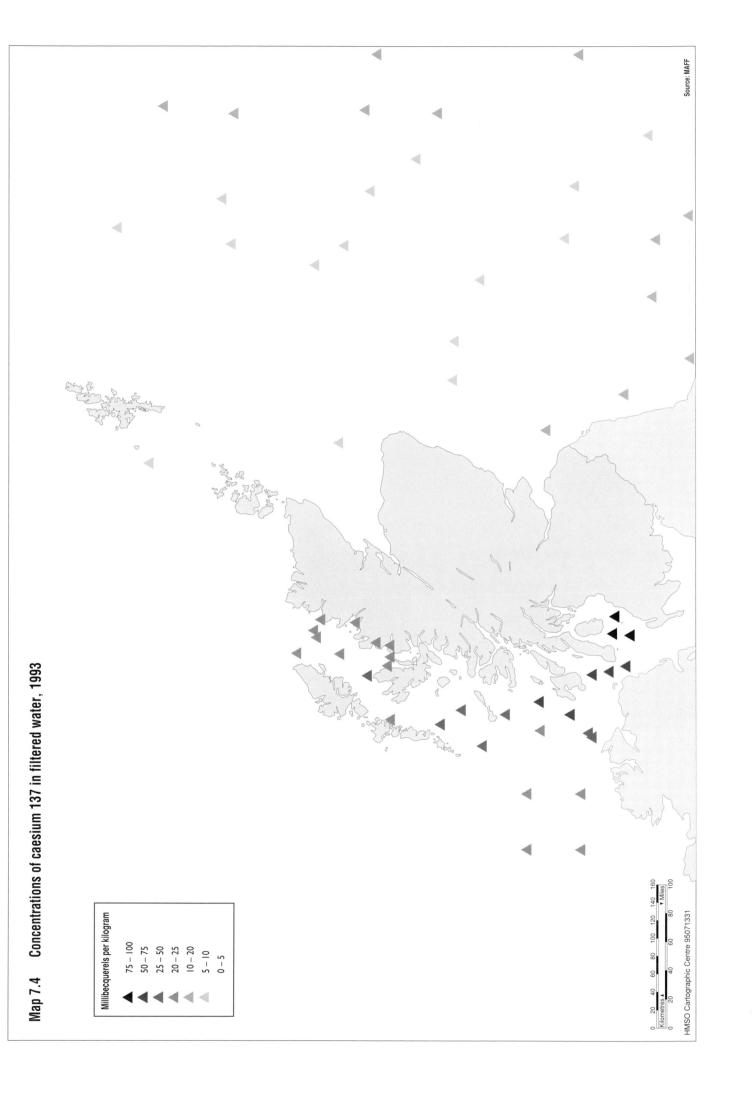

Millibecquerels per kilogram

75 – 100
50 – 75
25 – 50
20 – 25
10 – 20
5 – 10
0 – 5

Kilometres
0 20 40 60 80 100 120 140 160

Miles
0 20 40 60 80 100

HMSO Cartographic Centre 95071331

Source: MAFF

The following symbols have been used throughout the publication.

Symbol	Meaning	Symbol	Meaning
..	= not available	l	= litre
-	= nil or negligible	Ml	= megalitre
	(less than ½ the final digit shown)	Ml/d	= megalitre per day
ns	= not sampled	l/hd/d	= litres per head per day
nd	= not detected	mg/l	= milligrams per litre
na	= not analysed	mg/l O	= milligrams per litres of oxygen
		mg/l N	= milligrams per litre of nitrogen
<	= less than	Gw	= Giga watt
>	= greater than	Gwh	= Giga watt hour
≤	= less than or equal to	ppb	= parts per billion
≥	= greater than or equal to	pH	= measure of acidity/alkalinity (percentage hydrogen ions)
%	= per cent	Keq H+	= kilo equivalent of hydrogen
		GMT	= Greenwich Mean Time
(000)	= thousands	^{o}C	= degrees celsius
£(000)	= thousand pounds		
£m	= million pounds		
mm	= millimetre	bcm	= billion cubic metres
m	= metre	bcf	= billion cubic feet
m^2	= square metres		
m^3	= cubic metre	O	= oxygen
m3/sec	= cubic metres per second	N	= nitrogen
		NO_2	= nitrogen dioxide
km	= kilometre	SO_2	= sulphur dioxide
km^2 or sqkm	= square kilometre		
ha	= hectare	mSv	= millisievert
mg	= milligram	Bqm^{-3}	= bequerels per cubic metre
g	= gram		
kg	= kilogram		

Conversion factors

1 tonne	1,000 kilograms
1 mile	1,609.344 metres
1 hectare	10,000 square metres
1 square kilometre	100 hectares
1 gallon	0.00454609 cubic metres
1 litre	0.001 cubic metres
1 curie	3.17×10^{10} becquerels
1 becquerel	1 nuclear disintegration per second
1 microbecquerel	10^{-6} becquerels
1 tetrabecquerel	10^{12} becquerels
1 gigabecqerel	10^{9} becquerels
1 megabecquerel	10^{6} becquerels